FUNDAMENTALS OF INFORMATION SYSTEMS AND SYSTEMS DEVELOPMENT

FUNDAMENTALS OF INFORMATION SYSTEMS AND SYSTEMS DEVELOPMENT

Editor
Paul Seiffert

DPH

DISCOVERY PUBLISHING HOUSE
INDIA

Published by:

DISCOVERY PUBLISHING HOUSE
4383/4B, Ansari Road, Darya Ganj
New Delhi-110 002 (India)
Phone : +91-11-23279245; 23253475; 43596065
+91 9811179893 / +91 9871656464
E-mail : discoverybooksindia@gmail.com
orderdphbooks@gmail.com
namitwasan9@gmail.com
web : www.discoverypublishinggroup.com

Publisher and the editor expresses gratitude to these contributors for sharing their knowledge and expertise.

First Published: **2024**

ISBN: 978-81-19523-88-7

Fundamentals of Information Systems and Systems Development

Printed at:
Infinity Imaging Systems
Delhi

Preface

A company relies on various systems to support its managerial levels. These systems encompass transaction processing systems, management information systems, decision support systems, and dedicated business intelligence systems. The purpose of these information systems is to ensure accurate and timely information is readily available as and when required.

In an organization, executives at different levels of the hierarchy have distinct information needs. So, different types of information systems have emerged to cater to these diverse requirements. One common approach to examining the types of information systems utilized within organizations is through a vertical approach, which classifies them based on their roles at various levels of the organizational structure.

Information systems are widely regarded as one of the most critical fields, with modern studies focusing extensively on this area. Organizations strive to adopt novel technologies and facilities to support and enhance their information systems. The information component of these systems is considered their soul, as it drives their functionality and effectiveness. Therefore, achieving high performance necessitates a clear understanding of the different types of information systems and how they operate.

Technology plays a vital role throughout the life cycle of information systems, beginning with database (DB) technology. Databases are structured collections of information or facts that store current and future data, making it accessible at any time for organizational use. Additionally, data warehousing technology is employed to store data from both internal and external sources within an organization. The availability of past and current data serves as a valuable resource for supporting decision-making processes, providing the necessary information at any given time.

This book serves as a valuable resource for individuals seeking general and fundamental knowledge about information systems. It covers essential aspects related to the field, offering comprehensive insights into the subject matter.

The editor has collected reliable and scientifically proven information from various credible sources to provide readers with the latest and most accurate information available. The book is a compendium of contributions from various experts in the field, and the editor expresses gratitude to these contributors for sharing their knowledge and expertise.

Editor

Contents

1

Basic Concepts of Information Systems

Leila Zemmouchi-Ghomari
National Superior School of Technology, Algiers, Algeria

ABSTRACT

This chapter covers the basic concepts of the information systems (IS) field to prepare the reader to quickly approach the book's other chapters: the Definition of information, the notion of system, and, more particularly, information systems. We also discuss the typology of IS according to the managerial level and decision-making in the IS. Furthermore, we describe information systems applications covering functional areas and focusing on the execution of business processes across the enterprise, including all management levels. We briefly discuss the aspects related to IS security that ensure the protection and integrity of information. We continue our exploration by presenting several metrics, mainly financial, to assess the added value of IS in companies. Next, we present a brief description of a very fashionable approach to make the information system evolve in all coherence, which is the urbanization of IS. We conclude this chapter with some IS challenges focusing on the leading causes of IS implementation's failure and success.

Keywords: *information, system, information system, IS typology, Decision-making, IS applications, IS security, IS evaluation, IS evolution, and IS challenges*

1. INTRODUCTION

According to Russell Ackoff [1], a systems theorist and professor of organizational change, the content of the human mind can be classified into three categories:

1. **Data** represents a fact or an event statement unrelated to other things. Data is generally used regarding hard facts. This can be a mathematical symbol or text used to identify, describe, or represent something like temperature or a person. The data simply exists and has no meaning beyond its existence (in itself). It can exist in any form, usable or not. The data exists in different formats, such as text, image, sound, or even video.
2. **Information** is data combined with meaning. Information embodies the understanding of a relationship as the relationship between cause and effect [2]. Ex: The temperature dropped 15 degrees, then it started to rain. A temperature reading of 100 can have different meanings when combined with the term Fahrenheit or with the term Celsius. More semantics can be added if more context for the temperature read is added, such as the fact that this temperature concerns a liquid or a gas or the seasonal norm of 20°. In other words, information is data that has meaning through relational connection. According to Ackoff, information is useful data; it provides answers to the questions: "who," "what," "where," and "when."
3. **Knowledge** can be seen as information combined with experience, context, and interpretation. Knowledge constitutes an additional semantic level derived from information via a process. Sometimes this process is observational. Ackoff defines it as applying data and information; knowledge provides answers to the question "how" For example, what happens in cold weather for aircraft managers? Observational knowledge engineers interpret cold by its impact, which is the ice that can form on an aircraft by reducing aerodynamic thrust and potentially hampering the performance of its control surfaces [2].

IF temperature < = 0° C THEN cold = true;

Cold IF == right THEN notify personnel to remove ice from aircraft.

Indeed, knowledge is the appropriate collection of information such that it intends to be useful. Knowledge is a deterministic process. Memorization of information leads to knowledge. Knowledge represents a pattern and provides a high level of predictability regarding what is being described or will happen next.

Ex: If the humidity is very high and the temperature drops drastically, the atmosphere is unlikely to hold the humidity so that it rains.

This knowledge has a useful meaning, but its integration in a context will infer new knowledge. For example, a student memorizes or accumulates knowledge of the multiplication Table. A student can answer 2 × 2 because this knowledge is in the multiplication table. Nevertheless, when asked for 1267 × 300, he cannot answer correctly because he cannot dip into the multiplication table. To answer such a question correctly requires a real cognitive and analytical capacity that exists in the next level ... comprehension. In computer jargon, most of the applications we use (modeling, simulation, etc.) use stored knowledge.

2. SYSTEM DEFINITION

The system is an aggregated "whole" where each component interacts with at least one other component of the system. The components or parts of a system can be real or abstract.

All system components work toward a standard system goal. A system can contain several subsystems. It can be connected to other systems.

A system is a collection of elements or components that interact to achieve goals. The elements themselves and the relationships between them determine how the system works. Systems have inputs, processing mechanisms, outputs, and feedback mechanisms. A system processes the input to create the output [3].

- Input is the activity of collecting and capturing data.
- Processing involves the transformation of inputs into outputs such as computation, for example.
- Output is about producing useful information, usually in the form of documents and reports. The output of one system can become the input of another system. For example, the output of a system, which processes sales orders, can be used as input to a customer's billing system. Computers typically produce output to printers and display to screens. The output can also be reports and documents written by hand or produced manually.
- Finally, feedback or feedback is information from the system used to modify inputs or treatments as needed.

3. INFORMATION SYSTEM DEFINITION

An information system (IS) is a set of interrelated components that collect, manipulate, store and disseminate information and provide a feedback mechanism to achieve a goal. The feedback mechanism helps organizations achieve their goals by increasing profits, improving customer service [3], and supporting decision-making and control in organizations [4].

Companies use information systems to increase revenues and reduce costs.

In organizations, information systems are structured around four essential elements, proposed in the 1960s by Harold Leavitt (Figure 1). The pattern is known as the "Leavitt Diamond."

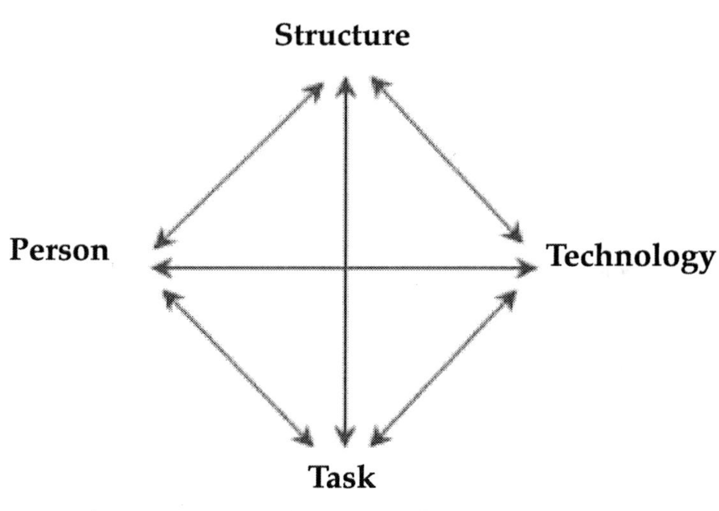

Figure 1.: *Leavitt's diamond: A socio-technical view of IS.*

1. **Technology**: The IT (Information Technology) of an IS includes the hardware, software, and telecommunications equipment used to capture, process, store and disseminate information. Today, most IS are IT-based because modern IT enables efficient operations execution and effective management in all sizes.
2. **Task**: activities necessary for the production of a good or service. These activities are supported by the flow of material, information, and knowledge between the different participants.
3. **Person**: The people component of an information system encompasses all the people directly involved in the system. These people include the managers who define the goals of the system, the users, and the developers.
4. **Structure**: The organizational structure and information systems component refers to the relationship between individuals people components. Thus, it encompasses hierarchical structures, relationships, and systems for evaluating people.

4. TYPOLOGY OF INFORMATION SYSTEMS

A company has systems to support the different managerial levels. These systems include transaction processing systems, management information systems, decision support systems, and dedicated business intelligence systems.

Companies use information systems so that accurate and up-to-date information is available when needed [5].

Within the same organization, executives at different hierarchy levels have very different information requirements, and different types of information systems have evolved to meet their needs. A common approach for examining the types of information systems used within organizations is to classify them according to their roles at different organizational structure levels, and this approach is called a vertical approach. Indeed, the organization is considered a management pyramid at four levels (Figure 2):

- **On the lowest level**, staff perform routine day-to-day operations such as selling goods and issuing payment receipts.
- **Operational management** in which managers are responsible for overseeing transaction control and deal with issues that may arise.
- **Tactical management,** which has the prerogative of making decisions on budgets, setting objectives, identifying trends, and planning short-term business activities.
- **Strategic management** is responsible for defining its long-term objectives and positioning concerning its competitors or its industry.

4.1 Transaction processing system (TPS)

At the operational level, managers need systems that keep track of the organization for necessary activities and operations, such as sales and material flow in a factory. A transaction processing system is a computer system that performs and records the routine (daily) operations necessary for managing affairs, such as keeping employee records, payroll, shipping merchandise, keeping records, accounting and treasury.

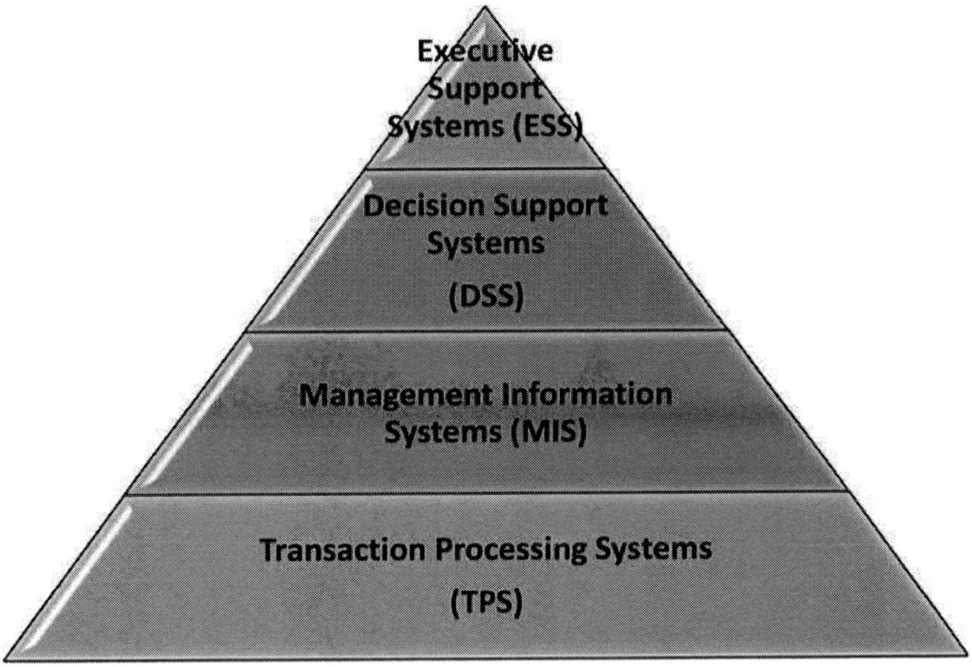

Figure 2.: *Information Systems types according to managerial level.*

At this level, the primary purpose of systems is to answer routine questions and monitor transactions flow through the organization.

At the operational level, tasks, resources, and objectives are predefined and highly structured. The decision to grant credit to a customer, for example, is made by a primary supervisor according to predefined criteria. All that needs to be determined is whether the client meets the criteria.

4.2 Management information systems (MIS)

Middle managers need systems to help with oversight, control, decision making, and administrative activities. The main question that this type of system must answer is: is everything working correctly?

Its role is to summarize and report on essential business operations using data provided by transaction processing systems. Primary transaction data is synthesized and aggregated, and it is usually presented in reports produced regularly.

4.3 Decision support systems (DSS)

DSS supports decision-making for unusual and rapidly evolving issues, for which there are no fully predefined procedures. This type of system attempts to answer questions such as: What would impact production schedules if we were to double sales for December? What would the level of Return on investment be if the plant schedule were delayed by more than six months?

While DSSs use internal information from TPS and MIS systems, they also leverage external sources, such as stock quotes or competitor product prices. These systems use a variety of models to analyze the data. The system can answer questions such as: Considering customer's delivery schedule and the freight rate offered, which vessel should be assigned, and what fill rate to maximize profits? What is the optimum speed at which a vessel can maximize profit while meeting its delivery schedule?

4.4 Executive support system (ESS)

ESS helps top management make decisions. They address exceptional decisions requiring judgment, assessment, and a holistic view of the business situation because there is no procedure to be followed to resolve a given issue at this level.

ESS uses graphics and data from many sources through an interface that senior managers easily understand. ESS is designed to integrate data from the external environment, such as new taxes or competitor data, and integrate aggregate data from MIS and DSS. ESSs filter, synthesize and track critical data. Particular attention is given to displaying this data because it contributes to the rapid assimilation of these top management figures. Increasingly, these systems include business intelligence analysis tools to identify key trends and forecasts.

5. DECISION MAKING AND INFORMATION SYSTEMS

Decision-making in companies is often associated with top management. Today, employees at the operational level are also responsible for individual decisions since information systems make information available at all company levels.

So decisions are made at all levels of the company.

Although some of these decisions are common, routine, and frequent, the value of improving any single decision may be small, but improving hundreds or even thousands of "small" decisions can add value to the business.

Not all situations that require decisions are the same. While some decisions result in actions that significantly impact the organization and its future, others are much less important and play a relatively minor role. A decision's impact is a criterion that can differentiate between decision situations and the degree of the decision's structuring. Many situations are very structured, with well-defined entrances and exits. For example, it is relatively easy to determine the amount of an employee's pay if we have the appropriate input data (for example, the number of hours worked and their hourly wage rate), and all the rules of relevant decision (for example, if the hours worked during a week are more than 40, then the overtime must be calculated), and so on. In this type of situation, it is relatively easy to develop information systems that can be used to help (or even automate) the decision.

In contrast, some decision situations are very complex and unstructured, where no specific decision rules can be easily identified. As an example, consider the following task: "Design a new vehicle that is a convertible (with a retractable hardtop), has a high safety rating, and is esthetically pleasing to a reasonably broad audience. No predefined solution to this task finalizing a design will involve many compromises and require considerable knowledge and expertise.

Examples of Types of decisions, according to managerial level, are presented in Table 1.

***Table 1.**: Types of decisions according to managerial level.*

Decision level	Characteristics of decisions	Examples of decisions
Top Management	Unstructured	Decide whether or not to come into the market
		Approve the budget allocated to capital
		Decide on long-term goals
Intermediate management	Semi-structured	Design a marketing plan
		Develop a departmental budget
		Design a website for the company
Operational management	Structured	Determine the overtime hours
		Determine the rules for stock replenishment
		Grant credit to customers
		Offer special offers to customers

Generally speaking, structured decisions are more common at lower levels of the organization, while unstructured problems are more common at higher business levels.

The more structured the decision, the easier it is to automate. If it is possible to derive an algorithm that can be used to make an efficient decision and the input data to the algorithm can be obtained at a reasonable cost, it generally makes sense to automate the decision.

Davenport and Harris [6] proposed a framework for the categorization of applications used for decision automation. Most of the systems they describe include some expert systems, often combined with DSS and/or EIS aspects. The categories they provided include Solution Configuration, Optimization of Performance, Routing or Segmentation of Decisions, Business Regulatory Compliance, Fraud Detection, Dynamic Forecasting, and Operational Control.

Many business decision situations are not very structured, and therefore cannot (or should not) be fully automated.

5.1 A particular type of decision support system: geographic information systems

Data visualization tools allow users to see patterns and relationships in large amounts of data that would be difficult to discern if the data had been presented in tabular form, for example.

Geographic Information Systems (GIS) helps decision-makers visualize issues requiring knowledge about people's geographic distribution or other resources. GIS software links the location data of points, lines, and areas on a map. Some GIS have modeling capabilities to modify data and simulate the impact of these modifications. For example, GIS could help the government calculate response times to natural disasters and other emergencies or help banks identify the best replacement for installing new branches or ATMs of tickets.

Geographic (or geospatial) information refers not only to things that exist (or are being planned) on specific locations on the Earth's surface but also to events such as traffic congestion, flooding, and other events such as an open-air festival [7].

Its scope and granularity characterize this information:

- Location, extent, and coverage are essential aspects of geographic information.
- Granularity, for example, geometric information, can be concise or fuzzy depending on the application.

GIS is used to capture, store, analyze, and visualize data that describes part of the Earth's surface, technical and administrative entities, and the results of geosciences, economics, and ecological applications.

- It is a computer system with a database observing the spatial distribution of objects, activities, or events described by points, lines, or surfaces.
- It is a comprehensive collection of tools for capturing, storing, extracting, transforming, and visualizing real-world spatial data for applications.
- It is an information system containing all the data of the territory, the atmosphere, the surface of the Earth, and the lithosphere, allowing the systematic capture, the update, the manipulation, and the analysis of these data standardized reference framework.
- It is a decision support system that integrates spatial data into a problem-solving environment.

Other definitions of GIS exist depending on the point of view of application [7], a GIS can be considered as

- A collection of spatial data with storage and retrieval functions
- A collection of algorithmic and functional tools
- A set of hardware and software components necessary for processing geospatial data
- A particular type of information technology
- A gold mine for answers to geospatial questions
- A model of spatial relations and spatial recognition.

Typically, a GIS provides functions for the storage and retrieval, interrogation and visualization, transformation, geometric and thematic analysis of information.

Indeed, geographic/geospatial information is ubiquitous, as seen on mobile devices such as cell phones, maps, satellite images, positioning and routing services, and even 3D simulations, gaining popularity from increasingly essential segments of the consumers.

Technological advances in recent years have transformed classical GIS into new forms of geospatial analysis tools, namely:

- Web-based and service-oriented approaches have led to a client–server architecture.
- Mobile technology has made GIS ubiquitous in smartphones, tablets, and laptops (opening up new markets).

6. INFORMATION SYSTEMS APPLICATIONS

IS applications cover functional areas and focus on the execution of business processes across the enterprise, including all management levels.

There are several categories of business applications: Enterprise Resource Planning (ERP), Supply Chain Management systems (SCM), Customer Relationship Management systems (CRM), electronic commerce or e-commerce, Knowledge Management systems or KM, and Business Intelligence or BI. The categories of business applications dealt with in this section cover all managerial levels since KMS are mainly intended for top management (ESS), SCMs, CRMs, and BI for mid-level management (MIS and DSS), ERP and e-commerce dedicated to the transactional level (TPS or basic or operational).

However, it is useful to specify that some ERP systems, such as the global giant SAP, offer versions of its software package covering these different categories, including SCM and CRM.

6.1 ERP, Enterprise resource planning

ERPs allow business processes related to production, finance and accounting, sales and marketing, and human resources to be integrated into a single software system. Information that was previously fragmented across many different systems is integrated into a single system with a single, comprehensive database that multiple business stakeholders can use.

An ERP system centralizes an organization's data, and the processes it applies are the processes that the organization must adopt [8]. When an ERP provider designs a module, it must implement the rules of the associated business processes. ERP systems apply best management practices. In other words, when an organization implements ERP, it also improves its management as part of ERP integration. For many organizations, implementing an ERP system is an excellent opportunity to improve their business practices and upgrade their software simultaneously. Nevertheless, integrating an ERP represents a real challenge: Are the processes integrated into the ERP better than those currently used? Furthermore, if the integration is booming, and the organization operates the same as its competitors, how do you differentiate yourself?

ERPs are configurable according to the specificities of each organization. For organizations that want to continue using their processes or even design new ones, ERP systems provide means for customizing these processes. However, the burden of maintenance falls on the organizations themselves in the case of ERP customization.

Organizations will need to consider the following decision carefully: should they accept the best practice processes embedded in the ERP system or develop their processes? If the choice is ERP, process customization should only concern processes essential to its competitive advantage.

6.2 E-commerce, electronic commerce

Electronic commerce is playing an increasingly important role in organizations with their customers.

E-commerce enables market expansion with minimal capital investment, improves the supply and marketing of products and services. Nevertheless, there is still a need for universally accepted standards to ensure the quality and security of information and sufficient telecommunications bandwidth.

The three main categories of e-commerce are Business-to-Consumer (B2C), Business-to-Business (B2B), and Consumer-to-Consumer (C2C).

- Business-to-Consumer (B2C) e-commerce involves the retailing of products and services to individual customers. Amazon, which sells books, software, and music to individual consumers, is an example of B2C e-commerce.
- Business-to-Business (B2B), e-commerce involves the sale of goods and services between businesses. The ChemConnect website for buying and selling chemicals and plastics is an example of B2B e-commerce.
- Consumer-to-Consumer (C2C), this type of e-commerce involves consumers selling directly to consumers. For example, eBay, the giant web-based auction site, allows individuals to sell their products to other consumers by auctioning their goods, either to the highest bidder or through a fixed price.

6.3 SCM, Information systems for supply chain management

Information systems for the management of the supply chain or SCM make it possible to manage its suppliers' relations. These systems help suppliers and distributors share information about orders, production, inventory levels, and delivery of products and services so that they can source, produce and deliver goods and services efficiently.

The ultimate goal is to get the right amount of products from their suppliers at a lower cost and time. Additionally, these systems improve profitability by enabling managers to optimize scheduling decisions for procurement, production, and distribution.

Anomalies in the supply chain, such as parts shortages, underutilized storage areas, prolonged storage of finished products, or high transportation cost, are caused by inaccurate or premature information. For example, manufacturers may stock an excessive amount of parts because they do not know precisely the dates of upcoming deliveries from suppliers. Alternatively, conversely, the manufacturer may order a small number of raw materials because they do not have precise information about their needs. These supply chain inefficiencies squander up to 25 percent of the company's operating costs.

If a manufacturer has precise information on the exact number of units of the product demanded by customers, on what date, and its exact production rate, it would be possible to implement a successful strategy called "just in time" (just-in-time strategy). Raw materials would be received precisely when production needed them, and finished products would be shipped off the assembly line with no need for storage.

However, there are always uncertainties in a supply chain because many events cannot be predicted, such as late deliveries from suppliers, defective parts or non-conforming raw materials, or even breakdowns in the production process. To cope with these kinds of contingencies and keep their customers happy, manufacturers often deal with these uncertainties by stocking more materials or products than they need. The safety stock acts as a buffer against probable supply chain anomalies. While managing excess inventory is expensive, a low stock fill rate is also costly because orders can be canceled.

6.4 CRM, Information systems for customer relationship management

CRM aims to manage customer relationships by coordinating all business processes that deal with customers' sales and marketing. The goal is to optimize revenue, customer satisfaction, and customer loyalty. This collected information helps companies identify, attract and retain the most profitable customers, and provide better service to existing customers and increase sales.

The CRM captures and integrates the data of the company's customers. It consolidates data, analyzes it, and distributes the results to different systems and customer touchpoints throughout the company. A point of contact (touchpoint, contact point) is a means of interaction with the customer, such as telephone, e-mail, customer service, conventional mail, website, or even a sales store, by retail.

Well-designed CRM systems provide a single view of the company's customers, which is useful for improving sales and customer service quality. Such systems also provide customers with a single view of the business regardless of their contact point or usage.

CRM systems provide data and analytical tools to answer these types of questions: "What is the value of a customer to the business" "Who are the most loyal customers?" "Who are the most profitable customers" and "What products are profitable customers buying?"

Businesses use the answers to these questions to acquire new customers, improve service quality, support existing customers, tailor offerings to customer preferences, and deliver escalating services to retain profitable customers.

6.5 KM, knowledge management

Some companies perform better than others because they know how to create, produce, and deliver products and services. This business knowledge is difficult to emulate, is unique, and can be leveraged and deliver long-term strategic benefits. Knowledge Management Systems or KMS enable organizations to manage processes better to collect and apply knowledge and expertise. These systems collect all the relevant knowledge and experiences in the company and make them available to everyone to improve business processes and decision management.

Knowledge management systems can take many different forms, but the primary goals are: 1) facilitating communication between knowledge workers within an organization, and 2) to make explicit the expertise of a few and make it available to many.

Consider an international consulting firm, for example. The company employs thousands of consultants across many countries. The consultancy team in Spain may be trying to resolve a client's problem, very similar to a consultancy team in Singapore that has already been solved. Rather than reinventing the solution, it would be much more useful for the Spain team to use the Singapore team's knowledge.

One way to remedy this situation is to store case histories from which employees worldwide can access (via the Internet) and search for cases (using a search engine) according to their respective needs. If the case documentation is of good quality (accurate, timely, complete), the consultants will share and benefit from each other's experiences, and the knowledge gained.

Unfortunately, it is often difficult to get employees to contribute meaningfully to the knowledge base (as they are probably more concerned with moving forward on their next engagements with customers rather than documenting their past experiences). For such systems to have any chance of success, the work organization must change, such as establishing a reward system for cases captured and well documented.

6.6 BI, business intelligence

The term Business Intelligence (BI) is generally used to describe a type of information system designed to help decision-makers learn about trends and identify relationships in large volumes of data. Typically, BI software is used in conjunction with large databases or data warehouses. While the specific capabilities of BI systems vary, most can be used for specialized reporting (e.g., aggregated data relating to multiple dimensions), ad-hoc queries, and trend analysis.

As with knowledge management systems, the value of business intelligence systems can be hampered in several ways. The quality of the data that is captured and stored is not guaranteed. Besides, the database (or data warehouse) may lack essential data (for example, ice cream sales are likely to correlate with temperature; without the temperature information, it may be difficult to identify why it is. There has been an increase or decrease in sales of ice cream). A third challenge is the lack of mastery of data analysts over the context of the organization's operations, even if they are proficient in BI software. In contrast, a manager has mastery of the organization but does not know how to use BI software. As a result, it is common to have a team (a manager associated with a data analyst) to get the most information (and/or knowledge) from a business intelligence system.

7. INFORMATION SYSTEMS SECURITY

Unlike physical assets, the information does not necessarily disappear when it has been stolen. If an organization holds confidential information such as a new manufacturing process, it may be uploaded by an unauthorized person and remain available to the organization.

Exposing information to unauthorized personnel constitutes a breach of confidentiality.

Another type of system failure happens when the integrity of information is no longer guaranteed. In other words, rather than unauthorized exposure of information, there are unauthorized changes of information. A corporate website containing documentation on how to configure or repair its products could suffer severe financial harm if an intruder could change instructions, leading to customers misconfigure or even ruin the purchased product.

Finally, the denial of access to information or the unavailability of information represents another type of information failure. For example, if a doctor is prevented from accessing a patient's test results, the patient may suffer needlessly or even die. A commercial website could lose significant sales if its website were down for an extended period.

Understanding the potential causes of system failure enables appropriate action to be taken to avoid them. There are a wide variety of potential threats to an organization's information systems.

Human threats are the most complicated to manage because they include a wide variety of behaviors. To illustrate how the level of detail can vary, some relevant subcategories include:

- Accidental behavior by members of the organization, technical support staff, and customers of the organization
- Malicious behavior by someone inside or outside the organization
- Other categories of threats include:
- A natural event: flood, fire, tornado, ice storm, earthquake, pandemic flu
- Environmental elements: chemical spill, gas line explosion.
- Technical Threat: Hardware or software failure
- Operational Threat: a faulty process that unintentionally compromises the confidentiality, integrity, or availability of information. For example, an operational procedure that allows application programmers to upgrade software without test or notification system operators can result in prolonged outages.

It is possible to categorize the various checks intended to avoid a failure, such as:

1. Management controls management processes that identify system requirements such as confidentiality, integrity, and availability of information and provide for various management controls to ensure that these requirements are met.
2. Operational controls: include the day-to-day processes associated with the provision of information services.
3. Technical controls: concern the technical capacities integrated into the IT infrastructure to support the increased confidentiality, integrity, and availability of information services.

A widely cited Gartner research report concludes that "people directly cause 80% of downtime in critical application services. The remaining 20% are caused by technological failures, environmental failure or a natural disaster".

Often, these failures are the result of software modifications such as adding new features or misconfiguring servers or network devices.

IT professionals should ensure that system changes are prioritized and tested and that all interested parties are notified of proposed changes.

8. INFORMATION SYSTEMS ASSESSMENT

Perceptible benefits can be quantified and assigned a monetary value. Imperceptible benefits, such as more efficient customer service or improved decision making, cannot be immediately quantified but can lead to quantifiable long-term gain [4].

System performance can be measured in different ways.

8.1 Efficiency

Efficiency is often referred to as "doing the things right" or doing things right. Efficiency can be defined as the ratio of output to input. In other words, a company is more efficient if it produces more with the same amount of resources or if it produces the same amount of output with a lower investment of resources, or - even better - produces more with less input. In other words, the company achieves improvements in terms of efficiency by reducing the waste of resources while maximizing Productivity.

Each time an item is sold or ordered, the manager updates the quantity of the item sold in the inventory system. The manager needs to check the sales to determine which items have been sold the most and restocked. This considerably reduces the manager's time to manage his stock (limit input to achieve the same output). So efficiency is a measure of what is produced divided by what is consumed [3].

8.2 Effectiveness

Effectiveness is measured based on the degree achieved in achieving system objectives. It can be calculated by dividing the objectives achieved by the total of the objectives set.

Effectiveness is denoted as "doing the right thing" or doing the things necessary or right. It is possible to define effectiveness as an organization's ability to achieve its stated goals and objectives. Typically, a business more significant is the one that makes the best decisions and can carry them out.

For example, to better meet its various customers' needs, an organization may create or improve its products and services founded on data collected from them and information accumulated from sales activities. In other words, information systems help organizations better understand their customers and deliver the products and services that customers desire. Collecting customer data on an individual basis will help the organization provide them with personalized service.

The manager can also ask customers what kind of products and services customers would like to buy in the future, trying to anticipate their needs. With the information gathered, the manager will order the customers' products and stop ordering unpopular products.

In what follows, we present several formulas established to measure efficiency and effectiveness resulting from the information systems use. Indeed, the impact of an information system on an organization can be assessed using financial measures.

8.3 Financial measures of managerial performance

When the information system is implemented, management will certainly want to assess whether the system has succeeded in achieving its objectives. Often this assessment is challenging to achieve. The business can use financial metrics such as Productivity, Return On Investment (ROI), net present value, and other performance metrics explained in the following:

8.3.1 Return on investment

Return on investment, denoted as a Return rate, is a financial ratio that measures the amount gained or lost compared to the amount initially invested.

An information system with a positive return on investment indicates that this system can improve its efficiency.

The advantage of using Return on investment is that it is possible to quantify the costs and benefits of introducing an information system. Therefore, it is possible to use this metric to compare different systems and see which systems can help the organization be more efficient and/or more effective.

8.3.2 Productivity

Developing information systems that measure Productivity and control is a crucial element for most organizations. Productivity is a measure of produced output divided by required input. A higher production level for a given entry-level means greater Productivity; a lower output level for a given entry-level means lower Productivity. Values assigned to productivity levels are not always based on hours worked. Productivity may be based on the number of raw materials used, the quality obtained, or the time to produce the goods or services. According to other parameters and with other organizations in the same industry, Productivity's value has to mean only compared to other Productivity periods.

8.3.3 Profit growth

Another measure of the SI value is the increase in profit or the growth in realized profits. For example, a mail-order company installs an order processing system that generates 7 percent growth in profits over the previous year.

8.3.4 Market share

Market share is the percentage of sales of a product or service relative to the overall market. If installing a new online catalog increases sales, it could help increase the company's market share by, for example, 20 percent.

8.3.5 Customer satisfaction

Although customer satisfaction is difficult to quantify, many companies measure their information systems performance based on internal and external feedback. Some companies use surveys and questionnaires to determine whether investments have resulted in increased customer satisfaction.

8.3.6 Total cost of ownership

Another way to measure the value of information systems has been developed by the Gartner Group and is called the Total Cost of Ownership (TCO). This approach allocates the total costs between acquiring the technology, technical support, and administrative costs. Other costs are added to the TCO, namely: retooling and training costs. TCO can help develop a more accurate estimate of total costs for systems ranging from small computers to large mainframe systems.

9. INFORMATION SYSTEMS EVOLUTION

The evolution of information technologies leads to the reflection on new approaches that set up more flexible, more scalable architectures to meet its agility needs. The urbanization of information systems is one such approach.

9.1 Definition of the urbanization of information systems

The company's information system's urbanization is an IT discipline consisting of developing its information system to guarantee its consistency with its objectives and business. By taking into account its external and internal constraints while taking advantage of the opportunities of the IT state of the art.

This discipline is based on a series of concepts modeled on those of the urbanization of human habitat (organization of cities, territory), concepts that have been reused in IT to formalize or model the information system.

Town planning defines rules and a coherent, stable, and modular framework, to which the various stakeholders refer for any investment decision relating to the management of the information system.

In other words, to urbanize is to lead the information systems' continuous transformation to simplify it and ensure its consistency.

The challenges of urbanization consist of managing complexity, communicating and federating work, considering organizational constraints, and guiding technological choices.

9.2 Stages of urbanization

9.2.1 Definition of objectives

Define and frame the objectives of the project, define the scope, develop the schedule.

9.2.2 Analysis of the existing situation

Carry out the inventory, organize the work, and present the deliverables. More precisely, list the assets and map the different layers (business, functional, application, and technical):

- Business Architecture
  Identify "business processes": Who does what and why? The description of the processes is done with BPMN, EPC formalisms, etc. This step is tricky and may require the use of exploration methods. However, it does improve the overall understanding and increase the possibilities for optimization
- Functional architecture
  Identify the "functional block": What do we need to carry out the business processes? Here, we are based on a classic division into zones (exchanges, core business, reference data, production data, support activities, management). This step's difficulty lies in choosing the right level of detail and remaining consistent with business processes. However, it provides a hierarchical presentation and makes it easier to break down the work.
- Application Architecture
  Identify the applications: How to achieve the functionalities? This step is based on a classic N-Tiers division. However, it is not easy to provide value and solutions compared to functional architecture. This stage lays the foundations for the realization (major technological choices, etc.).
- System Architecture
  Identify the technical components: With what and where the applications work, it is based on a classic division into technical areas (security, storage, etc.). It is not easy to make the connection between applications and servers. This step brings concrete and structuring and is essential to assess the cost of the system.

9.2.3 Identification of the target IS

Impact on the different layers, consideration of constraints (human, material, etc.), design of costed scenarios, and arbitration of the choice of a target.

9.2.4 Development of the trajectory

How to organize the work, frame and then refine the budgets, design and plan projects, define the support strategy, set up an organization, contributions, roles, and responsibilities of actors.

At the end of this process, a Land Use Plan (LUP) is defined. It is a report consisting of:

- Summaries of the orientations chosen as well as the justifications for the options selected.
- A definition of areas, neighborhoods, and blocks.
- Existing and target maps (process, functional, application, and technical mapping).
- Additional documents (interview reports, list of people and organizational entities, etc.)

The goal is to identify the gaps between the existing and the principles of urbanization and establish changes by describing the actions and their corresponding cost.

In practice, the urbanization process is very cumbersome to implement. On the one hand, it requires the participation of many actors in the organization, and on the other hand, the analysis is very long. As a result, needs to change, and LUP is no longer necessarily suitable.

10. INFORMATION SYSTEMS CHALLENGES

The reasons for a successful or unsuccessful IS implementation are complex and contested by different stakeholders and from the various perspectives involved. Developers tend to focus on the system's technical validity in terms of execution, operation, and evolution. Other qualities are often considered, such as security, maintainability, scalability, stability, and availability. All of these criteria are considered to be signs of successful IS Development.

The failure of an IS can be defined as: either the system put in place does not meet the user's expectations or does not function properly. The reasons for failure are as divergent as the projects.

The perspective of project management, on the other hand, tends to focus on the consumption of resources. The project delivered with the initial budget and within the allotted time is considered a successful project. Nelson [9] analyzed 99 SI projects and identified 36 classic errors. He categorized these errors into four categories: process, people, product, and technology. The last category concerns the factors leading to IS failures based on the misuse of modern technologies.

The seminal article by DeLone and McLean [10] suggested that IS success should be the preeminent dependent variable for the IS domain. These researchers proposed a taxonomy of six interdependent variables to define the IS' success as the system's quality, the quality of information, the IS, user satisfaction, individual impact, and organizational impact.

One of the significant extensions to this proposition is the dimension of the IT department's quality of service [11].

Either way, the use of the system is seen as a sign of its success. The IS use level is incorporated into most IS success models [11, 12]. These models show the complexity of measuring user satisfaction because, even in the same organization, some user groups may be more or less enthusiastic than others to use the new information system.

In the current global context of the covid pandemic, it appears clear that information systems that integrate web and mobile technologies can positively contribute to the monitoring of contaminated cases and therefore minimize the risks of contamination provided that users adhere to this movement for the benefit of all [13]. A truly global, rapid, and efficient decision-making process is enabled by the integration of information systems from distributed sources [14].

11. CONCLUSION

To conclude this introductive chapter, we present its key ideas:

- Levels of information are data, information, and knowledge.
- The system is an aggregated "whole" where each component interacts with at least one other system component to achieve a goal.

- An information system can be defined as a set of interconnected components that gather, process, store and dispense information to support decision making and control in an organization. An IS can be seen as a socio-technical system. The technical part includes the technology and the processes, while the social part includes the people and the structure.
- The role of information systems is to solve an organization's problems concerning its information needs
- A company has systems to support the different managerial levels: transaction processing systems, management information systems, decision support systems, and systems dedicated to business intelligence.
- Decisions can be operational or strategic.
- There are several categories of business applications: enterprise resource planning, supply chain management systems, customer relationship management systems, knowledge management systems, and business intelligence.
- Among the failures that can affect IS a violation of confidentiality, integrity, and availability of information.
- The controls intended to avoid the IS's security failures include management controls, operational controls, and technical controls.
- The information system's performance can be measured according to efficiency, effectiveness, Return on investment, Productivity, customer satisfaction, etc.
- Urbanizing an information system means directing its continuous transformation to guarantee its consistency
- The reasons for a successful or unsuccessful implementation of an IS are complex and contested by the various stakeholders and from the various perspectives involved.

REFERENCES

1. Ackoff R L. From Data to Wisdom. Journal of Applied Systems Analysis; 1989, 16, 3-9.
2. Watson R T. Information Systems. Global Text Project, University of Georgia, Collection open source textbooks; 2007, 1-33.
3. Stair R M, Reynolds G. Fundamentals of business information systems. Thomson Learning; 2008, 118-129
4. Laudon K C, Laudon J P. Management information systems: managing the digital firm. Edition 12, Prentice Hall; 2012.
5. Van Belle J P, Nash J, Eccles M. Discovering Information Systems: an exploratory approach. University of Cape Town; 2010.
6. Davenport T H, Harris J G. Automated Decision Making Comes of Age. Sloan Management Review; 2005, 46(4), 83-89.
7. Kresse, W., & Danko, D. M. Springer handbook of geographic information. Springer Science & Business Media; 2012.

8. Bourgeois, D. T. Information Systems for Business and Beyond. Washington: The Saylor Academy; 2014.
9. Nelson, R. R. (2007). IT project management: infamous failures, classic mistakes, and best practices. MIS Quarterly Executive, 6 (2), 67-78.
10. DeLone, W.H., and McLean, E.R. (1992) Information systems success: The quest for the dependent variable. Information Systems Research, 3 (1), 60-95.
11. Petter, Stacie, William DeLone, and Ephraim R. McLean. (2013). Information systems success: The quest for the independent variables. Journal of Management Information Systems 29 (4), 7-62.
12. Delone, William H., and Ephraim R. McLean, (2003). The DeLone and McLean model of information systems success: a ten-year update. Journal of management information systems 19 (4), 9-30.
13. Ågerfalk, P. J., Conboy, K., & Myers, M. D. (2020). Information systems in the age of pandemics: COVID-19 and beyond.
14. O'Leary, D. E. (2020). Evolving information systems and technology research issues for COVID-19 and other pandemics. Journal of Organizational Computing and Electronic Commerce, 30(1), 1-8.

2

Exploring the Benefits of an Agile Information System

Pankaj Chaudhary, Micki Hyde and James A. Rodger

Information Systems and Decisions Sciences Department, Eberly College of Business and IT, Indiana University of Pennsylvania, Indiana, USA.

ABSTRACT

Information Systems (IS) agility is a current topic of interest in the IS industry. The study follows up on work on the definition of the construct of IS agility and attributes for sensing, diagnosis, and selection and execution in an agile IS. IS agility is defined as the ability of an IS to sense a change in real time; diagnose it in real time; and select and execute a response in real time. Architecting an agile IS is a complex and resource-intensive task, and hence examination of its benefits is highly desired and appropriate. This paper examines the benefits of an Agile Information System. Benefits of an agile IS were derived from related academic literature and then refined using practitioner literature and qualitative data. The benefits considered were the first order or direct benefits. These benefits were then empirically validated through a survey of IT practitioners. The results of the survey were analyzed and a rank order of the benefits was arrived at. An exploratory factor analysis was also done to find the common dimensions underlying the benefits. It is suggested that organizations can use the empirically validated benefits from this study to justify and jump-start their capital and labor expenditure to build agility into their Information System.

Keywords: *Information Systems Agility Benefits, Agile Information Systems Benefits, Agility*

1. INTRODUCTION

Change is the rule of the game in the current business environment. Not only are the changes occurring at an increasing rate, they are becoming increasingly unpredictable. This unpredictability can involve when a known change will occur, what an unknown change will look like, or the combination of these. The rapid rate of change implies that an organization needs to become an expert at changing and morphing itself rapidly in response to a change. As per the ORACLE cloud agility survey [1] the ability of the competitor to launch innovative services more rapidly was identified as a top threat by 27% of the respondents. Also, as per the survey, a majority of businesses believe they are agile but cannot flexibly manage workloads or rapidly develop, test, and launch new applications, leaving them poorly prepared to deal with competitive threats. Retention of leadership and/or competitive position requires that an organization should be able to change at will in any direction, without significant cost and time, to counter a threat or capitalize on an opportunity. Such an organization may be characterized as an agile organization. For most of organizations the survival and/or retention of market share demands that the organization should be able to change faster than, or as fast as, new entrants and rivals. The ORACLE survey found that the impact of agility on competitiveness is critically important to businesses.

Information Systems (IS) pervade all aspects of modern organizational functioning and play an integral role in information processing activities of an organization. Information Systems are needed for organizational agility on account of their ability to provide shared, distributed and integrated, current, and fast-flowing information [2] - [8] .

Modern business processes in organizations use IS as a core resource or component. In many and most of cases, IS may completely or significantly embed a business process (e.g., Internet banking). The pivotal role of IS in modern organizational business processes means that an organization (agile or striving to be) cannot change its business processes unless the IS changes as well. Thus an agile organization would need an agile IS. As per the ORACLE cloud agility survey, 81% of the respondents stated that the ability to rapidly develop, test, and launch new business applications is critically important or important to the success of the business. In particular 29% of the respondents believed that effective mobilization of applications and services is the most important factor in business success today [1] . What Brandt and Boynton [9] indicated in 1993 still holds true—current IS are not easy to change though several are getting better at it in some aspects.

So what is an agile IS? We arrive at the definition or construct of an agile IS based on prior work done by the authors in this area. Agility in general is defined [10] [11] as a formative construct comprised of the ability to sense a change, diagnose a change, select a response, and execute the response in real- time:

1) Sense: Ability to sense the stimuli for change (as they occur) in real-time;
2) Diagnose: Ability to interpret or analyze stimuli in real-time to determine the nature, cause, and impact of change;
3) Respond: Ability to respond to a change in real-time, further disaggregated into select and execute.

a) Select: Ability to select a response in real-time (very short planning time) needed to capitalize on the opportunity or counter the threat.
b) Execute: Ability to execute the response in real-time.

Real-time is defined as the span of time in which the correctness of the task performed not only depends upon the logical correctness of the task performed but also upon the time at which the result is produced. If the timing constraints of the system are not met, system failure is said to have occurred [12] .

Thus an Agile IS may be defined as one that has the ability to sense a change in real-time, diagnose the change in real-time, select a response in real-time, and execute the response in real-time. Due to the formative nature of the construct, several, or some, of these abilities might exist in the absence of others.

The IT industry over the last few years has made strides in enhancing IS agility. Perhaps the most important development has been in the area of Cloud computing with services like Infrastructure as a Service (IaaS), Platform as a Service (PaaS), Storage as a Service, Security as a Service, Database as a Service, and Software as a Service (SaaS), amongst others. In the area of software development, methodologies like eXtreme Programming (XP), SCRUM, Feature Driven Design, Microservices, and others have been implemented to facilitate continuous change to the software by incorporating new requirements as opposed to the freezing of requirements in the Waterfall methodologies. In the area of continuous deployment, DevOps has made great strides into the industry. However the adoption of these technologies and frameworks involves some learning curve and is not as rapid as anticipated. As per the ORACLE cloud agility survey, only 32% of respondents state that they fully understand what PaaS is, rising to 37% in the US, while 29% admit that they do not understand it at all. For those that say they do understand PaaS, only 31% cite reduced time frames for application development as a main benefit [13] .

Having an agile IS is no simple task and needs a variety of abilities for sensing a change in real-time [14] , diagnosing a change in real-time [15] , and selecting a response and executing a response in real-time [16] . These abilities require a significant investment of resources in both the people and IT components of an IS. A relevant question then one may pose is what are the benefits of an agile IS? While many benefits may be apparent, it is still worthwhile to undertake an empirical investigation of this question. This is the research question addressed in this manuscript. It should be mentioned that there is literature specifically linking the role of IS to organizational agility [17] . The question explored here is specific to the benefits of IS agility, which may include both first order and higher order benefits.

2. LITERATURE REVIEW

Peer-reviewed academic literature alludes to several benefits of IS agility. While the authors clearly distinguish between flexibility and agility [11] , the published literature often does not make this distinction and hence pertinent literature from both areas is examined. Also literature from other areas like supply chain management and manufacturing (which was and is at the forefront of the agility phenomenon) is also examined.

Based on the Resource-Based View (RBV) of the firm, we consider IS as a key resource of a firm. Even though many systems can be purchased from the marketplace, the use and customization of these systems is recognized as anchoring the IS competencies of the firm. [18] [19] view IS infrastructure as an IS competence, because not all the firms can equally capitalize on information technology (IT) without using a flexible IS infrastructure. Firm competencies inherit the following properties: they are valuable, rare, inimitable, and non-substitutable. These attributes cannot be easily imitated by competitors in the short-run because capabilities are deeply rooted in the history of the firm, and some capabilities could arise just by being in the right place at the right time [20] . Agility of an IS would further enhance an organization's competitive advantage.

Traditionally IS planning was conducted on an ad-hoc basis, because IS was considered as a support system performing back-end service functions. Therefore, the main function of IS management was to choose those systems that could perform back-end functions efficiently. Since the 1980s, however, IS planning started playing an important role in business planning. However, both business planning and IS planning exercises were done in isolation. Even though business managers acknowledged the key role of IS, they did not take notice of IS competencies [20] [21] . Today, we look upon IS in an agile manner that can add benefit to the organization through sensing, directing, executing and diagnosing information in real time. A model proposed by [22] proposes to examine how IT capabilities (i.e., flexible IT infrastructure and IT assimilation) affect firm performance through absorptive capacity and supply chain agility, in the supply chain context [22] . Their research shows that absorptive capacity and supply chain agility fully mediate the influences of IT capabilities on firm performance.

There are many examples of agile IS in the literature. For example, Shin et al. [23] explored the nature and role of agility as a strategic intent and its influence on operational and firm performance. [24] claim that agile development has now become a well-known approach to collaboration in professional work life. Yanan et al. [25] believe that there has been a significant effect that the design of a plant can have on its agile and dynamic performance. Sangari et al. [26] contend that supply chain agility is a key determinant of competitiveness and they developed a practical evaluation framework that serves to identify critical factors for achieving supply chain agility. Gilgor et al. [27] feel that traditionally, researchers have claimed agility as an attribute closely tied to the effectiveness of strategic supply chain management that is closely associated with customer effectiveness. Goldsby et al. [28] claim that the relationship between agility and cost efficiency is not clear due to limited empirical scrutiny from researchers and shed light on the relationship between agility and efficiency. Narayanan et al. [29] demonstrate that several studies in the buyer-supplier relationship literature have addressed the impact of collaboration on agility performance and claim that some but not all studies have concluded that collaboration leads to beneficial effects while others have questioned the positive effects of collaboration on relationship performance. Chung et al. [30] examine how organizational workers improve their perceived job performance, while also investigating the impact of perceived organizational agility and location independence on technology acceptance. Sherehiy and Karwowski [31] believe that organizational agility requires development of an adaptable workforce that is able to deal with unexpected and dynamic changes in the business environment. They utilize an Agility Strategy Scale, Work Organization Scale, and Workforce Agility Scale to study autonomy at work as one of the most important predictors of workforce agility. Yang [32] developed and empirically tested a conceptual framework to investigate the antecedents of manufacturers' supply chain agility and the connection of their agility with performance. They postulated that technical (vvv and relational factors (information sharing and trust, and operational collaboration) are the antecedents of a manufacturer's supply chain agility.

Barthe-Delanoë et al. [33] propose that the modern business environment tends to involve a large network of heterogeneous people, devices, and organizations that engage in collaborative processes among themselves that lead to a high degree of interoperability between partner IS and that these processes need to be agile. Yusuf et al. [34] assesses the link between dimensions of an agile supply chain, competitive objectives, and business performance, and identify the most important dimensions and attributes of supply chain agility. Yusuf et al. [34] also researched the pressures that persist on organizations to master and profit from oil and gas energy. While most results suggest that clusters enhance and enable higher levels of agile practices, their findings indicate that there is no strong empirical basis to make a direct link between clusters and competitiveness. DeGroote and Marx [35] investigated the impact of information technology (IT) on supply chain agility measured by the ability to sense and respond to market changes, and the impact supply chain agility has on firm performance, and their results suggest that IT improves the supply chain's ability to sense market changes by improving the adequacy, accuracy, accessibility, and timeliness of the information flows among members of the supply chain. Balaji et al. [36] propose that Agility is perceived as the principal competitive medium for all organizations in an ambiguous and changing business environment and that enterprises are converging to a point where they need to be smarter, faster, flexible, and more reactive to changes in order to sustain in the demanding market. Seethamraju and Sundar [36] postulate that past research on the effect of ERP systems on agility is contradictory, and research on the post implementation effects of ERP systems on agility is limited and found that the inadequacies in implementation and poor process optimization prior to ERP implementation are restricting process agility. Galster and Avgeriou [37] investigate how variability facilitates the design of software products that can be adapted for a wide range of customers or contexts. They found that in agile development, software products begin to be built before the desired product is fully understood. Sheffield and Lemétayer [38] believe that there is considerable debate among practitioners and researchers on the nature of software development agility and conditions under which it is linked to project success. They found that software development agility was indicated by the project environment factor of organizational culture and a project factor of empowerment of the project team.

Krotov, et al. [39] identify several ways in which mobile technology is used to improve operational, customer, and partnering agility. A flexible IS infrastructure, according to Bharadwaj [18] , is an integrated shared system that is built piece by piece over time. That means, as a firm learns to work with a system and gradually becomes proficient in using the system, it continually works to add other pieces in the infrastructure that can set it apart from other firms. A flexible IS infrastructure allows sharing of data and applications through communication networks (Wasko and Faraj [40] . It pertains to the arrangements of hardware, software, and networks so that data and applications can be accessed and shared within and between suppliers, customers, and vendors [41] . A flexible IS infrastructure helps in integrating disparate and geographically distributed systems and make IS applications cost effective in their operations and supports, therefore, flexible infrastructure becomes a critical source of advantage to the firm [42] . Weber et al. [43] pointed out that in both academics and industry, companies increasingly adopt process-aware information systems (PAISs), which offer promising perspectives for more flexible enterprise computing. Seebacher and Winkler [44] believe that recent economic developments indicated that greater flexibility in manufacturing is more important than ever and they present an applicable approach that shows exactly how to evaluate the manufacturing flexibility and how to measure an improvement of flexibility in business practice.

The literature points to several benefits of agility and more importantly the need for agility, in general, to an organization in areas like supply chain, enhanced partnership with customers, timely information, etc. Though the unit of analysis-IS within an organization, in this manuscript is different, several of these benefits may be rolled into higher order benefits of an agile IS.

3. RESEARCH APPROACH AND OBJECTIVES

IS agility is an area where practitioners have taken the lead. In the practitioner literature, IS agility is equated to a set of technologies that enable seamless interconnection and collaboration between the IT components to achieve rapid configuration changes. The conceptualization of IS agility used in this study is much broader and more comprehensive in scope. To arrive at the benefits of an agile IS, a comprehensive survey of the practitioner literature was done. This included having Google alerts for the topic and continually refining the benefits. In addition, existing literature on agility was also examined to arrive at a list of benefits of an agile IS. Specifically, the following steps were taking to arrive at a list of benefits:

1) Arrive at a conceptualized set of benefits of an agile IS. Such benefits would arise due to the ability of an IS to respond to internal, organizational, and external changes through sensing a change in real-time, diagnosing the change in real-time, and selecting and executing a response in real-time (Pankaj, 2005).
2) Verify and refine the conceptualized set of benefits of an agile IS based on the feedback from practitioners and to arrive at a comprehensive set of benefits.
3) Validate the benefits through a survey.

4. PERCEIVED BENEFITS OF AN AGILE IS

As stated earlier benefits due to the ability of an agile IS to sense, diagnose, and select and respond in real-time are based on the comprehensive and continual review of the practitioner literature as well as published academic literature. The agility literature describes the benefits of agility as ranging from survival to enhancement of the competitive position. Since an agile IS contributes to the agility of an organization, the benefits of IS agility may span a similar range. The net effect of IS agility would be on the financial performance of the organization but it may have several other immediate or first order effects like reduction in the time needed for changing IS, etc. Table 1 gives a list of benefits of an agile IS from the classical agility literature. It may be noted that most of these are higher order benefits. For the purpose of this manuscript, the focus is on first order benefits to ensure that the effects of investments in an agile IS are observable and not confounded by other variables.

Table 1.: *Benefits of organizational agility.*

Description	References
Enhanced value to customers	Vokurka, Zank, & III, [54] ; Christian, Govande, Staehle, & Jr., [55]
Advantage from the changing situation; benefit from change	Yoffie & Kwak, [56]
Competitive advantage and/or competitive performance	Bessant, Francis, Meredith, & Kalinsky, [57] ; Schonsleben, [58] ; Cho, Jung, & Kim, [59] ; Bal et al., [3] ; Vernadat, [60] ; O'Connor, [61] ;
Profitable operations	Sahin, [62] ; Vokurka & Fliedner, [63] ; Vokurka et al., [54] ; Devor, Graves, & Miles, [64] ; Noaker, [65]
Survive unprecedented threats, viability	Sharifi & Zhang, [7] ; Cho et al., [59] ; Dove, [45] ;
Growth in a competitive market	Y. Y. Yusuf et al., [34] ;
Capture new market	Vernadat, [59]
Leadership	Dove, [45]

Overall, an agile IS will lead to a reduction in time for changing the IS. The resulting changes would also be more robust [45] . The benefits of having an agile IS for an organization are summarized in Table 2.

Table 2.: *Benefits of an agile information system.*

1) Reduction in time to implement changes in IS.
2) Increase in the robustness of the implemented changes.
3) Benefits from response to internal changes.
   a) Increase in efficiency and effectiveness of the existing business processes.
   b) Increase in efficiency and effectiveness of information processing.
   c) Build spare capacity.
   d) Build enhanced capabilities for future use.
   e) Maintain the desired levels of service as per the service level agreements for the IS.
   f) Enable fast recovery in case of outages to minimize the down time.
4) Benefits from response to organizational changes.
   a) IS is aligned to business process requirements at all times.
   b) Business processes can change rapidly (in real time).
   c) Higher financial benefits to the organization.
5) Benefits from response to environmental changes.
   a) Avoid technology obsolescence through provision of needed latest IT/IS solutions.
   b) Allow business process innovation through incorporating the latest IS solutions.
   c) Protect the IS and the organization against unfavorable licensing terms and vendor induced situations.
   d) Allow rapid response to security threats like virus attacks, cyber-attacks, etc.

Benefits of having an agile IS come from a real-time response to internal, organizational, and environmental changes. Internal changes in IS that are geared for improvements, build spare capacity and enhance capabilities. Monitoring for internal changes enables the IS to predict outages and other potential problems and thus enables fast response by the IS to maximize the uptime and maintain desired levels of services at all times. In case of outage, the properties of an agile IS enable fast recovery and minimize downtime. An IS that changes easily in response to organizational changes ensures that the IS is aligned with the business processes at all times thereby increasing the efficiency, productivity, and effectiveness of the business processes and related information processing tasks. The efficiency and effectiveness may also lead to reduction in costs. An agile IS allows for rapid changes in the business processes thereby enabling the organization to maintain or enhance profits by countering the moves of competitors. The ability to respond to an actual or anticipated IS innovation (environmental change) in real-time enables an IS to provide the latest solutions for the business processes thereby increasing the effectiveness of the business processes. It also enables business process innovation through the use of the latest IS solutions, and protects against technology obsolescence. Being responsive to the environment also enables the IS to protect itself and the organization against unfavorable events like expensive licensing terms, security vulnerabilities, cyber-attacks, and viruses.

5. IMPROVING AND REFINING THE BENEFITS OF AN AGILE IS

Ten executives were interviewed to elicit their opinions on the benefits of an agile IS. The interviews were comprehensive in the sense that they were introduced to the definition of IS agility, asked to validate it, comment on it, and discuss it, and then asked to comment on the attributes of an agile IS (published elsewhere). Subsequent to that they were asked about the benefits of an agile IS outlined in Table 2. They were requested to modify, add, and delete to and from the list. They were also requested to give a balanced perspective on different aspects of an agile IS ranging from organizational rules and policies to IT components. As per Bonoma's verification guidelines [46] , multiple interviews were proposed for purposes of literal replication. The interviewees selected were participants in a discussion round table for a research center in a major university. The participants' organizations/ companies were examined by the participating researchers and were deemed to have a need for IS agility based on an informal assessment of the antecedents of IS agility for these organizations [10] .

The interviewees' demographics demonstrated diversity (industry and size; diversity in role and responsibilities; and diversity in organizations in terms of their approach to developing and managing IS). The interviewees' roles spanned from strategic, to a mix of strategic and technical, to more specialized technical roles.

Content analysis was done on the interviews [10] . Interviewees commented on the benefits of an agile IS but only the first order benefits of an agile IS were considered. Some of the first order benefits of IS agility mentioned were better recoverability, faster development of products and services, better responsiveness, higher availability of IS and conformance to Service Level Agreements (SLAs), cost savings on IS changes, use of IS as a strategic tool, targeted information for various tasks, increased problem resolution, better utilization of IS, availability of needed functionality in IS, process improvement, quick changes to operational processes, and alignment of IS with the business needs. Of these benefits, faster development of products and services and the use of IS as a strategic tool was not included in the original list of benefits and so these were included as a benefit of responding to organizational changes. Interviews also mentioned burnout effects resulting from changing too fast and too often. Changing fast and trying to be on the cutting edge of the technology may leave the organization with IS that use technologies that do not become mainstream, and a lot of new IS that stretch the IS staff. Poor vendor support for these cutting-edge technologies and their lack of maturity further aggravates the situation. As such, being agile does not necessarily mean that the IS should always use a cutting-edge technology. This aspect is stressed in the work that details the theory behind the definition of agility [10] , where it has been mentioned that that a reconfiguration of an IS in response to change should result in a stable configuration. The criterion of stability will often preclude technologies that are not mature and proven, and are difficult to maintain. Most new and cutting-edge technologies share these characteristics, and so being agile may not necessarily mean being on the cutting-edge of technology, though such new technologies may often facilitate higher levels of IS agility.

Table 2 illustrates the perceived benefits of an Agile Information System. A refined set of attributes for sensing is presented in Table 3. New attributes have been italicized. These changes are meant to demonstrate how our study leads to improving and refining the original perceived benefits of an Agile IS. These refinements make a contribution to the literature and increase our understanding of the Agile IS construct. The benefits of an Agile IS will lead to optimization of enterprise performance with improved organizational knowledge, memory and learning. Our improved model leads to enterprise-wide intelligent information management principle adoption.

6. SURVEY DEVELOPMENT & ADMINISTRATION

Survey development and administration was performed using the well-documented steps for survey development, administration and analysis [47] [48] [49] [50] . The development and validation of the survey was performed as per the guidelines by Churchill [51] : generate sample items, pilot test, and develop final measures.

The survey contained 18 items for benefits of an agile IS along with other items relating to sensing, diagnosis, selection and execution [14] [15] [16] [52] . The survey contained 6 items pertaining to demographics. There, demographic items were based on a sample of ten surveys designed by peer researchers. The demographic information collected included the title and department of the re-

spondent, industry, the number of IS personnel, annual IS budget, and annual revenue. The draft survey was pilot-tested with four practitioners and three MIS researchers for assessing the understandability of the questions, clarity of the instructions, unambiguity in the wording of the items, and the overall format of the questionnaire. Though the questionnaire was a long, pilot-testers agreed that the survey could be completed within a reasonable time, and without extensive effort. It was suggested that items be grouped together. For example, items relating to personnel may be grouped together and items relating to the IT components may be grouped together. Additional changes suggested included the rephrasing of five items and the layout of the balloon graphic providing the definition of agility on the second page.

Table 3.: Post interview benefits of an agile information system.

1) Reduction in time to implement changes in IS.
2) Increase in the robustness of the implemented changes.
3) Benefits from response to internal changes.
   a) Increase in efficiency and effectiveness of the existing business processes.
   b) Increase in efficiency and effectiveness of the information processing.
   c) Build spare capacity.
   d) Build enhanced capabilities for future use.
   e) Maintaining the desired levels of service as per the service level agreements for the IS.
   f) Enable fast recovery in case of outages to minimize the down time.
4) Benefits from response to organizational changes.
   a) IS is aligned to business process requirements at all times.
   b) Business processes can change rapidly (in real time).
   c) Higher financial benefits to the organization.
   d) Faster development of products and services.
   e) Ability to use IS as a strategic tool.
5) Benefits from response to environmental changes.
   a) Avoid technology obsolescence through provision of needed latest IT/IS solutions.
   b) Allow business process innovation through incorporating the latest IS solutions.
   c) Protect the IS and the organization against unfavorable licensing terms and vendor induced situations.
   d) Allow rapid response to security threats like virus attacks, cyber-attacks, etc.

The pilot test for the web questionnaire was done using students and was oriented towards visual appeal, layout and design, and not content. The survey was tested on different browsers to verify that all the buttons and scripts worked and there were no run-time errors. The pause-and-resume functionality; clarity of the images and fonts; visual appeal of colors; amount of scrolling at standard resolution of 800 × 600; and download times were tested. Some changes in fonts and layout were done as a result of the tests.

Survey Administration

The survey was mailed to IS executives for self-administration. This list was purchased from a professional marketing company. The questionnaire was mailed to 2718 executives (IS staff strength of between 100 - 1500). The survey included a cover letter, a paper copy of the questionnaire and a prepaid return envelope. The only incentive for responding to the survey was to share the results of the survey. The cover letter specified that the survey could also be completed online if desired by the respondent. A reminder for the survey was mailed approximately three weeks after the original mailing. After mailing the questionnaires, emails were sent to about 30 potential respondents using referrals from IS executives known to the researchers. The emails contained an executive summary of the research concepts, a copy of the questionnaire, and a link to the web-based questionnaire. A second mailing of the survey was done. The survey was mailed to 2448 addresses and a reminder postcard was mailed approximately three weeks after the mailing.

7. SURVEY ANALYSIS & RESULTS

A total of 154 responses were received (105 paper and 49 web responses). 11 responses were likely from referrals. There were a total of 2539 solicitations (accounting for incorrect addresses). This gives a 5.7% response rate. This response rate was considered acceptable considering the questionnaire had 112 items (pertaining to sensing, diagnosis, selection, execution, benefits, and self-assess- ment), budgetary constraints on the survey, and the fact that these executives likely receive several surveys with some financial incentive (gift card) for completion.

All the data was entered into SPSS for analysis. The demographic data item categories (except for the title and department) were assigned numerical codes. The rating for all items for benefits and attributes were entered as marked on the questionnaire except for "Not Applicable" which was assigned a code of 0 (zero). To verify the correctness of data entry from the paper survey, a random sample of 20 questionnaires was selected and checked by a fellow researcher. No data entry errors were found. There were few missing values in the entire data set. Missing values were treated as pair-wise exclusive for correlational analyses like factor analysis. They were treated as list-wise exclusive otherwise, e.g. for purposes like calculating descriptive statistics.

7.1. Respondent Demographics

The demographics of the respondents are shown in Tables 4-7. Education, government, finance, healthcare, and information technology companies are prominently represented in the survey. 62% of the respondents had fewer than 250 IS personnel, 61% of the organizations had an annual IS budget between $1 million and $50 million, and 40% of the respondents had revenues between $1 billion and $25 billion.

Table 4.: *Industry distribution of survey respondents.*

Industry	Frequency	Percent
Retail	3	2.0%

Conti.

Table 4.: *Conti.*

Finance & Insurance	23	15.0%
Government	24	15.7%
Information Technology	18	11.8%
Mining & Oil	1	0.7%
Manufacturing	9	5.9%
Education	32	20.9%
Recreation & Leisure	1	0.7%
Utilities	3	2.0%
Trading (Wholesale)	4	2.6%
Media/Publishing/Broadcasting	5	3.3%
Professional Services	3	2.0%
Healthcare	20	13.1%
Other	7	4.6%
Total Valid	153	100.0%
Missing	1	
Total	154	

Table 5.: *IS personnel distribution of survey respondents.*

IS Personnel	Frequency	Percent	Cumulative Percent
1 - 100	39	25.3%	25.3%
101 - 250	56	36.4%	61.7%
251 - 500	29	18.8%	80.5%
501 - 750	12	7.8%	88.3%
751 - 1000	3	1.9%	90.3%
1001 - 1500	3	1.9%	92.2%
1501 - 2000	1	0.6%	92.9%
2001 - 5000	3	1.9%	94.8%
>5000	8	5.2%	100.0%
Total	154	100.0	

Table 6.: *Distribution of annual IS budget of survey respondents.*

Annual IS Budget ($millions)	Frequency	Percent	Cumulative Percent
<0.5	11	7.2%	7.2%
0.5 - 1	10	6.5%	13.7%
1 - 50	93	60.8%	74.5%
50 -100	20	13.1%	87.6%
100 - 500 Million	15	9.8%	97.4%
500 - 1000	3	2.0%	99.3%
>1000	1	0.7%	100.0%
Total Valid	153	100.0%	
Missing	1		
Total	154		

Table 7.: *Distribution of annual revenue of survey respondents.*

Annual Revenue	Frequency	Percent	Cumulative Percent
<$1 Million	8	5.5%	5.5%
$1 Million - $50 Million	18	12.4%	17.9%
$50 Million - $100 Million	9	6.2%	24.1%
$100 Million - $500 Million	25	17.2%	41.4%
$500 Million - $1 Billion	21	14.5%	55.9%
$1 Billion - $25 Billion	58	40.0%	95.9%
>$25 Billion	6	4.1%	100.0%
Total Valid	145	100.0%	
Missing	9		
Total	154		

In summary, the survey had respondents from various segments of the population and it captured opinions from a variety of organizations in different industries both small and large in terms of annual revenue, IS budget, and number of IS personnel.

7.2. Non-Response Bias

Since the survey was anonymous, it was not possible to test for differences between the respondents and the non-respondents. The respondents from the two mailings were, however, compared for differences. The number of responses for each medium and for each mailing is detailed in Table 8. The number of responses in the second mailing was about half of those in the first mailing.

Cross-tabulations on the demographic variables of industry, IS personnel, IS budget, and annual revenue were calculated and compared for differences. Chi-square tests were not conducted since many of the cells had an expected count of less than 5 and combining various categories led to mitigation of the differences with respect to the categories for the two mailings of the survey. There was no noticeable difference between the two mailings in terms of the demographic variables. The mean ratings of benefits of an agile IS from the responses of the two mailings were compared using independent sample t-tests. The means of the ratings were not different at a significance level of 0.01.

The 18 benefits of an agile IS were presented to the survey respondents for rating on a scale of 1 to 7, 1 being not important to 7 being very important. Table 9 shows the frequency, mean, and standard deviation of the ratings of the benefits of an agile IS.

Benefits of an Agile IS

The item with the largest mean rating of 6.54 was "Rapid response to security threats like viruses and cyber-attacks", and indicating the emphasis that IS executives attach to security and quickly taking remedial actions to alleviate the threat. Security has been a constant focus in mainstream practitioner and academic literature recently, and so the expectation of an agile IS to excel in the area of security is understandable. In the same vein, "Recovery from failure" was rated as an important benefit of an agile IS (mean rating of 6.32). The benefit with the second highest mean was "Information systems changes are made in a timely fashion". This is the reason for having an agile IS and is an obvious benefit. The fact that it did not score as the top benefit is somewhat of a surprise but perhaps amply demonstrates the focus on security. Interestingly, "Quick building of capacity for handling peak loads and/or sudden loads" was not rated as one of the top benefits (it is 9th in the ranking) of an agile IS, yet this is the area where many IT providers are focused through various cloud initiatives like PasS, SaaS, IasS, etc.

***Table 8.**: Paper and web responses for first and second survey mailing.*

First		Mailing		Total
		Second		
Type of	Paper	67	38	105
Medium for Survey	Web	36	13	49
Total		103	51	154

***Table 9.:** Survey ratings of the benefits of an agile information system.*

Benefit of an Agile IS	Frequency of Rating[1]								N	Mean[2]	Std. Dev
	1	2	3	4	5	6	7	N/A			
Rapid IS response to security threats like viruses and cyber attacks	0	1	0	2	13	23	114	1	154	6.61**	0.79
IS changes are made in a timely fashion	0	0	0	2	15	37	100	0	154	6.53**	0.73
Fast IS recovery from failures/ outages	0	0	4	6	14	42	87	1	154	6.32**	0.98
Increase in efficiency and effectiveness of business processes supported by IS	0	1	0	6	22	54	71	0	154	6.21**	0.91
Effective information processing	0	2	3	9	23	54	61	2	154	6.02**	1.09
Alignment of IS with the business process requirements at all times	2	0	4	12	26	42	63	3	152	5.94**	1.23
Use of IS as a strategic business tool	0	1	7	10	26	54	54	2	154	5.89**	1.14
IS can meet the service level agreements (SLAs) for capacity and performance	0	1	6	8	42	52	42	3	154	5.75**	1.09
Quick building of capacity for handling peak loads and/or sudden loads	0	2	5	17	34	50	46	0	154	5.71**	1.78
Faster development of products and services	1	0	2	18	40	49	42	2	154	5.70**	1.10
Efficient information processing	1	2	4	18	38	43	47	1	154	5.66**	1.24
Increased financial benefits to the organization	2	2	6	12	33	52	44	3	154	5.68**	1.28
Rapid change in business processes	3	1	5	19	36	52	36	2	154	5.53**	1.29

Conti.

***Table 9.:** Conti.*

Increased robustness of changes made to the IS	4	2	7	15	55	39	32	0	154	5.34**	1.34
Enhancement of IS capabilities	2	0	4	16	57	48	27	0	154	5.24**	1.11

Notes: [1]The shaded boxes show the rating with the highest frequencies. [2]Items are arranged in ascending order of mean rating. **Mean is significantly greater than 4 at 0.00 level of significance in a two-tailed test.

The low rating for "use of the latest technologies to avoid technology obsolescence", shows that the use of the latest technologies did not seem to be a priority for most IS organizations. Also, in spite of the trend towards applications service providers, off-the-shelf software products, outsourcing, and off-sourcing, managing vendor risk did not seem to be a major concern for most IS executives, as denoted by the low rating on "protection of IS and the organization from vendor induced risks (bankruptcy, etc.)".

7.3. Exploratory Factor Analysis of Benefits of an Agile IS

An exploratory factor analysis (EFA) was conducted to identify possible dimensions underlying the benefits of an agile IS. Though broad categories were defined when arriving at attributes and it would be possible to do a confirmatory factor analysis, it was felt that an EFA is appropriate given the exploratory nature of the study. There were 18 items for benefits of an agile IS. Given the sample size of 154, the case-to-variable ratio is 8.55:1. This ratio satisfies the rule of thumb of 5:1 and thus the sample size was considered as acceptable for an EFA. Kaiser-Meyer-Olkin's Measure of Sampling Adequacy (KMO MSA) for the correlation matrix was 0.88. This is considered at meritorious level, signifying that the correlation matrix can be used for factor analysis.

An EFA was conducted using principal axis factoring since the objective was to identify underlying dimensions based on the common variance shared by the attributes. Varimax rotation was used to arrive at a simple factor structure. Other rotations including varimax, oblimin, quatrimax, and promax were tested. Varimax rotation provided the simplest and most interpretable structure. The number of factors to be extracted was based on a combination of the scree-test, eigen-value criterion, and simple structure. Simplicity of structure was given preference over parsimony. Initial factor extraction was based on the criteria of the eigen-value being greater than 1. Then, the scree plot was examined for a visible elbow such that all factors with an eigen-value of greater than 1 were included in the solution. The factor analysis was run again with the number of factors indicated by the elbow. Both solutions were examined and the factor structure that was simple and interpretable was chosen. The cut-off for factor loading was taken as 0.4. While no set criteria for the factor loading exist in the literature, guidelines suggest [53] loadings of greater than ± 0.3 to meet the minimal level while loadings of ± 0.40 are considered more important.

The criteria of eigen-values greater than 1 yielded four factors. The scree plot did not indicate a distinct elbow, though the slope seemed to decrease at factor 5.

The five-factor solution was not superior in any sense to the four-factor solution and so the four-factor solution was retained. These four factors together explain 62% of the variance. Table 10 depicts the factors: The strategic benefits factor reflects a top down approach and provides guidance for all levels of the organization's managers.

The first factor was labeled as the "Technology Leverage" factor. Though "protection of IS and the organization" and "increased robustness of changes" may be seen more as mitigating risks, these benefits in recent times have emerged due to the use of new and better technologies. In some cases, the benefits have arisen due to leveraging existing technologies and using them in an innovative way. The item "faster development of product and services" cross-loaded onto this factor. Faster development of product and services may be another benefit of leveraging technologies and hence the loading of the item could be considered appropriate. It must be understood that the technology leverage factor deals with improving the enterprise through technology attributes such as improved flexibility and expertise. This is often a bottom up phenomenon. The second factor was labeled as "Strategic Benefits". The item "faster development of products and services" that loaded on this factor and cross-loaded on the first factor may also be considered as a strategic benefit to the organization. The strategic benefits factor reflects a top down approach and provides guidance for all levels of the organization's managers. The third factor was labeled as "Cost Saving" since the items that loaded onto it primarily dealt with efficiency and effectiveness of information processing which would lead to cost savings and increase in revenues. The fourth factor was labeled as "Top Performance" and included rapid response to various situations and sustaining performance levels.

Table 10.: *Factors for benefits of an agile information system.*

Benefit of an Agile IS	Factor			
	1 (Technology Leverage)	2 (Strategic Benefits)	3 (Cost Savings)	4 (Top Performance)
Use of the latest technologies to avoid technology obsolescence	0.795			
Business process innovation through use of latest IS technologies	0.719			
Protection of IS and the organization from vendor induced risks (bankruptcy, etc.)	0.663			
Increased robustness of changes made to the IS	0.569			

Conti.

Table 10.: *Conti.*

Enhancement of IS capabilities	0.483			
Alignment of IS with the business process requirements at all times		0.719		
Use of IS as a strategic business tool		0.652		
Faster development of products and services	0.449	0.541		
Rapid change in business processes		0.488		
Increased financial benefits to the organization				
Effective information processing			0.822	
Efficient information processing			0.717	
Increase in efficiency and effectiveness of business processes supported by IS			0.525	
Rapid IS response to security threats like viruses and cyber attacks				0.726
Fast IS recovery from failures/outages				0.551
IS can meet the service level agreements (SLAs) for capacity and performance				0.542
Quick building of capacity for handling peak loads and/or sudden loads				0.428
IS changes are made in a timely fashion				

The only cross-loading was of "faster development of products and services" on two factors, both of which appear to be relevant. It may need to be further investigated.

Two of the items did not load on any factor. The first was "IS changes are made in a timely fashion". In the rating of the benefits, this particular item was consistently rated high. It deals with changes that are undertaken in a planned or proactive fashion and may just not be attributable to agility but other factors like good project management and may be more related to planning related attributes. In hindsight, the item is an obvious benefit of IS agility and may easily apply to more than one factor or all the four factors. It may need to be worded more specifically; in which case, it is more likely to load on the "Strategic Benefit" factor. The item loaded on to "Top Performance" factor with a loading of 0.305. The second item in question that did not load on to a factor was "increased financial benefits to the organization". This item had a near 0.4 (0.379) loading on "Strategic Benefit Factor" and greater than 0.3 loading on the "Cost Savings" and "Technology Leverage" factors. It is more of a higher order benefit as compared to others. In hindsight, this item sounds fairly generic and may be split into at least two or maybe three distinct items. First would be cost savings, second would be an increase in revenue due to leveraging of technology and third may be increase in revenue by successfully keeping up with changes in the marketplace. The item "faster development of product and services" may also be split into two items: one that deals with innovation in products and services and the second that deals with maintaining competitiveness through emulating competitors or making incremental changes. These suggestions may be explored in future research.

8. LIMITATIONS

There are some methodological limitations to this study which have alluded to earlier for example in the EFA section. Some items may need to be further refined to avoid cross-loadings and non-loading items in EFA. The response rate for the survey was 5.7% and though this response rate was considered acceptable for the purpose of this survey there is still room to improve the response rate. This could be done, for example, through collaboration with some special interest groups and research groups with an interest in the area of IS agility.

In view of the rapid evolvement of new paradigms like the cloud model and machine to machine communication the issues and benefits may shift since, like all research such as this, this research represents the state at a particular point in time. The research may need to be continually refreshed to be more meaningful with the times.

9. SUMMARY AND COMMENTS

The survey data provides support to the hypothesized benefits of an Agile IS. The top benefit of an agile IS was "rapid IS response to security threats like viruses and cyber-attacks" and the third most important benefit was "fast IS recovery from failures/outages". Thus IS agility may be present in some form in most of organizations in the IS especially in the recovery area.

These empirically supported benefits may provide the justification for investment in initiatives to increase the agility of an IS. Specifically, investments in areas that enhance sensing a change in real time [14] , diagnosing a change in real-time [15] , and selecting a response and executing a response in real-time [52] may be undertaken.

It is unarguable that the current IT industry has come to accept the requirement for agility in the IS. The industry approach though is somewhat fragmented along applications, databases, infrastructure and so forth and may lack a holistic framework in line with what has been proposed in this study. This is somewhat understandable given the complexity and distributed vendor driven nature of these new paradigms. The empirically-justified benefits from this study may provide support for an organization to invest in these initiatives through both capital and labor expenditures. Over a period of time with the benefits that have been established in this study and other new benefits, agile ISs will become a mainstream in organizations.

REFERENCES

1. ORACLE (2015) New Oracle Research Reveals That Businesses Are Unaware of Competitive Advantages of Cloud Agility.
2. Bajgoric, N. (2000) Web-Based Information Access for Agile Management. International Journal of Agile Management Systems, 2, 121-129.
3. Bal, J., Wilding, R. and Gundry, J. (1999) Virtual Teaming in the Agile Supply Chain. The International Journal of Logistics Management, 10, 71-82.
4. Christopher, M. (2000) The Agile Supply Chain: Competing in Volatile Markets. Industrial Marketing Management, 29, 37-44.
5. Hoek, R.I.V. (2000) The Thesis of Leagility Revisited. International Journal of Agile Manufacturing Management Systems, 2, 196-201.
6. Mason-Jones, R. and Towill, D.R. (1999) Total Cycle Time Compression and the Agile Supply Chain. International Journal of Production Economics, 62, 61-73.
7. Sharifi, H. and Zhang, Z. (1999) A Methodology for Achieving Agility in Manufacturing Organizations: An Introduction. International Journal of Production Economics, 62, 7-22.
8. Yusuf, Y.Y., Sarahadi, M. and Gunasekaran, A. (1999) Agile Manufacturing: The Drivers Concepts and Attributes. International Journal of Production Economics, 62, 33-43.
9. Boynton, A.C. (1993) Achieving Dynamic Stability through Information Technology. California Management Review (Winter), 50, 58-77.
10. Pankaj (2005) An Analysis and Exploration of Information Systems Agility. Ph.D. Thesis, Southern Illinois University, Carbondale.
11. Pankaj, Hyde, M., Ramaprasad, A. and Tadisina, S. (2009) Revisiting Agility to Conceptualize Information Systems Agility. In: Lytras, M. and Pablos, P.O.D., Eds., Emerging Topics and Technologies in Information Systems, IGI-Global, Hershey, 19-54.
12. Unknown (2002) Comp.realtime: Frequently Asked Questions (FAQs) 3.6.
13. IT-Online (2015) Are You as Agile as You Think?
14. Pankaj, Hyde, M. and Rodger, J.A. (2013b) Sensing Attributes of an Agile Information System. Intelligent Information Management, 5, 150-161.
15. Pankaj, Hyde, M. and Rodger, J.A. (2013a) Attributes for Change Diagnosis in an Agile Information System. International Journal of Computers & Technology, 10, 2095-2109.
16. Pankaj, C., Micki, H. and James, A.R. (2015) Attributes for Executing Change in an Agile Information System. International Journal of Technology Diffusion (IJTD), 6, 30-58.
17. Blessing Mavengere, N. (2014) Role of Information Systems for Strategic Agility in Supply Chain Setting: Telecommunication Industry Study. Electronic Journal of Information Systems Evaluation, 17, 100-112.

18. Bharadwaj, A.S. (2000) A Resource-Based Perspective on Information Technology Competences and Firm Performance: An Empirical Investigation. MIS Quarterly, 24, 28.
19. Rockart, J.F., Earl, M.J. and Ross, J.W. (1996) Eight Imperatives for the New IT Organization. Sloan Management Review, 38, 13.
20. Barney, J.B. (1991) Firm Resources and Sustained Competitive Advantage. Journal of Management, 17, 24.
21. Chakravarty, A., Grewal, R. and Sambamurthy, V. (2013) Information Technology Competencies, Organizational Agility, and Firm Performance: Enabling and Facilitating Roles. Information Systems Research, 24, 976-997.
22. Hefu, L., Weiling, K., Kwok, K.W. and Zhongsheng, H. (2013) The Impact of IT Capabilities on Firm Performance: The Mediating Roles of Absorptive Capacity and Supply Chain Agility. Decision Support Systems, 54, 1452-1463.
23. Shin, H., Lee, J.N., Kim, D. and Rhim, H. (2015) Strategic Agility of Korean small and Medium Enterprises and Its Influence on Operational and Firm Performance. International Journal of Production Economics, 168, 181-196.
24. Gren, L., Torkar, R. and Feldt, R. (2015) The Prospects of a Quantitative Measurement of Agility: A Validation Study on an Agile Maturity Model. Journal of Systems and Software, 107, 38-49.
25. Cao, Y., Swartz, C.L.E., Baldea, M. and Blouin, S. (2015) Optimization-Based Assessment of Design Limitations to Air Separation Plant Agility in Demand Response Scenarios. Journal of Process Control, 33, 37-48.
26. Sangari, M.S., Razmi, J. and Zolfaghari, S. (2015) Developing a Practical Evaluation Framework for Identifying Critical Factors to Achieve Supply Chain Agility. Measurement, 62, 205-214.
27. Gligor, D.M., Esmark, C.L. and Holcomb, M.C. (2015) Performance Outcomes of Supply Chain Agility: When Should You Be Agile? Journal of Operations Management, 33, 71-82.
28. Goldsby, T.J., Griffis, S.E. and Roath, A.S. (2006) Modeling Lean, Agile, and Leagile Supply Chain Strategies. Journal of business logistics, 27, 57-80.
29. Narayanan, S., Narasimhan, R. and Schoenherr, T. (2015) Assessing the Contingent Effects of Collaboration on Agility Performance in Buyer-Supplier Relationships. Journal of Operations Management, 33, 140-154.
30. Chung, S., Lee, K.Y. and Kim, K. (2014) Job Performance through Mobile Enterprise Systems: The Role of Organizational Agility, Location Independence, and Task Characteristics. Information & Management, 51, 605-617.
31. Sherehiy, B. and Karwowski, W. (2014) The Relationship between Work Organization and Workforce Agility in Small Manufacturing Enterprises. International Journal of Industrial Ergonomics, 44, 466-473.
32. Yang, J. (2014) Supply Chain Agility: Securing Performance for Chinese Manufacturers. International Journal of Production Economics, 150, 104-114.

33. Barthe-Delanoe, A.M., Truptil, S., Bénaben, F. and Pingaud, H. (2014) Event-Driven Agility of Interoperability during the Run-Time of Collaborative Processes. Decision Support Systems, 59, 171-179.

34. Yusuf, Y.Y., Gunasekaran, A., Musa, A., Dauda, M.M., El-Berishy, N. and Cang, S. (2014) A Relational Study of Supply Chain Agility, Competitiveness, and Business Performance in the Oil and Gas Industry. International Journal of Production Economics, 147, 531-544.

35. DeGroote, S.E. and Marx, T.G. (2013) The Impact of IT on Supply Chain Agility and Firm Performance: An Empirical Investigation. International Journal of Information Management, 33, 909-916.

36. Balaji, M., Velmurugan, V., Sivabalan, G., Ilayaraja, V.S., Prapa, M. and Mythily, V. (2014) ASCTM Approach for Enterprise Agility. Procedia Engineering, 97, 2222-2231.

37. Galster, M., Weyns, D., Tofan, D., Michalik, B. and Avgeriou, P. (2014) Variability in Software Systems—A Systematic Literature Review. IEEE Transactions on Software Engineering, 40, 282-306.

38. Sheffield, J. and Lemétayer, J. (2013) Factors Associated with the Software Development Agility of Successful Projects. International Journal of Project Management, 31, 459-472.

39. Krotov, V.V.K.A.A.A., Junglas, I.I.C.F.E. and Steel, D.S.U.E. (2015) The Mobile Agility Framework: An Exploratory Study of Mobile Technology Enhancing Organizational Agility. Journal of Theoretical & Applied Electronic Commerce Research, 10, 1-17.

40. Wasko, M.M. and Faraj, S. (2005) Why Should I Share? Examining Social Capital and Knowledge Contribution in Electronic Networks of Practice. MIS Quarterly, 29, 35-57.

41. Broadbent, M., Weil, P. and St.Clair, D. (1999) The Implications of Information Technology Infrastructure for Business Process Redesign. MIS Quarterly, 23, 159-182.

42. Clemons, E.K. and Row, M.C. (1991) Sustaining IT Advantage: The Role of Structural Differences. MIS Quarterly, 15, 275-292.

43. Weber, B., Reichert, M. and Rinderle-Ma, S. (2008) Change Patterns and Change Support Features—Enhancing Flexibility in Process-Aware Information Systems. Data & Knowledge Engineering, 66, 438-467.

44. Seebacher, G. and Winkler, H. (2014) Evaluating Flexibility in Discrete Manufacturing Based on Performance and Efficiency. International Journal of Production Economics, 153, 340-351.

45. Dove, R. (1995) Agile Benefits: Viability and Leadership. Production, 1, 16-17.

46. Bonoma, T.V. (1985) Case Research in Marketing: Opportunities, Problems, and a Process. Journal of Marketing Research, 22, 199-208.

47. Bailey, J.E. and Pearson, S.W. (1983) Development of a Tool for Measuring and Analyzing Computer User Satisfaction. Management Science, 29, 530-545.

48. Goodhue, D.L. (1988) Supporting Users of Corporate Data. Ph.D. Doctoral, Massachusetts Institute of Technology, Boston.

49. Ives, B., Olson, M.H. and Baroudi, J.J. (1983) The Measurement of User Information Satisfaction. Communications of the ACM, 26, 785-793.

50. Ricketts, J.A. and Jenkins, A.M. (1985) The Development of an MIS Satisfaction Questionnaire: An Instrument for Evaluating User Satisfaction with Turnkey Decision Support Systems. Retrieved from Bloomington, Indiana:
51. Churchill, G.A. (1979) A Paradigm for Developing Better Measures of Marketing Constructs. Journal of Marketing Research, 16, 64-73.
52. Chaudhary, P., Hyde, M. and Rodger, J.A. (2015) Attributes for Executing Change in an Agile Information System. International Journal of Technology Diffusion (IJTD), 6, 30-58.
53. Hair Jr., J.H., Anderson, R.E., Tatham, R.L. and Black, W.C. (1995) Multivariate Data Analysis. Prentice Hall, Upper Saddle River, New Jersey.
54. Vokurka, R.J., Zank, G.M. and Lund III, C.M. (2002) Improving Competitiveness through Supply Chain Management: A Cumulative Improvement Approach. CR, 12, 14-25.
55. Christian, P.H., Govande, V., Staehle, W. and Zimmers Jr., E.W (1999) Advantage through Agility. IIE Solutions, 31, 26-33.
56. Yoffie, D.B. and Kwak, M. (2001) Mastering Strategic Movement at Palm. Sloan Management Review, 43, 55-63.
57. Bessant, J., Francis, D., Meredith, S. and Kalinsky, R. (2001) Developing Manufacturing Agility in SMEs. International Journal of Technology Management, 22, 28-54.
58. Schonsleben, P. (2000) With Agility and Adequate Partnership Strategies towards Effective Logistics Networks. Computers in Industry, 42, 33-42.
59. Cho, H., Jung, M. and Kim, M. (1996) Enabling Technologies of Agile Manufacturing and its Related Activities in Korea. Computers and Industrial Engineering, 30, 323-335.
60. Vernadat, F.B. (1999) Research Agenda for Agile Manufacturing. International Journal of Agile Management Systems, 1, 37-40.
61. O'Connor, L. (1994) Agile Manufacturing in a Responsive Factory. Mechanical Engineering, 3, 54-57.
62. Sahin, F. (2000) Manufacturing Competitiveness: Different Systems to Achieve the Same Results. Production and Inventory Management Journal, 1, 56-65.
63. Vokurka, R.J. and Fliedner, G. (1997) Agility: Competitive Weapon of the 1990s and Beyond? Production and Inventory Management Journal, 38, 19-24.
64. Devor, R., Graves, R. and Miles, J.J. (1997) Agile Manufacturing Research: Accomplishments and Opportunities. IIE Transactions, 29, 813-823.
65. Noaker, P.M. (1994) The Search for Agile Manufacturing. Manufacturing Engineering, 113, 5-11.

3

Information Systems Security Threats and Vulnerabilities: A Case of the Institute of Accountancy Arusha (IAA)

Adam Aloyce Semlambo, Didas Malekia Mfoi and Yona Sangula

Department of Informatics, Institute of Accountancy Arusha (IAA), Arusha, Tanzania.

ABSTRACT

All modern computer users need to be concerned about information system security (individuals and organisations). Many businesses established various security structures to protect information system security from harmful occurrences by implementing security procedures, processes, policies, and information system security organisational structures to ensure data security. Despite all the precautions, information security remains a disaster in Tanzania's learning institutions. The fundamental issue appears to be a lack of awareness of crucial information security factors. Various companies have different security issues due to differences in ICT infrastructure, implementations, and usage. The study focuses on identifying information system security threats and vulnerabilities in public higher learning institutions in Tanzania, particularly the Institute of Accountancy Arusha (IAA). The study involved all employees of IAA, academics, and other supporting staff, which totalled 302, and the sample size was 170. The study utilised a descriptive research design, where the quantitative methodology was used through a five-point Likert scale questionnaire, and found that key factors that affect the security of information systems at IAA include human factors, policy-related issues, work environment and demographic factors. The study proposed regular awareness and training programs; an increase in women's awareness of information system security; proper policy creation and reviews every 4 years; promote actions that lessen information system security threats and vulnerabilities, and the creation of information system security policy documents independently from ICT policy.

Keywords: *Information Systems, Information Security, Public Higher Learning Institutions, IAA*

1. INTRODUCTION

Information security can be defined as the process of maintaining information confidentiality, integrity and availability against both internal and external vulnerabilities. Dependence on ICT infrastructure for daily use in achieving organisation objectives has made higher learning institutions a target of malicious activities from both within and from external factors [1]. Researchers have analysed different factors that contribute to poor Information System security in the learning environment. For example, the use of online learning facilities such as portals, online learning systems and mobile apps have increased security threats to learning environments [2] [3] [4]. Studies show that the number of internet users in Tanzania increased to 43.62 million just by 2018 [5]. This is about 45% of all adult citizens [6] and the majority of these users are from higher learning institutions with no proper knowledge on how to defend themselves/their institutions from hackers and online attacks. The threats to information system security have been reported to increase for both organisations and individuals [7]. The case is more alarming in learning environments of Tanzania as these incidences do not have formal ways of being documented, which are likely to reverse. Security attacks can result in loss of business, trust, reputation and money [8]. For example, researchers in reference [5] had their research showing the impact of cyber security attacks on learning environments in Tanzania. The study aims at identifying and categorising these threats and vulnerabilities and proposing appropriate solutions in the case of the learning environment of Tanzania.

There is a wealth of information on information system security around the world in the literature and international reports. According to Kaspersky's estimate, there were 445 million attacks in 2020 [9]. According to research in reference [10], 50% of Internet users admit to having experienced security breaches. According to research in reference [11], the typical data breach results in the loss of 25,575 records annually, costing an enterprise an estimated $3.92 million USD. Investors and customers may become less trusting of the impacted companies as a result of the data leak and stop doing business with them [12]. Collectively, it is clear that cyberattacks are on the rise [13]; as a result, it is important for stakeholders to remain aware of the variables affecting the security of information systems in learning environments.

As a result, studies about variables influencing information system security are provided in the literature. By concentrating on users' compliance with ICT policies, researchers in reference [14] analyse elements that affect the security of information systems. According to the report, disregarding ICT policies has a negative impact on the security of information systems. Reference [15] highlighted low adherence to the security culture as one of the causes of online vulnerability in a different study. The study in reference [16], in contrast, concentrated on the role of people in defending an organisation from attacks. In addition, references [17] and [18] hypothesised that variables including a lack of managerial backing, a woefully inadequate information security policy, and a dearth of information security education programmes all play a role in the deficient security of corporate-owned information systems security. In this context, it is clear that there is no consensus on what influences information system security in the modern world. In order to identify the aspects affecting the security of information systems, this study does such analysis in public higher learning institutions in Tanzania, particularly the Institute of Accountancy Arusha (IAA).

There is evidence that the use of information systems is becoming more and more important to human activity, especially in learning environments like public higher learning institutions. Information systems are necessary for human activities and decision-making. The rising usage of computers and computer systems is due to the requirement for a reliable information system to fulfil consumer satisfaction [18]. In Tanzania, for example, ICT use is growing at a rate of 4.9 percent per year [19]. Currently, 60% of individuals worldwide are subscribers, compared to 50% of people in Tanzania who use the internet [10]. With this rise, it's clear that efficient use requires reliable information systems to improve the performance of the user organisation [18]. The study focuses on the efficient use of ICT infrastructures within the learning environment to eliminate information system security threats and vulnerabilities.

Evidently, safe supporting infrastructure and accompanying resources are necessary for information system reliability [2] [3] [20]. Nevertheless, according to reference [20] and [21], a number of factors influence the necessary level of online safety in eliminating information system security threats and vulnerabilities. These variables include administrative, technological, and human-related variables. Reference [22] asserts that more information system risks are being published online every day. Phishing, social engineering, supply chain attacks, zero-day and polymorphic attacks, IoT, and infrastructure attacks are a few of these dangers [23] [24]. This study aims to find out if these factors are the same for the higher learning environments in Tanzania.

Policies controlling the use of ICT provide the organisation with a solid administrative basis necessary to combat these challenges [25] [26]. This is why the current study assesses information system security threats and vulnerabilities in the learning environments.

2. METHODOLOGY

Through a descriptive design, the study employed a quantitative methodology. The 302 employees (both teaching and supporting staff) at IAA made up the study's population. Using the n = N/1 + N(e)2 formula proposed by Kothari [27], through a random sampling procedure, a sample of 170 participants was obtained at a 95% confidence level, 5% margin of error, and 50% population proportion from the population size of 302. Participants were instructed to select their thoughts by checking only one cell in the concept column on questionnaires that contained items ordered in the logical sequence of a 5-point Likert scale. Passionately 1) strongly disagree, 2) disagree, 3) neither agree nor disagree, 4) agree, and 5) strongly agree. The validity and reliability of the data were ensured. Before distributing questionnaires, the participants' permission was taken into account. Additionally, questionnaires were forwarded to specialists for evaluation of their validity and reliability in relation to the goal of the study. A descriptive analysis was used in the study to analyse the information gathered through SPSS V26.

3. FINDINGS AND DISCUSSIONS

This section concentrates its analysis of information system security threats and vulnerabilities on the Institute of Accountancy Arusha (IAA). The study was inspired by the fact that, like all other organisations, more and more security events affecting all kinds of businesses are being reported from the continent but very few within learning environments. The purpose of this study was to ascertain why information system security remains a concern for most learning institutions as well as for individual users. According to the research in reference [17], the elements affecting the security of information systems should be divided into a human, information security policy, work environment, and demographic aspects. Quantitative data were collected through questionnaires consisting of statements arranged in the logical order of a 5-point Likert scale, directing participants to choose their ideas by ticking only one cell in the concept column. 1) Strongly disagree, 2) disagree, 3) neither agree nor disagree, 4) agree, and 5) agree strongly.

Table 1.: *Determinants of information system security threats and vulnerabilities.*

SN	Proposition	SDA %	DA %	NS %	A %	SA %
1) Human Factors						
1.1	It is a high-security risk to share personal credentials (user name and password) with anyone in the office or at the institute.	9.2	8.2	9.2	50.0	23.5
1.2	In our institution, information access is restricted accordingly by taking into account information that is public, protected, and restricted / secret.	21.4	35.0	14.0	29.6	6.1
1.3	We usually discuss office-related matters and share official documents on social networking sites such as WhatsApp groups.	2.0	20.4	20.6	24.3	32.7
1.4	I prefer to use my personal computer at work and connect to the institute network, as there are no restrictions on doing so.	9.2	17.3	12.2	28.0	33.3
1.5	I usually do notlock the screen or log out of my workstation while idle.	26.5	24.4	24.5	14.3	10.3

Conti.

Table 1.: *Conti.*

1.6	It is not important to have training on new ICT facilities before purchasing them as our experts (IT department) are competent with enough expertise to know everything.	2.0	20.4	20.6	24.3	32.7

Source: Researchers (2022).

3.1. Human Factor

Reference [16] takes into account human variables, including how people behave physically and psychologically in connection to information system security. Additionally, the study in reference [28] noted that the suitability of user behaviours when using the system is crucial to an organisation's information system security success. This area of human variables includes carelessness, lack of skills, and trust. Details on the information in Table 1 are provided in the next section.

Trust: According to this study, trust is the human component having the greatest impact on the security of information systems. Because of recommendations from co-workers or personal experience, one comes to trust another individual [29]. Although trust seems admirable, if safety measures are not implemented, it can turn into a point of attack [30]. Employees exchanging login information or data without taking security into account are one of the dangerous behaviours related to trust [31] [32]. These actions exacerbate the risks to information system security [33]. Though findings show that about 73.5% of respondents know the risk of sharing personal credentials, there is still a small number of people who do not understand this risk, which can result in catastrophic information system security risks and vulnerabilities at the institute. The same applies to the restriction of information based on public, protected, and restricted (secret) (Item 1.2).

Carelessness: According to reports, human carelessness also has an impact on the security of information systems in a learning environment. Carelessness is defined as an individual's activity or behaviour that deliberately or unknowingly jeopardises the information system's security. For instance, discussing work-related matters in emails or on public networks, where it is estimated that the average email user sends up to 112 emails per day and that about one in every seven of these emails is connected to office gossip [34]. Social media chitchat about work-related issues can be irresponsible and reveal confidential information to unwanted or unauthorised parties, increasing security risks and vulnerabilities for a firm. Results showed that more than half of respondents (Item 1.3) agreed to discuss office-related issues on social media, which results in numerous information system security threats and vulnerabilities. Additionally, additional actions like allowing a visitor to use a company computer or connecting a personal computer to the network without taking the proper security procedures raise alarms about security (Item 1.4). Security hazards can also be brought about by leaving workplace computers unattended (Item 1.5), introducing new hardware or software to users without proper training (Item 1.6), and operating ICT infrastructures without an ICT/IS security policy (Item 1.7). Additionally, employing old technology and software, among many other negligent practices (Item 1.8), is thought to put corporate information security at risk.

Lack of skills: Table 1 found a further human element affecting information security in a learning environment, namely a lack of skills. According to research by in reference [35], many people lack faith in the information system security expertise and experience of their specialists to handle current security concerns. Due to the high cost of most information security certifications for individuals (Item 1.9), this is a challenge. Additionally, the majority of businesses are reluctant to sponsor their staff members for professional qualifications [36]. On the other hand, as demonstrated the study in reference [37], common users also lack capabilities. This combination eventually has an impact on initiatives to protect the security of information systems.

3.2. Inadequate Information Systems Security Policies

An organisation's personnel's duties and responsibilities for safeguarding its information systems are specified in its information security policy [38]. Policies ensure proper administration of technology resources if they are followed [39]. If not addressed properly, this group of factors can lead to information system security threats and vulnerabilities, as explained in the following subsections.

Lack of Information System Security Policy Training: The most prevalent component within the policy category is a lack of information security policy training. Users would receive training to equip them with the necessary knowledge to ensure information system security [25] [40]. Users who go through training are given reliable tools and the know-how to keep company information secure. Table 1 shows that most of the people who answered the survey at IAA did not get any training on ICT or information system security policies (Item 2.1). This means that they use ICT facilities without knowing the right rules and safety features to protect themselves and their institution.

Poor Creation of Information System Security Policies: one of the information system security threats and vulnerabilities cause is the poor creation of information system security policy. Findings of this study show that participants were unaware of such policies, which means they were not involved in their creation as stakeholders (Item 2.2). Studies in reference [13] provide guidelines to adhere to and minimum standards for a security policy. Data security, Internet and network services governance, use of company-owned devices, physical security, incident handling and recovery, monitoring and compliance, and policy administration are the parts of the security policy that they advise including. In addition to these requirements, reference [25] stressed how important it was to include all security stakeholders in the process of writing the policy. They will be able to share their expertise, thoughts, and ideas because the organisation's weak spots will be exposed [41]. A good policy will be made if you make sure to include important stakeholders and follow the standards that are suggested.

Poor Implementation of Information Systems Security Policies: Poor information systems security policy application, as shown in Table 1, is one of the variables that without proper addressing, can lead to information system security threats and vulnerabilities in an organisation (item 2.3). According to the study in reference [42], policy implementation challenges arise because the majority of policies are created for compliance reasons rather than to address actual security requirements. Also, say that when information systems policies aren't put into place properly, they become useless documents that make the system more vulnerable. With the right implementation of information system security policies [20], the company could find implementation issues, limitations, and technological changes that need to be taken into account when making policies.

3.3. Work Environment

This definition is adapted from refence [43] and [44] and refers to the social elements and physical circumstances in which users of information systems carry out their work. The category of elements most frequently identified to have an impact on the security of information systems in the workplace is Individual factors of this sub-category are detailed in the next sub-section according to Table 1.

Inadequate Management Support: inadequate management support for information system security in an organisation can lead to security threats and vulnerabilities. Findings show that IAA management does not provide awareness and training in information system security policies to employees (item 3.1). Senior managers should serve as role models for the organisation by ensuring appropriate training and awareness campaigns, as well as by positively influencing their security behaviour [15] [45]. Other strategies used by management to assist subordinates include idealising security impact inside an organisation, giving each person special consideration, and inspiring drive [46]. According to researchers in reference [47] and [48], management's failure to support security programmes increases the organisation's information system security risk and vulnerabilities.

Organizational Security Culture: Another issue that is frequently mentioned in relation to information system security is organisational security culture. Establishing policies, norms, and guidelines that direct employees' behaviour within a company becomes part of the organisation's culture [16]. The organisation's inability to establish the proper security culture has led to a rise in security threats associated with information systems [15] [33]. Themanagement must establish the proper security culture and integrate it into the long-term agenda. Sadly, research indicates that IAA does not operate in this way (Item 3.2).

Workload: Another aspect included in the work environment category that has been noted is workload. The workload in this essay refers to the volume of work that must be finished within the allotted time and resources [49]. Findings show that there are no restrictions on the use of optimisation software at IAA, which can lead to information system security threats and vulnerabilities. According to studies, employees' ambition to optimise production with limited resources leads to a number of information system security threats and vulnerabilities. Over time, the organisation's pressure on workers to meet higher financial targets raises the possibility that they will violate security [50]. Because of the constant pressure to stretch resources, employees put performance over security concerns [51].

Internet and Network Use: This describes how much a company relies on the Internet and networks to run its operations. The need for an Internet connection in the current business climate is essential to being competitive [7] [52]. The usage of the Internet becomes a risk to the security of information systems if the organisation uses it to support its operations without properly weighing the security concerns [53]. Findings show that respondents are unaware of any restrictions regarding the use of internet and network facilities at IAA (Item 3.4). This can result in the inappropriate use of such services, which leads to information system security risks and vulnerabilities.

Access Control: As users demand greater privileges when interacting with the system, access controls typically become less effective [54]. Instead of just making someone happy at the expense of overall security, the company must regulate system accessibility based on an individual's tasks and responsibilities [55]. The information must be classified into three types: public, protected, and restricted. A system is vulnerable to threats if system access policies are not defined [56]. Respondents of the study have mixed feelings on the exitance of such controls at IAA (Item 3.5).

3.4. Demographic Variables

This section presents information on a variety of demographic variables that have been implicated in information system security threats and vulnerabilities. Gender, age, level of education, experience, and managerial function, according to reference [57], can all be used to predict a person's intention to adhere to information system security as described below.

Gender: According to this study, gender can lead to various information system security threats and vulnerabilities. Findings show that it is the perception of the majority of respondents that information system security is more likely to be a male practice than a female one (Item 4.1). This perception leaves behind the majority of female employees, who are competent enough and can bring the required change in securing the organisations' information systems. Researcher in reference [58] found that females are more likely than males to perceive high levels of security threats. In a different study, reference [20] found that men are more likely than women to exhibit superior information security behaviours. Researchers in reference [36] say that since information system is thought of as a male-dominated field, it is important to get more women to sign up for information systems security courses and get them interested in a career in information system security.

Work Experience: The presumption is that an individual's employment history, both technical and non-technical, has some bearing on how appropriate their information security behaviour is. According to reference [59], experienced staff are safer thanks to their prior exposure to handling various security events. Additionally, work experience offers the chance for training, which imparts important knowledge for defence against assaults [56]. According to the findings of this study, experience in a less secure environment cannot provide an employee with security knowledge and experience (item 4.2). As explained in previous subcategories, without an adequate information system security training and awareness program, it is likely for the institute to have vulnerabilities and threats in its information systems.

Internet User Age: These study findings show that the internet use habits of young people have more information system security incidents compared to senior employees (items 4.3 and 4.4). According to the researcher in reference [60], younger individuals are more likely than older people to be aware of information system security threats and vulnerabilities. They are similarly irresponsible with their security knowledge [61]. Additionally, when undergoing new changes, youthful people are simple to teach, which is important when the firm changes its security procedures [60]. Based on these results, more work needs to be done to deal with how careless young people are and to teach adults more about security vulnerabilities and threats at IAA.

Level of Education: The results of this study show that the people who took part in it think that a level of education in the internet, cyber security, and information system security can protect the institute from vulnerabilities and threats to information system security (Item 4.5). According to research in reference [62], businesses face a variety of information security risks as a result of the information being shared via the Internet. These difficulties with maintaining information integrity and confidentiality depend on the understanding, education, and conduct of the end user. A trained cyber-literate workforce and an education system that can create such a workforce are necessary for successfully defending the organisation's vital infrastructure against cyberattacks [63].

4. CONCLUSION AND RECOMMENDATIONS

The Institute of Accountancy Arusha (IAA) was used as a case study to understand the main factors that contribute to the information system security threats and vulnerabilities in a learning environment. This research put information system security threats and vulnerabilities into four groups. The first category comprises human elements, including carelessness, level of skill, and trust. The inadequacy of information security policies, which includes problems with policy creation, implementation, and a lack of security training, was the second category. The study also looked at the "work environment", which includes things like support from management, organisational security culture, workload, Internet and network use, and access control. Last but not least, the study included variables related to gender, age, education level, and work experience under the category of "demographic variables". The study findings showed that almost all these categories received negative responses and contributed highly to the information system risk and vulnerabilities at the institute. Moreover, there is an unregulated level of trust, negligence, and inadequate security measures. According to these results, the study suggests that:

1) Organisations should regularly train their staff to improve their information system security proficiency.
2) Given that women are disproportionately affected, the institutes should make a concerted effort to increase their awareness.
3) The institute should create up-to-date policies that fully handle the issues with contemporary information system security and update in a minimum of every four (4) years.

4) The institute ought to promote actions that lessen exposure to information system security concerns.
5) The institute should consider creating an independent information system security policy document as currently, information system security policy is just a section within ICT policy which hinder its adequacy and relevance.

REFERENCES

1. Kundy, E.D. and Lyimo, B.J. (2019) Cyber Security Threats in Higher Learning Institutions in Tanzania A Case Study of University of Arusha and Tumaini University Makumira. Olva Academy—School of Researchers, 2, 1-37.
2. Semlambo, A., Almasi, K. and Liechuka, Y. (2022) Perceived Usefulness and Ease of Use of Online Examination System: A Case of Institute of Accountancy Arusha. International Journal of Scientific Research and Management (IJSRM), 10, 851-861.
3. Semlambo, A., Almasi, K. and Liechuka, Y. (2022) Facilitators' Perceptions on Online Assessment in Public Higher Learning Institutions in Tanzania: A Case Study of the Institute of Accountancy Arusha (IAA). International Journal of Scientific Research and Management (IJSRM), 10, 34-42.
4. Lubua, E.W., Semlambo, A. and Pretorius, P.D. (2017) Factors Affecting The Use of Social Media in the Learning Process. South African Journal of Information Management, 19, a764.
5. Nfuka, E.N., Sanga, C. and Mshangi, M. (2015) The Rapid Growth of Cybercrimes Affecting Information Systems in the Global: Is this a Myth or Reality in Tanzania? International Journal of Information Security Science, 3, 182-199.
6. Tanzania Communication Regulatory Authority. (2022) 2022 Quarterly Statistics Reports. Tanzania Communication Regulatory Authority, Dar es Salaam.
7. Saunders, J. (2017) Tackling Cybercrime—The UK Response. Journal of Cyber Policy, 2, 4-15.
8. Lewis, J. (2018) Economic Impact of Cybercrimes-No Slowing Down. McAfee, Santa Clara.
9. Kaspersky (2021) Top Ransomware Attacks of 2020. Kaspersky, Moscow.
10. International Telecommunication Union (2021) Cyber Security in Tanzania: Country Report. International Telecommunication Union, Geneva.
11. International Business Machine Cooperation (IBM) (2021) Cost of Data Breach Report. International Business Machine Cooperation, Armonk.
12. Gordon, L.A., Loeb, M.P. and Zhou, L. (2011) The Impact of Information Security Breaches: Has There Been a Downward Shift in Costs? Journal of Computer Security, 19, 33-56.
13. Lubua, E.W. and Pretorius, P.D. (2019) Ranking Cybercrimes Based on Their Impact on Organisations' Welfare. 2019 THREAT Conference Proceedings, Johannesburg, 26-27 June 2019, 1-11.

14. Al-Omari, A., El-Gayar, O. and Deokar, A. (2012) Security Policy Compliance: User Acceptance Perspective. 2012 45th Hawaii International Conference on System Sciences, Maui, 4-7 January 2012, 1-10.
15. AlHogail, A. (2015) Design and Validation of Information Security Culture Framework. Computers in Human Behavior, 49, 567-575.
16. Alhogail, A., Mirza, A. and Bakry, S.H. (2015) A Comprehensive Human Factor Framework for Information Security in Organisations. Journal of Theoretical and Applied Information Technology, 78, 201-211.
17. Arbanas, K. and Hrustek, N.Ž. (2019) Key Success Factors of Information Systems Security. Key Success Factors of Information Systems Security, 43, 131-144.
18. Almazán, D.A., Tovar, Y.S. and Quintero, J.M. (2017) Influence of Information Systems on Organisational Results. Contaduría y Administración, 62, 321-338.
19. Tanzania Communication Regulatory Authority (TCRA). (2022) Communication Statistics Quarter 2 2021/2022. Tanzania Communication Regulatory Authority, Dar es Salaam.
20. Alotaibi, M., Furnell, S. and Clarke, N.L. (2016) Information Security Policies: A Review of Challenges and Influencing Factors. 2016 11th International Conference for Internet Technology and Secured Transactions, Barcelona, 5-7 December 2016, 352-358.
21. Assefa, T. and Tensaye, A. (2021) Factors Influencing Information Security Compliance: An Institutional Perspective. SINET: Ethiopian Journal of Science, 44, 108-118.
22. Williams, S. (2021) Cyberattacks on Organisations Worldwide Surge 40% in 2021. Security Brief, New Zealand.
23. Broadhurst, R.G., Skinner, K., Sifniotis, N., Matamoros-Macias, B. and Ipsen, Y. (2018) Phishing and Cybercrime Risks in a University Student Community. SSRN Electronic Journal.
24. Lohani, S. (2019) Social Engineering: Hacking into Humans. International Journal of Advanced Studies of Scientific Research, 4, 385-395.
25. Alqahtani, F.H. (2017) Developing an Information Security Policy: A Case Study Approach. Procedia Computer Science, 124, 691-697.
26. ISO/IEC 27000:2018. (2018) Information Technology—Security Techniques—Information Security Management Systems—Overview and Vocabulary. International Organization for Standardization.
27. Kothar (2004) Research Methodology; Methods and Techniques. New Age International Publishers, New Delhi.
28. Glaspie, H.W. and Karwowski, W. (2018) Human Factors in Information SecurityCulture: A Literature Review. Proceedings of the AHFE 2017 International Conference on Human Factors in Cybersecurity, Los Angeles, 17-21 July 2017, 269-281.
29. Rajaonah, B. (2017) A View of Trust and Information System Security under the Perspective of Critical. Revue des Sciences et Technologies de l'Information—Série ISI: Ingénierie, 22, 109-133.
30. Sapronov, K. (2020) The Human Factor and Information Security. Kaspersky, Moscow.

31. Astakhova, L.V. (2016) The Ontological Status of Trust in Information Security. Scientific and Technical Information Processing, 43, 58-65.
32. Robinson, S.C. (2019) Factors Predicting Attitude toward Disclosing Personal Data Online. Journal of Organizational Computing and Electronic Commerce, 28, 214-233.
33. Brock, V. and Khan, H.U. (2017) Big Data Analytics: Does Organizational Factor Matters Impact Technology Acceptance? Journal of Big Data, 4, Article No. 21.
34. Mitra, T. and Gilbert, E. (2012) Have You Heard? How Gossip Flows Through Workplace Email. Proceedings of the 6th International AAAI Conference on Weblogs and Social Media, Dublin, 4-7 June 2012, 242-249.
35. Kagwiria, C. (2020) Cyber Security Skills Gap in Africa. African Advanced Level Telecommunications Institute, Nairobi.
36. Patrick, H., Niekerk, B.V. and Fields, Z. (2018) Information Security Management: A South African Public Sector Perspective. In: Fields, Z., Ed., Handbook of Research on Information and Cyber Security in the Fourth Industrial Revolution, IGI Global, Hershey, 382-405.
37. Cisco (2016) Mitigating the Cybersecurity Skills Shortage. Cisco, San Francisco.
38. Bulgurcu, B., Cavusoglu, H. and Benbasat, I. (2010) Information Security Policy Compliance: An Empirical Study of Rationality-Based Beliefs and Information Security Awareness. MIS Quarterly, 34, 523-548.
39. Watters, P.A. and Ziegler, J. (2016) Controlling Information Behaviour: The Case for Access Control. Behaviour & Information Technology, 35, 268-276.
40. Ghazvini, A. and Shukur, Z. (2016) Awareness Training Transfer and Information Security Content Development for Healthcare Industry. International Journal of Advanced Computer Science and Applications, 7, 361-370.
41. Hina, S. and Dominic, P.D. (2018) Information Security Policies' Compliance: a Perspective for Higher Education Institutions. Journal of Computer Information Systems, 60, 201-211.
42. Lopes, I. and Oliveira, P. (2015) Implementation of Information Systems Security Policies: A Survey in Small and Medium Sized Enterprises. In: Rocha, A., Correia, A., Costanzo, S. and Reis, L., Eds., New Contributions in Information Systems and Technologies, Springer International Publishing, Bragança, 459-468.
43. Greene, G. (2010) Assessing the Impact of Security Culture and the Employee-Organization Relationship on IS Security Compliance I. 5th Annual Symposium on Information Assurance, Albany, 16-17 June 2010, 1-8.
44. Humaidi, N. and Balakrishnan, V. (2015) The Moderating Effect of Working Experience on Health Information System Security Policies Compliance Behaviour. Malaysian Journal of Computer Science, 28, 70-92.
45. Kearney, W.D. and Kruger, H.A. (2016) Can Perceptual Differences Account for Enigmatic Information Security Behaviour in an Organisation? Computers & Security, 61, 46-58.
46. Choi, M. (2016) The leadership of the Information Security Manager on the Effectiveness of Information Systems Security for Secure Sustainable Computing. Sustainability, 8, 638-648.

47. Padayachee, K. (2012) Taxonomy of Compliant Information Security Behavior. Computers & Security, 31, 673-680.
48. Dotto, M.H. (2015) Effectiveness of the Electronic Records Management System in the Selected Courts of Tanzania. Collage of Business Education (CBE), Dar es Salaam.
49. Vernon-Bido, D., Grigoryan, G., Kavak, H. and Padilla, J. (2018) Assessing the Impact of Cyberloafing on Cyber Risk. Proceedings of the Annual Simulation Symposium, Baltimore, 15-18 April 2018, Article No. 11.
50. Martin, N., Rice, J. and Martin, R. (2016) Expectations of Privacy and Trust: Examining the Views of IT Professionals. Behaviour & Information Technology, 35, 500-510.
51. Amraoui, S., Elmaallam, M., Bensaid, H. and Kriouile, A. (2019) Information Systems Risk Management: Litterature Review. Computer and Information Science, 12, 1-20.
52. Khan, H.U. and AlShare, K.A. (2019) Violators Versus Non-Violators of Information Security Measures in Organisations—A Study of Distinguishing Factors. Journal of Organisation Computing and Electronic Commerce, 29, 4-23.
53. Tawalbeh, L., Muheidat, F., Tawalbeh, M. and Quwaider, M. (2020) IoT Privacy and Security: Challenges and Solutions. Applied Sciences, 10, Article No. 4102.
54. Sindiren, E. and Ciylan, B. (2018) Privileged Account Management Approach for Preventing Insider Attacks. International Journal of Computer Science and Network Security, 18, 33-42.
55. Pesic, D. and Veinović, M.Đ. (2016) Privileged Identities—Threat to Network and Data Security. International Scientific Conference on ICT and E-Business Related Research, Belgrade, 22 April 2016, 154-160.
56. Connolly, L., Lang, M. and Tygar, D. (2014) Managing Employee Security Behaviour in Organisations: The Role of Cultural Factors and Individual Values. 2014 International Federation for Information Processing, Marrakech, 2-4 June 2014, 417-430.
57. Barlow, J., Warkentin, M., Ormond, D.K. and Dennis, A.R. (2018) Don't Even Think About It! The Effects of Antineutralization, Informational, and Normative Communication on Information Security Compliance. Journal of the Association for Information Systems, 19, 689-715.
58. McGill, T. and Thompson, N. (2018) Gender Differences in Information Security Perceptions and Behaviour. Australasian Conference on Information Systems 2018, Sydney, 3-5 December 2018, 1-10.
59. Erceg, A. (2019) Information Security: Threat from Employees. Tehnički Glasnik, 13, 123-128.
60. Fatokun, F.B., Hamid1, S., Norman, A. and Fatokun, J.O. (2019) The Impact of Age, Gender, and Educational level on the Cybersecurity Behaviors of Tertiary Institution Students: An Empirical Investigation on Malaysian Universities. Journal of Physics: Conference Series, 1339, Article ID: 012098.
61. Levesque, F.L., Fernandez, J.M. and Batchelder, D. (2017) Age and Gender as Independent Risk Factors for Malware Victimisation. Proceedings of the 31st British Computer Society Human Computer Interaction Conference, Sunderland, 3-6 July 2017, Article No. 46.

62. Bostan, A. (2015) Impact of Education on Security Practices in ICT. Tehnicki Vjesnik, 22, 161-168.

63. Catota, F.E., Morgan1, G. and Sicker, D.C. (2019) Cybersecurity Education in a Developing Nation: The Ecuadorian Environment. Journal of Cyber Security, 5, tyz001.

4

The Grand Challenges in Information Systems

Chandra Amaravadi
School of Computer Sciences, Western Illinois University, Macomb, USA.

ABSTRACT

The field of information systems has historically suffered from a pre-dominance of behavioral approaches. As a result, it is not surprising that in spite of decades of research, dozens of conferences and journals and thousands of researchers, very few breakthroughs have been achieved. This paper advocates a technical approach that focuses on improving existing systems in organizations by viewing them from the point of roles i.e. functions fulfilled by IS in organizations. These are understood as: 1) supporting operations, 2) providing information, 3) supporting decision making, 4) providing knowledge, 5) supporting knowledge and clerical work, and 6) supporting organizational design. It is generally agreed that the field's understanding of fulfilling roles "1", "2", "3" and "6" is mature while understanding of areas "3" (for unstructured decisions), "4", and "5" are still incomplete. The challenges in these areas are difficult problems that we refer to as grand challenges and discuss in this paper.

Keywords: *Challenges in Information Systems, Information Systems Challenges, Research in IS, IS Research, Technology Support*

1. INTRODUCTION

The field of information systems was established in 1968 when the University of Minnesota initiated its master's and Ph.D. programs in information systems.

With an excess of 3200 scholars, dozens of journals, and thousands of papers, the field has progressed tremendously since its inception. In spite of a large number of scholars and exuberant participation in conferences, there have been few technical breakthroughs that inspire confidence in the discipline. Groundbreaking innovations such as HTML, social media, data analytics, and deep learning have originated from related areas outside the academic field and frequently from industry participants. The debate on "research that matters" highlights the fact that there is a paucity of IS research that has made an impact on the world [1]. As scholars, we need to collectively acknowledge that we have not produced much useable research during the five decades that the field has been in existence.

Part of the reason is the behavioral approach that predominates in the field [1]. For example, whenever a new technology emerges, rather than study ways of improving it, there are studies that identify critical success factors in its implementation and conclude among other things that top management support is critical to its success. The utilization of information systems in organizations does not present the difficulties that it previously did due to the prevalence of visual interfaces (GUI) and the high level of technological proficiency among the general public. The case study of Siemens Sharenet illustrates this. The ICN division of Siemens was able to develop a very successful knowledge management system that was used by 19,000 employees at its peak [2]. The implementation did not use any of the academic theories pertaining to system usage. In the software industry, user acceptance testing (UAT) is a mandatory part of any release, so there is little value in researching acceptance issues or similar behavioral issues involving technology.

On the other hand, system approaches are far and few in between. One study found that only 15% of research articles in journals used the Software Engineering Approach [3], which is often referred to as the Design Science Approach. Real progress in the field is hard to achieve unless it is directly focused on improving information systems used in organizations. To achieve breakthroughs at the system levels, information systems research should focus on the technologies and how they can support organizations. Roles are a convenient way of focusing this effort. These are widely understood as [4]: 1) support operations, 2) provide information, 3) provide knowledge, 4) support structured decision making, 5) support unstructured decision making, 6) support knowledge and clerical work, 7) support organizational design and strategy. The field's technical/research understanding of "1", "2", "4" and "7" is mature but still incomplete, requiring mopping up operations. For example, the technology to support company operations across organizational boundaries is poorly understood. On the other hand, the IS field is lagging in its understanding of "3", "5", and "6" [5] [6] [7]. Coupled with these are improvements to the software development process, particularly where analyzing and developing specialized systems are concerned. Achieving success in these requires breakthroughs in certain fundamental areas which I will refer to as the "Grand Challenges of IS." These are based on personal experience and represent, it is hoped, the holy grail of information systems research [8]. These are called as such because resolving them would improve the fulfillment of information systems roles. Save for one or two, the majority are recognized problems in related disciplines, so the contribution here is in identifying the agenda for IS researchers.

2. THE GRAND CHALLENGES

The grand challenges range across a number of different areas from supporting decision making to file formats to knowledge representation. When these are addressed it will be possible to better support organizations and their employees.

2.1. Supporting Decision Making

DSS is a mature technology in organizations, providing support for structured and semi-structured decisions, mostly in production, operations, marketing and transportation [9]. Support for unstructured decisions is still primitive. In a pathological case, an executive at a Japanese electronics company used a version of "rock, paper or scissors" to make a $20 m decision [10]. The key to supporting these types of decisions still lies in understanding how they are made. The phases of decision making are widely understood as Intelligence, Design and Choice although these are not necessarily sequential [11]. The Intelligence phase concerns the identification of the problem, an area that has received much attention in the organizational literature as problem formulation. According to [12], managers become aware of problems through informal channels of communication. Then they attempt to pigeonhole the problem into "categories" such as "mission and goals," "organizational structure," "resources" etc. [12] [13]. Cognitive scientists believe that categorization is followed by a mental representation of the problem that includes details such as constraints, objects, procedures and operators which enables them to solve it [14]. Both the problem formulation and categorization stages involve retrieving information from stored schemata, an area that technology could support. This stage overlaps with the Design phase of the decision-making process. Choices are made to maximize decision-maker utility, as in the classical literature with experienced managers giving extra attention to see that decision constraints are fulfilled [14]. Understanding these stages will certainly contribute to the state-of-the-art of DSS.

In the meantime, specific contributions are required in three areas. The first is Decision Representation—to develop a graphical method of representing a decision, similar to the representation of a process (see also challenge#9). A universal methodology, like UML for representing alternatives, constraints, information, rationale, micro-decisions, actions and impacts of a decision is required. Along with this, a tool that provides an unconstrained interface to formulate the problem and additionally to find a solution is required. With the tool, a decision-maker should be able to "sketch" decision alternatives, sub-problems, assumptions, weights, etc. and freely hop among these (see [15] for a similar idea). Drawing a diagram with the Microsoft Visio tool, using different symbol sets, is a comparable design metaphor. Such a "doodling" tool is one of the great challenges in IS. The second challenge is modeling subparts of the decision with existing DSS models such as L.P., Probabilistic, or simple algebraic models. For example, can we model the impacts of a decision as a mathematical relationship between the decision objective and a possible action [16] ? Is such an approach feasible? What information will the subparts require? Is it available from the decision situation as depicted by the model?

How can we aggregate results from these sub-decisions? If it is not possible to model subparts with DSS models, is it at least possible to have a schemata for each category of problem, in a manner somewhat analogous to word/email templates? This is the third area where research is required.

2.2. Designing Natural Language Interfaces

Natural language interfaces (NLI) will be the ultimate interface to information systems since no menus or user training is required. NLIs have been developed for databases [17], visualization software, medical and tourist information systems [18] [19]. But not all domains lend themselves to NLI applications, and graphical software being one example. So the first question to address is, for what types of software are NLIs best suited to? Perhaps it is not the software as much as certain actions that are suited to NLI. What are those? Assuming this is addressed, other issues arise during the process of interacting with the software [20]:

1) Understanding the User's Request—there are two approaches to understanding the user's request. The first is to break the request into parts of speech to understand the subject and object of the request. This presents the usual problems of processing NL which will be addressed in time. The second and more promising approach is to map the request into a pre-defined pattern. The request and its intent have to be understood in the context of the user's previous actions as well his/her current software context in order to select a sequence of actions.
2) Mapping the Request into a Sequence of Actions—once the request is understood, the next step is to identify a sequence of actions that will fulfill the objective. Classical issues in means-ends analysis and hierarchical planning arise (see for example [21]). A compromise approach where the complexity is limited should be taken to ensure that these problems do not arise. What then is the right level of complexity that can be handled by the system without running into planning problems? Additional questions that arise are, are there canonical forms for task-execution sequences? Can execution sequences be somehow auto-generated from the software itself to avoid coding them explicitly?
3) Determining the User's Context—the most important problem here is identifying the user's present context. Issues arising here are how can context be determined within an application in relation to the task that the user is carrying out? What knowledge should the system have about previous and current actions? About his/her computing environment? If the user is asking for a heading change in a file, how does the system recognize the file the user referring to?
4) Error handling and help—the system needs to interact with the user when their request is not understood, incorrect or poorly phrased. What are effective ways of dealing with help and error handling? Should the system present alternative formulations of the request? Suggest a list of functions that the user can use? Or fill in missing parameters from what it knows?

2.3. Providing Task/Functional Support

Task or functional support is concerned with technological support for performing daily tasks. A simple example is a researcher preparing a research paper that has a list of references at the end. He / she ought to be able to ask the system to use IEEE referencing style for formatting them, but this is not possible in current systems without using specialized software. Despite the plethora of information technologies available, office workers are poorly supported in their work [6]. They cannot automatically send emails or collect information from an email message (some of this capability is appearing in contemporary systems). Technology support for professionals is even poorer. It has not evolved past the use of specialized software such as CAD / CAM, LexisNexis database or a business intelligence tool. So an engineer carrying out a design cannot ask the system a question such as "What is the yield point for a 2" thick 10' long I beam?"

Functional support requires four types of capabilities on the part of office systems [6]: 1) Answer requests for information from documents stored in the system, 2) Store and retrieve assorted information such as a vendor offering a particular type of discount, 3) Answer questions about the employee's domain / work (essentially knowledge management) and 4) Carry out an action or a sequence of actions. The system should support the office worker like an assistant [6].

The first requirement is to answer requests for information that is in the system. The field of information retrieval focuses primarily on retrieving documents using keywords / terms [22], but in this realm, retrieval of parts of documents is an important problem [6]. It is up to IS researchers to identify different scenarios in which this requirement arises and then pursue a solution using techniques from the field of information extraction (see for example [23]). The second capability in the list requires suitable organization of information and perhaps the use of AI technologies [5]. The third requirement, question answering capability requires knowledge to be encoded using a suitable representation method (challenge#6) as well as natural language interfaces (challenge#2). Although there are some proposals [24] [25], research is still required to operationalize these schemes to develop technologies for a production implementation. Lastly, the requirement to provide clerical support for mundane tasks requires re-architecting office systems so that its functionality is available as services to end-users as well as other applications [6]. For example, it should be possible to send an email while editing a document or to schedule a meeting from an email client. Here also different usage scenarios need to be identified. This and NL capability (challenge#2) will allow requests such as "Email the Frankfurt report to all VPs of the company" to be fulfilled by the system [6].

2.4. Designing Universal Formats for Information Storage and Retrieval

The information and internet revolutions have spawned a number of different file formats for documents, images and data. For example, there are docx, html, xml, pdf, txt, and rtf formats for documents and bmp, jpg, png, and gif formats for images. At present, we will confine our discussion to physical file formats for documents only. A variety of applications including workflows, patient records, maintenance records, web searches and IoT (Internet of Things) related communications require standardized archival file formats that have to withstand the test of time. Is such a universal document format possible? XML has been introduced as such a standard but it has several shortcomings [26]. The first is ambiguity in the meaning of tags used since these are user-generated and subject to linguistic problems. Secondly, it lacks mechanisms for encoding relationships between elements *i.e.* other than as a hierarchy of elements [26]. Thirdly XML is verbose and requires a DTD file for interpreting it correctly. Fourthly, it is possible to encode *only* the linear or hierarchical structure of document elements, e.g. "a", "b", "c" (linear) or "a" ("b" ("c")) (hierarchical) where a, b and c are elements of the document. So a table structure is awkward to encode [27]. A similar problem occurs with office forms [6]. Modeling of form components as normalized tables makes it difficult to model operations on them in the same way that hierarchical structure in hierarchical databases made queries difficult [6]. An intermediate representation therefore presents a layer of complexity. A possible solution is to go beyond basic data types (e.g. integer, character, text, etc.), standardize more complex data types such as data ranges, min-max values, list of tasks, meeting minutes, etc. and incorporate them into the interpreter/browser. Conceivably these could be implemented as XML extensions. It will enable any document type to be modeled independently of the technology. For example, document A could be encoded as a + b, while document B could be a + b + c, and document C could be b + d where "a" "b", "c" and "d" are components of a document. As a concrete example, "a" could be user profile on a web site and "b" could be a list of patient medications, dosages, etc., so "a + b" would be a patient record. Only a comprehensive use-case analysis can reveal the complex types that are required. This addresses only part of the problem. The second issue is to have a more elegant solution to describe the appearance of the document, that would integrate well with the semantic model. Markup languages such as HTML may be thought of as a possible solution, but in these, data is stored without interpretation. For example, items such as graphs would be stored simply as images rather than with their semantic content, *i.e.* what is the graph about?

2.5. Designing Executive Information Systems

Executive information systems (EIS) have been introduced in the eighties. Their main functions are to provide high-level summarized information (from operational databases) and to provide support for analyzing this information. The information can be internal or external but generally speaking, external information is more valuable than summarized data from operational databases. The data and analysis capability are currently provisioned by Business Intelligence (BI) tools [28] [29]. These can provide summarized information in a variety of formats with an almost infinite variety of data couplings. BI tools appear to have replaced EIS completely, but some fundamental problems remain even with the addition of data/analysis capability.

The first is access to external information. Most EISs do not provide access to external information [30], presumably to avoid exposing sensitive company information. BI tools tend to be standalone tools with the ability to import data. Top management needs access to soft, non-financial data and strategic information that is currently a gap in EIS capabilities [29]. Regardless of the source and type of information, executives use it to make strategic decisions [31] and this is another bottleneck in the hyper-reactive 21st century business environment. To keep up with this velocity, it is necessary to rely on AI techniques to process and analyze trends; for example, to assess how a company's valuation is affected by a change in regulation. This has been missing in EIS research and is obviously the most important problem in this area. While there has been some research, there are no good models of how an organization or an organizational unit is affected by environmental forces (see also challenge#1). Secondly, there is no support for analyzing environmental information, such as creating scenarios or simulations [31]. The third issue is with respect to filtering the information. Critical success factors (CSFs) or strategic business objectives are often used as development methodologies for executive information [32] but in practice the volume of information is vast and dynamic, making CSFs an unsuitable paradigm. When executives are responding to a specific situation, they will need to obtain and analyze very specific information. For this reason, filtering information is an important research problem. Filtering requires the user's context which is typically ignored in Information Retrieval systems [33]. For executives, the user's context translates into markets, products, customers, etc. but these will not be simple encodings. So there is a need for user representations of context and at the same time, representations of document content are also needed to enable retrieval, spilling into other related challenges (challenges #3 and #6).

2.6. Knowledge Engineering for Professional Knowledge

Professional knowledge is deep knowledge associated with a particular domain such as stock trading, marketing, banking, engineering, etc. [24]. It describes objects, events, actions, situations, concepts, objectives or policies but consists mostly of abstract concepts [24]. In professional knowledge, there are complex relationships between such concepts including mathematical, axiomatic, logical, temporal, structural, etc. Traditionally rules have been used to model this knowledge but these are not useful for representing declarative knowledge such as "a 'trade' (an 'action') being one of 'options', 'stocks', 'bonds' or 'mutual funds' ". This is a typical class-subclass relationship (structural) that is better modeled with declarative schemes. Professional knowledge is filled with abstract concepts that are defined in terms of other abstract concepts, creating a knowledge engineering challenge [24]. In the previous example, "trade", "options", "stocks" etc. are all abstract concepts with structural relationships among them. There could be elaborations or restrictions on both concepts and relationships such as conditions under which the relationship is valid or some sort of agreement that enforces the relationship. For example, the allowable condition of a trade is that there should be sufficient funds in the account. These funds could consist of "cash" or "unsettled trades" or both. Thus concepts can have elaborations on relationships, but there are additional requirements for the representational mechanism. Firstly, the knowledge stored in the system should be viewable/editable by employees, so it should be at the "conceptual level" rather than at the "implementation level" of Brachman's knowledge levels. Graphical representations are easier to comprehend so this is a requirement. Secondly, the representation scheme should support the formation of abstractions so that concepts may be defined in terms of other concepts. Class-subclass relationships and concept definitions are common abstraction mechanisms. Thirdly, the scheme should support modularity which takes the form of partitioning. It should not be a monolithic graph that will present difficulties in comprehension, update or assertions of facts. In other words, it should be easy to divide the representation into parts and perhaps store these parts or make assertions independently. Fourthly, the scheme should be extensible, so that new concepts/constructs can be easily added. Lastly, since the amount of information in organizations is large, the techniques should scale up to accommodate volume [5].

2.7. Knowledge Management Support with Technology

Knowledge management (KM) is the explicit management of organizational knowledge, including tools and processes to create, store, access and disseminate organizational knowledge [34]. KM ideas have been in existence for at least two decades now, yet very little progress has been achieved in terms of technology. The prevailing approach in IT is to use knowledge repositories [35] with little consideration being given to the problem of retrieval or the need for keeping thousands of knowledge items up to date [5]. The trend toward virtual organizations and exploding knowledge in high-tech industries exceeds the bounded rationality of organizations, if not their budgets. The leader in addressing KM problems was not academia but Siemens with its Sharenet [2]. The repository approach is not practical if the use case requires answers to fine-grained queries (see also Challenge #2 and #3) such as "What should be the blade angle for a jet engine, if it needs 16,000 lbs of thrust at an altitude of 25,000 feet, facing a head wind of 15 knots?" Such queries can be answered only through AI approaches [5]. But these are poorly developed at best [24]. Progress in representing complex knowledge is needed as outlined in Challenge #6. Since knowledge in a repository has to be updated, it should be both human and machine processable. For this reason, graphical representations should be used [24]. Further, the knowledge should be checked for consistency, so maintaining knowledge integrity is another challenge for researchers. A philosophical issue here is when knowledge is updated, should it replace existing knowledge or should it be another version of the same knowledge? Would having ten versions of the same knowledge item defeat the purpose of a KM system? The details and functionality of the KM engine should be worked out as well as the best way to enhance the user experience (UX). These issues are definitely within the scope of IS research.

2.8. Achieving Large-Scale Distributed AI within a Smart-Device Ecosystem

The internet of things (IoT) is upon us with billions of smart devices that communicate with other smart devices. Designing applications that rely on IoT and communications with other systems to achieve distributed intelligence will be a major challenge for the future [36]. A car that has been sold in a dealership should be able to communicate to a Dealer Inventory database as well as to the Department of Motor Vehicles to update its registration [3]. How to achieve this without causing chaos or conflicts while preserving security and privacy is the "mother of all problems" and can serve as a gateway for many useful applications.

The basic IoT architecture is a wireless sensor network that collects data from sensors (e.g. a utility meter). This data could be sent to a local data store or a cloud-based server [37]. In some cases, actions can be taken based on the data, such as turning on a pump. For some applications, the data is cleaned and processed while in others such as meter readings, it is collected for other purposes. Data can also be aggregated and mined for patterns/conclusions [38]. There are networking/architectural challenges in having common transport and application protocols given the heterogeneity of sensor/actuator devices and networks [37]. Maintaining security and privacy in a ubiquitous data rich environment is also a major hurdle [39]. For IS researchers, the challenge lies in developing a framework that can facilitate data sharing (at the user level) since this will be a crucial component of distributed AI. The necessary protocols for handling this need to be developed. Issues that arise are: What data is public vs private? What checks have to be carried out before allowing information access from a device such as a health monitor? If a building detects a person with a weapon entering it, can it identify the person and check his/her firearm permit? Can it alert law enforcement if there is no permit? Philosophically, where should the intelligence that carries this out be located? Who should update it?

2.9. Universal Method for Specifying System Requirements

Software engineering is a massive but mature industry. Potential developers are confronted by a bewildering array of tools and methodologies for specifying requirements. Existing methodologies can be classified into two main branches based on whether the development approach is traditional or agile, using object-oriented development [40]. There are a number of methodologies in each of these for specifying the development. In the traditional approaches, there are tools such as DFDs, structure charts, data dictionaries [41], while for the latter approach there are tools such as UML diagrams, sequence and interface diagrams. Most research approaches have focused on specialized systems or on individual tools. See for example, [42] [43]. There is a compelling need for a uniform and integrated specification method (that is not unwieldy) to document or define: 1) objects and their relationships, 2) processes, 3) process calling sequences, 4) data relationships, 5) decisions 6) interfaces and interface relationships, 7) system features, 8) business rules and 9) organizational knowledge. Such a universal method ensures that the same methodology can be used for different types of systems and additionally, for creating a system's entire documentation in an integrated fashion. UML has been proposed as one such standard, but it has several limitations [44]. Among these is the inability to capture: 1) system-actor interactions (for example, a system informing an actor of its unavailability), 2) organizational context (for example, interactions between actors), 3) use case relationships (for example, part/subpart), 4) state-dependent system behavior (for example, a use case depends on a system's state). Modeling of information flows is also awkward in UML, but is a basic requirement of a specification methodology [44]. A universal methodology that overcomes these limitations and adapted to specifying/documenting different types of systems is required.

3. CONCLUSION

The field has suffered a behavioral emphasis for a long time as manifested in the design science debate [2]. It can only progress with application to business needs as defined at the outset. Behavioral work was relevant to the industry in the "initiation stage" of information systems in the "70"s and "80"s, but with the widespread adoption of information technologies by the masses (adults and infants alike!), this assumption is rapidly losing currency. For example, product manufacturers handle their own usability studies rather than utilize findings from academia. Previous works have viewed research issues in a broad sense, such as research being required in Databases, GDSS, etc. [45]. This paper advocates a technical approach to designing systems for organizations. Some of the topics discussed include decision modeling systems, designing natural language interfaces based on understanding simple requests, systems supporting employees' daily tasks, such as filling time sheets, universal data formats based on document algebra, and a universal method of specifying systems among others. Ultimately, all of these will boil down to models of various situations/objects, such as models of decision making, knowledge representation, semantic models of files, etc. It is the task of IS researchers to design these. There are other candidates for the grand challenges such as security and large-scale architectures for organizing data/processes on the cloud, but they appear surmountable with existing methods and cannot be considered grand challenges.

REFERENCES

1. Österle, H., Becker, J., Frank, U., Hess, T., Karagiannis, D., Krcmar, H. and Loos, P. (2010) Memorandum on Design-Oriented Information Systems Research. European Journal of Information Systems, 20, 7-10.
2. MacCormack, A.D., Volpel, S. and Herman, K. (2002) Siemens ShareNet: Building a Knowledge Network. Harvard Business School Case 603-036.
3. Morrison, J. and George, J.F. (1995) Exploring the Software Engineering Component in MIS Research. Communications of the ACM, 38, 80-91.
4. Valacich, J. and Schneider, C. (2013) Information Systems Today: Managing in the Digital World. 6th Edition, Prentice Hall, Upper Saddle River.
5. Amaravadi, C.S. (2005) Knowledge Management for Administrative Knowledge. Expert Systems, 22, 53-61.
6. Amaravadi, C.S. (2014) Office Information Systems: A Retrospective and Call to Arms. Journal of Software Engineering and Applications, 7, 700-714.

7. Huttenegger, G. (2004) Knowledge Management and Information Technology: Goals/Problems, Practical Approaches and Proposal Solution. Doctoral Dissertation, University of Vienna, Vienna.
8. Amaravadi, C.S. (2016) Ten Grand Challenges in Information Systems. Australian Conference on Information Systems, Workshop on Grand Challenges, Wollongong.
9. Eom, S. and Kim, E. (2006) A Survey of Decision Support System Applications (1995–2001). Journal of the Operational Research Society, 57, 1264-1278.
10. Vogel, C. (2005) Rock, Paper, Payoff: Child's Play Wins Auction House an Art Sale. New York Times.
11. Mintzberg, H., Raisinghani, D. and Théorêt, A. (1976) The Structure of Unstructured Decision Processes. Administrative Science Quarterly, 21, 246-275.
12. Lyles, M. and Mitroff, I. (1980) Organizational Problem Formulation: An Empirical Study. Administrative Science Quarterly, 25, 102-119.
13. Smith, G.F. (1995) Classifying Managerial Problems: An Empirical Study of Definitional Content. Journal of Management Studies, 32, 679-706.
14. Nokes, T.J., Schunn, C.D. and Chi, M.T.H. (2010) Problem Solving and Human Expertise. International Encyclopedia of Education, 5, 265-272.
15. Acar, W. and Druckenmiller, D. (2006) Endowing Cognitive Mapping with Computational Properties for Strategic Analysis. Futures, 38, 993-1009.
16. Saaty, T.L. (1978) Modeling Unstructured Decision Problems—The Theory of Analytical Hierarchies. Mathematics and Computers in Simulation, 20, 147-158.
17. Androutsopoulos, I., Ritchie, G.D. and Thanisch, P. (1995) Natural Language Interfaces to Databases—An Introduction. Natural Language Engineering, 1, 29-81.
18. Rector, A.L., Solomon, W.D., Nowlan, W.A, Rush, T.W., Zanstra, P.E. and Claassen, W.M. (1995) A Terminology Server for Medical Language and Medical Information Systems. Methods of Information in Medicine, 34, 147-157.
19. Malaka, R. and Zipf, A. (2000) Deep Map: Challenging IT Research in the Framework of a Tourist Information System. In: Fesenmaier, D.R., Klein, S. and Buhalis, D., Eds., Information and Communication Technologies in Tourism 2000, Springer, Vienna, 15-27.
20. Srinivasan, A. and Stasko, J. (2017) Natural Language Interfaces for Data Analysis with Visualization: Considering What Has and Could Be Asked. Proceedings of the Eurographics/IEEE VGTC Conference on Visualization: Short Papers, Barcelona, 12-16 June 2017, 55-59.
21. Yang, Q. (1997) Hierarchical Planning. In: Amarel, S. Biermann, A., et al, Eds., Intelligent Planning, Artificial Intelligence, Springer, Heidelberg, 163-188.
22. Manning, C.D., Raghavan P. and Schütze, H. (2008) Introduction to Information Retrieval. Cambridge University Press, Cambridge.
23. Muslea, I. (1999) Extraction Patterns for Information Extraction Tasks: A Survey. In: The AAAI-99 Workshop on Machine Learning for Information Extraction.

24. Amaravadi, C.S. (2020) A Representation Scheme for Managing Complex Professional Knowledge. Advanced Aspects of Engineering Research, 1, 13-37.
25. Rosner, D., Grote, B., Hartman, K, Hofling, B. and Guericke, O. (1998) From Natural language Documents to Sharable Product Knowledge: A Knowledge Engineering Approach. In: Borghoff, U.M. and Pareschi, R., Eds., Information Technology for Knowledge Management, Springer, Berlin, 35-51.
26. Renear, A., Dubin, D., McQueen, C.M. and Huitfeldt, C. (2002) Towards a Semantics for XML Markup. Proceedings of the 2002 ACM symposium on Document Engineering, McLean, 8-9 November 2002, 119-126.
27. Walsh, N. (1998) A Technical Introduction to XML.
28. MicroStrategy (2017) Basic Reporting Guide, version 10.9.
29. Marx, F., Mayer, J.H. and Winter, R. (2012) Six Principles for Redesigning Executive Information Systems—Findings of a Survey and Evaluation of a Prototype. ACM Transactions on Management Information Systems, 2, 1-19.
30. Salmeron, J.L., Luna, P.L. and Martinez, F.J. (2001) Executive Information Systems in Major Companies: Spanish Case Study. Computer Standards and Interfaces, 23, 195-207.
31. Papageorgiou, E. and De Bruyn, H. (2011) Challenges of Executive Information Systems in Listed Johannesburg Stock Exchange Companies. SA Journal of Information Management, 13, Article No. a448.
32. Boynton, A. and Zmud, R. (1984) An Assessment of Critical Success Factors. Sloan Management Review, 25, 17-27.
33. Pasi, G. (2010) Issues in Personalizing Information Retrieval. IEEE Intelligent Informatics Bulletin, 11, 3-7.
34. Prusak, L. (1997) Introduction to Knowledge in Organizations. Butterworth-Heinemann, Boston, ix-xv.
35. Kankanhalli, A., Tanudidjaja, F., Sutanto, J. and Tan, B.C.Y. (2003) The Role of Information Technology in Successful Knowledge Management Initiatives. Communications of the ACM, 46, 69-73.
36. Amaravadi, C.S. (2003) World and Business Computing in 2051. The Journal of Strategic Information Systems, 12, 373-386.
37. Farhan, L., Kharel, R., Quiroz, M., Alissa, A. and Abdulsalam, M. (2018) A Concise Review on Internet of Things (IoT)-Problems, Challenges and Opportunities. 11th International Symposium on Communication Systems, Networks & Digital Signal Processing (CSNDSP), Budapest, 18-20 July 2018, 1-6.
38. Stolpe, M. (2016) The Internet of Things: Opportunities and Challenges for Distributed Data Analysis. ACM SIGKDD Explorations Newsletter, 18, 15-34.
39. Aggarwal, C.C., Ashish, N. and Sheth, A. (2013) The Internet of Things: A Survey from the Data-Centric Perspective. In: Aggarwal, C., Ed., Managing and Mining Sensor Data, Springer, Boston, 383-428.

40. France, R.B., Wu, J., Petrie, M.L. and Bruel, J.M. (1996) A Tale of Two Case Studies: Using Integrated Methods to Support Rigorous Requirements Specification. Proceedings of the Methods Integration Workshop, Leeds, 25-26 March 1996, 1-18.
41. Page-Jones, M. (1980) The Practical Guide to Structured Systems Design. Yourdon Press, New York.
42. Gulla, J.A. (2004) Understanding Requirements in Enterprise Systems Projects. 12th IEEE International Requirements Engineering Conference, Kyoto, 10 September 2004, 176-185.
43. Escalona, M.J. and Koch, N. (2003) Requirements Engineering for Web Applications—A Comparative Study. Journal of Web Engineering, 2, 193-212.
44. Glinz, M. (2000) Problems and Deficiencies of UML as a Requirements Specification Language. 10th International Workshop on Software Specification and Design, San Diego, 7 November 2000, 11-22.
45. Galliers, R.D. (1993) Research Issues in Information Systems. Journal of Information Technology, 8, 92-98.

5

Interdisciplinary Integrated Tools to Problem Solving 2.0

Maria J. Espona

ArgIQ, Argentina Information Quality, Buenos Aires, Argentina

ABSTRACT

Everyone understands the events they witness or read about according to their mental models, and that is one of the main reasons there are a lot of disagreements at workplaces and between friends and families. Considering this situation, plus the difficulty that most people face when trying to conceptualize problems, I suggest a course that includes series methodologies, working synergistically to deal with this problem that goes from understanding the differences between people to test multiple hypotheses and planning the solution implementation. Since 2014, I have been teaching with some colleagues this tool in the format of a short course that articulates systems thinking, mapping studies, information quality, and competing hypotheses. This course has been presented often not only in Argentina and also in Peru with great success. Considering the pandemic situation, since 2020, it has been taught virtually. The latest modification to the original structure of the course was the incorporation of the Gantt chart to design the implementation of the solution found. This paper will present our course and the logic behind it, its outcomes, and how it evolved with the different iterations.

Keywords: *problem-solving, systemic thinking, information quality, decision making*

1. INTRODUCTION

Being part of the information society and live in this time has a lot of advantages but pose a lot of challenges. The superabundance of information and the difficulties we face to evaluate its quality complicates our decision-making processes.

The COVID-19 pandemic has shown us clearly the impact of misinformation and how the constant influx of a lot of information -of which we know just little-affects our emotional and physical health and our understanding of reality and its evolution.

Since we are running like headless chickens most of the time after many objectives that become difficult to identify, when it comes the moment to think and conceptualize a problem, we need extra help to do it properly and get the expected result. This situation also affects how we look for information and based on which parameters we select it or not, how we validate our hypothesis, and how we plan what we need to do to implement the desired solution.

Here, I will describe the course and the different methodologies included in it and show how they articulate to give the students an easy way to understand and solve their problems.

2. RELATED RESEARCH

There are several problem-solving methods, nevertheless, almost all of them follow this logic (Figure 1). But only a few of them include methodologies to implement the different steps in a structured and auditable way. Also, in most of the cases, the people involved in the problems are not considered as no not only as possible sources of solutions but as the ones who know the most about the situation and, at the end, the ones who will be involved in the change.

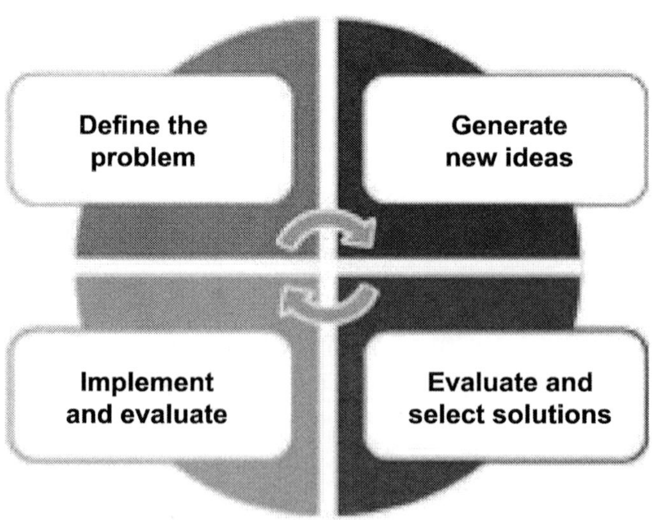

Figure 1.: *Problem-solving logic [1].*

Methodologies as the TRIZ/USIT [2], Six Sigma [3], the VSM (Viable Systems Model) [4] and the many problem-solving in 4 steps or 6 steps that exists in the literature offer different tactics to approach the problems and find a solution [5]. Even when they are helpful in many specific fields, they are not do not look for a fluid tool, easy to implement in all possible problems as the one presented here.

The Six Step Problem Solving Model [6], developed at the University of Arkansas at Pine Bluff, is worth to highlight because of its characteristics and reasoning close to the one that laid behind I designed. This method includes for each step one or more tools and considers the participation of the people involved.

In closing, even though many problem-solving methodologies exist, the one presented in this paper could be consider as a combination of the best of others that exist with a twist of innovation.

3. THE COURSE

This problem-solving course entails integrating five methodologies: systems theory, mapping studies, data quality, and competing hypothesis, plus the Gantt chart. Together, they allow us to go from the problem conceptualization to the hypothesis testing and plan the solution in a methodologically consistent, unbiased, and structured way.

Using a combination of methodologies in an articulated way has its origin in a request made by the Peruvian Air Force. They wanted to have a dedicated course on research methodologies. After that, the course has been successfully presented in many places. Finally, the INAP (National Institute for the Public Administration, Argentina) requested an upgrade to include implementing the solution found, and the Gantt chart was included. So now the course goes from problem identification to solution implementation.

This course starts with a discussion about mental models and how their impact in the understanding of the reality. In this specific context, helps to realize why we all disagree about problems or circumstance and facilitate the communication and agreements [7].

3.1 General systems theory

This problem-solving course starts with understanding the first out of the five methods that conform to this proposal, the systemic method, developed after the general systems theory. This tool is well known and widely used in many disciplines.

Ludwig Von Bertalanffy, the biologist who developed the general systems theory, recognized that his theory started to be developed back in Aristotle times when he said: "the whole is greater than the sum of its parts", describing the synergy, one of the core characteristics of the system when working [8].

Von Bertalanffy included the three premises that set the basis of the General Systems Theory in his book published in 1969 [9]. Those assumptions are:

1. Systems exist within systems;
2. The systems are open; and
3. The functions of a system depend on its structure.

Von Bertalanffy has described the systems' functioning considering the inputs, processes and components and output (Figure 2).

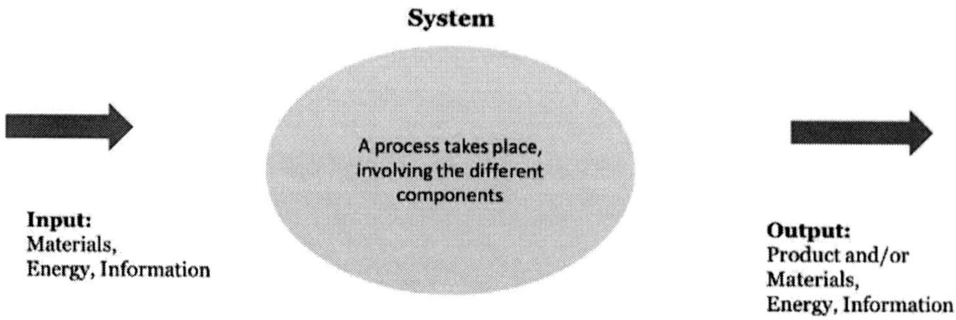

Figure 2.: *How the system works (designed by the author).*

In the representation of how the systems work, it is implicit a time spam since the input enters into the system, then a process takes place, and finally the product of the process exits the system as output. Therefore, applying this method to understand a problem or situation provides us with a dynamic vision of reality, including its components.

One of the most intuitive examples of a system is the ecosystem. The word itself results from the merge of eco (house) and system. According to the Encyclopaedia Britannica, a definition of the term is: "Ecosystem, the complex of living organisms, their physical environment, and all their interrelationships in a particular unit of space" [10].

A graphic representation of the ecosystem definition using systems theory could be (Figure 3):

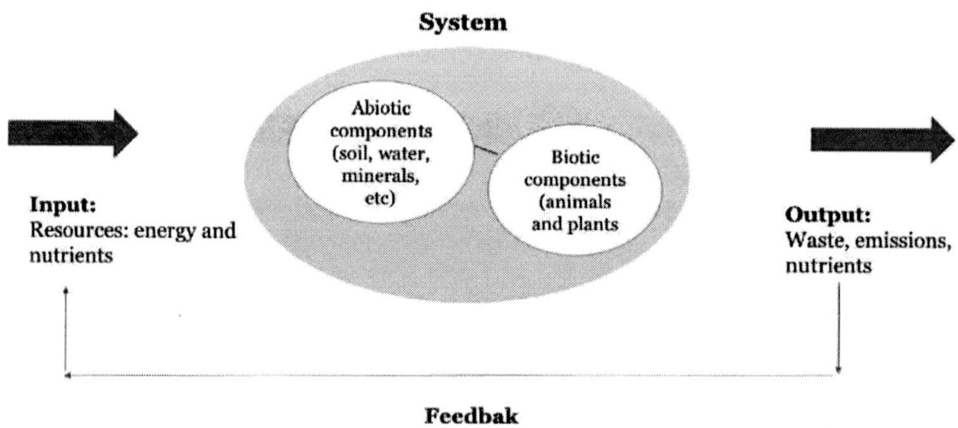

Figure 3.: *Representation of an ecosystem using the systems theory (designed by the author).*

The components of an ecosystem are related so a balance between them is achieved. This is another property of the systems, and it is called homeostasis.

Feedback is one of the essential properties of the systems and what means is that the system's output re-enters again as an input. This cyclic process is also linked with the homeostasis.

Let us analyze the feedback in other system, for example in a workplace where a modification is included. One role it will play will be informing if the changes have a positive or a negative impact.

The study of the systems has two possible approaches, one is the study of the system and its components and the processes that take place between them; and another is considering the border of the system, characterizing and studying what happens there. But in both cases the context is considered and the inputs and outputs (and feedback).

During the course, since this is the starting point, this method is used to conceptualize the problem and understand its components, the process, and its dynamic.

At this point, the students decide with which problem or situation they want to analyze and solve. By doing this, they move out from thinking to drafting and putting in words their ideas. This process takes time and requires reflection, and also decisions should be made to set up the limits (system border) and the components -and relations between them- of the problem under study.

When doing this conceptualization process, the system is developed with a specific objective and if the objective changes, the system will also do.

3.2 Structured searches

Once the problem is identified and described the look for answers and solutions start. At this point two possibilities exists: look for an existing solution or innovate if nothing has been done successfully by others. In both cases the search of the information in a structured way is optimal.

Considering the abundance of information, it is relevant to search on the internet following specific parameters and minimize the impact of our cognitive bias.

Systematic literature review or systematic mapping studies is the name of a methodology to execute searches in a structured way by following a detailed procedure.

The origins of this technique can be traced back to the problems the clinicians faced when relying in the available literature for their decision-making process. "In answer to this challenge, the worldwide Cochrane Collaboration was formed in 1992 to provide an expanding resource of updateable systematic reviews of randomized controlled trials (RCTs) relating to health care. Thus began the modern incarnation of the review article, a tool that had for many centuries been the mainstay for updating scientific knowledge" [11].

Later, this methodology was discovered and widely implemented by academics from the areas of systems engineering and informatics mostly to develop the state of the art of research topics. And later, considering its usefulness, it was adopted by other sciences and also used in projects design.

The author who is a reference for this methodology is Barbara Kitchencham [12] from Keele University. And Dr. Marcela Genero Bocco from the Alarcos Group

(University of Castilla La Mancha -UCLM- Spain) is leading the field in Spanish-speaking countries [13].

This method is relevant in this problem-solving tool because it helps to minimize the impact of our cognitive bias when doing a search, particularly for selecting among the results. As humans, we have the tendency to tend to choose what agrees with our mental models or the concept or ideas we have in mind. Because of this, we may avoid reading relevant articles with a different perspective on the topic under study.

The methodology includes three phases: planning the review, executing it and writing the report.

In the first phase, many tasks will take place. First, the need for a review must be identified, particularly considering that applying this methodology takes time and effort and it is not for a simple quick search. By doing a review, it is possible to summarize all the information on a topic, in a format that resembles a database.

To begin with the practical steps of this tool, the research questions formulation is the next step. These research questions will be the tool to select the publications, considering whether they answer or not to them, and not how they do (this is important for the later analysis of the results). This way of selecting the publications helps to minimize the impact of our cognitive bias, allowing us to have the whole set of possible answers, and not only the ones we like.

Before performing the search, a protocol must be developed. This plan includes:

1. with what? Identification of the search terms, and also their synonyms and other alternative terms (the use OR and AND, or other Boolean operators is recommended);
2. where will the search be performed? The sources of information must be chosen and specified (use virtual libraries, Google or other search engines);
3. inclusion and exclusion criteria; and
4. a form to transfer the selected publications and the research questions must be designed, usually an Excel sheet.

In the second phase, the review takes place, and what was planned on the first phase here it is executed.

Once the search engine is selected, the terms are introduced, and the results appear. Now, it is important to check all the results, one by one, and the publications that answer the research questions will be transferred to the Excel file and the different fields will be completed. The inclusion and exclusion criteria will help to filter the results obtained, and finally the result will be a set of publications that fulfill the requirements and answer the research questions.

This methodology was designed to be implemented on virtual libraries. But it works perfectly in Google and other search engines like it.

After doing the search and filling the Excel, it will be possible to identify if an adjustment of the protocol is needed or not (new keywords, rephrase of the research questions, etc).

The publications database we will have as a result will include fields specific to each publication (author, date, publisher, title, etc.), and other relevant information, considered metadata, which will help perform a broader analysis.

The methodology concludes with the report writing. The text must include a detailed presentation of the protocol, an explanation of how the search was executed, and all the decisions made during the process to make the search repeatable and auditable.

The report will also include the analysis of the answers to the research questions, not only in writing but graphs could be performed considering the information will be included in an Excel.

This file will be the starting point to the execution of these methodologies, information quality (to evaluate the quality of the selected publications) and competing hypothesis (to identify the scenario with more support in the available literature).

3.3 Information quality core concepts

Having the possibility to access many sources of information when looking for something is fantastic. Still, the growing amount of data and information and the difficulties in knowing its quality created the need to develop a specific method to evaluate its properties [14].

Experts at the Massachusetts Institute of Technology (MIT) (Cambridge, Massachusetts, USA) developed an information quality method. Lately, professionals from other universities and countries expanded and added more elements to it.

The part of the method which will used in this problem-solving methodology is the one of categories and dimensions. The other two, that explore the role of the different stakeholders involved in the information management and the total data quality management (TDQM) cycle will not be considered here.

Table 1.: *MIT information quality categories and dimensions (designed by the author, adapted from [15]).*

Categories	Dimensions
Intrinsic	Accuracy, believability, objectivity, and reputation
Contextual	Value-added, relevancy, timeliness, completeness, and amount of data
Representational	Interpretability, ease of understanding, representational consistency and representation conciseness
Accessibility	Access and security

Wang and Strong [15], back in 1996 developed a framework to evaluate and hierarchically organize information. To create this method, they sent a survey to information consumers and master's in business administration (MBA) students asking about the most critical attributes that information should have. The result was a list of 179 attributes. After that, they performed a second survey to learn and understand the importance of the attributes identified. Finally, they come out with a list of 15 dimensions, grouped into four categories (see Table 1).

3.4 Competing hypothesis

The competing hypothesis methodology was developed by Richards J. Heuer Jr., an intelligence analysis expert from the Central Intelligence Agency (CIA), during the Cold War, and a few years later was provided to the public [16].

This tool is especially useful in cases of complex problems, with many possible scenarios and a lot of evidence to analyze. It allows to study simultaneously all likely hypothesis and verify them with all the available information simultaneously. The outcome will be a table including the evidence and the hypotheses and the results of the evaluation performed (Table 2).

Table 2.: Resulting table as consequence of the execution of the competing hypothesis method (designed by the author, adapted from [16]).

	Hypothesis 1	Hypothesis 2
Evidence	+	+
Evidence	++	—
Evidence	+	Not apply
Evidence	Not apply	—
Evidence	—	+
Total	4+, 1- = 3+	2+, 3- = −1

In this evaluation, the level correlation is showed:
(+) the evidence supports the hypothesis.
(++) the evidence highly supports the hypothesis.
(–) the evidence does not support the hypothesis.
(–-) the evidence does not support the hypothesis strongly.
Not apply: there is no relation between the hypothesis and the evidence.

The winning hypothesis, in the Table 2 example will be the hypotheses 1, is according to Heuer [16]: "The result of the methodology is which hypothesis has more support according to with the available evidence and not which is the hypothesis with a higher probability of occurrence."

This next to the last step will allow taking the publications selected in the structured searches after the quality evaluation and considering them as the evidence for this method. The hypotheses will be elaborated considering the objective of the systemic method along with the research questions.

This step will identify the winning hypothesis, which means the solution to the problem with more support in the available information.

3.5 Gantt chart

Now that the solution has been found, it is time to design its implementation. To do it, the Gantt chart will be used as method.

To design a Gantt chart, identify objectives and tasks for each implementation phase: design, planning, execution and evaluation.

The objectives preferable must be SMART, which means:

S: Specific, what do you want to achieve? Who needs to participate? When do you want to accomplish your objective? Why is it important?

M: measurable, how can the be progress measured? How do you know if the objective has been achieved?

A: Attainable or Achievable, can you achieve the objective? Do you have the skills needed to achieve the objective? If not, could you build them?

R: Relevant, why it is important? The impact?

T: Timely (or time-bound), when the objective must be accomplished? Is it possible?

George T. Doran coined the concept of SMART objectives, and he published them in the November 1981 issue of Management Review [17]. Since then, some authors added more letters to the acronym, and others created different ones. Still, the general concept remains the same: the objectives gain meaning when a task to be performed is associated to them.

In this final step of the problem-solving tool, the first step is to go back to the systemic method and use it as starting point. Over this scenario, the diagnosis will be performed, but also considering the winning hypotheses from the previous method applied. Considering this information, the specific objectives, and tasks (including the intended duration) must be identified. At this point, a qualitative evaluation is recommended. Asking the people involved in the project for their opinions and suggestions could bring relevant information to the objectives and tasks design for the whole project.

Next to the diagnosis, the planning of what needs to be done is the next stage. It is critical to carefully plan and link the objectives and tasks from this planning stage to the ones in the implementation or execution phase. One of the most common errors is to plan activities that have no correlation on the execution phase or design activities not planned in advance. And also, to put both phases in parallel, when they must be one after the other, sequentially.

Finally, the evaluation phase, it is time to measure if what was implemented has led to the desired scenario or to another. At this point, a qualitative evaluation is recommended.

4. EXECUTING THE TOOL

When we initiate the course discussing the mental models, the participants think about how they see the world and why we all have different opinions. Also, they usually increase their awareness about how bias they are because of their high engagement with the situation they are trying to improve.

It is like they experience Eureka moments.

After this, they can reduce the tension associated with the analysis of the situation and how they consider the other people. This is a first step that facilitates the following ones, when they apply the different methodologies to their problem.

Using the systemic thinking to conceptualize the situation or problem the participants are trying to solve is the next step. This stage is time and energy consuming since a lot of self-questioning and reflection upon not only the scenario but its components, relationships, inputs and outputs and understanding the objective of the system.

Often the participants think they have a problem, but after this phase of deep analysis, they discover sometimes that they were right and in others that it was not the case.

Forcing the participants to prepare the systemic method diagrams, helps them to visualize clearly the situation and they get ready for the next step, which is finding a solution.

Looking for answers and solutions in a structured way is what the participants to this course do when executing the mapping studies.

When performing this task, they complaint a lot because of the effort it takes, but later they realize how important is to have an Excel file that acts as database which condenses all the information.

The link between this method and the systemic thinking is given by the objective of the system which becomes the main research question in the structured search. Using this main question as cornerstone, the relevant aspects to it (and to find answers to the problem) can be easily identified.

Once the relevant publications are selected, its quality is measured using the information quality method. By doing this, since many options or potentials solutions are now identified, this evaluation could be a way to consider which of the available answers have better support.

Competing hypothesis method uses as evidences the publications obtained during the structured search, that also has been evaluated to measure their quality, and ranked. The hypotheses are related to both the objective of the systemic method and the research questions of the mapping. The winning hypotheses, since sets of hypotheses linked to the different aspects of the problem are expected, will be the ones considered to design the implementation plan using the Gantt chart.

The different phases of the Gantt chart, diagnosis, planning, execution and evaluation are developed following the objective of the system (3.1), as guidance, and using winning hypotheses (3.4) as clues to internally organize what must be done to solve the components or aspects of the main problem.

Using this tool, participant to the course solved and implemented problems related to the administrative functioning of a workplace; design new regulations; design and implement customer care systems, etc.

5. CONCLUSIONS

This problem-solving course has been presented in different formats over a dozen times, always successfully. A previous publication summarizes the accomplishments until 2016 [18], which were largely surpassed with the new editions of the course and the new venues where it was taught.

Considering the audience and their specific needs, the focus on the different methodologies changes. Usually, the most demanding stage is the implementation of the systemic method in order to conceptualize the problem and also the Gantt design.

The problems that were considered during the courses range from improving to make significant changes. Often, the students implemented what they design during the course, and the results were the ones expected. The effectiveness of this method is proved.

The methodologies included led to finding the solution to many problems, in an unbiased, structured, auditable and at the same time, simple way.

Finally, I consider there is still room for improvements, and maybe shortly more methods or resources will be added to have a more usable and easier to implement tool. Those that are under evaluation are the formal incorporation at the beginning of the curse of an introduction to different decision-making models so the participants would have more information to be applied not only during the problem conceptualisation phase but also to use them at the time of communicating and implemented the solutions. Other resource under evaluation to be added after the Gantt chart is the elaboration of dashboards, which will be useful to monitor the different processes under implementation.

REFERENCES

1. ASG – Excellence Through Quality.
2. Nakagawa T. Creative Problem-Solving Methodologies TRIZ/USIT: Overview of My 14 Years in Research, Education, and Promotion. The Bulletin of the Cultural and Natural Sciences in Osaka Gakuin University, No. 64, March 2012.
3. Douglas A, Middleton S, Antony J, Coleman S. Enhancing the Six Sigma problem-solving methodology using the systems thinking methodologies. International Journal of Six Sigma and Competitive Advantage. 2009;5(2):144. DOI: 10.1504/ijssca.2009.025166
4. Richter J, Basten D. Applications of the Viable Systems Model in is Research - A Comprehensive Overview and Analysis, 2014 47th Hawaii International Conference on System Sciences. Waikoloa, HI, USA: IEEE Institute of Electrical and Electronics Engineers; 2014. pp. 4589-4598. DOI: 10.1109/HICSS.2014.565
5. Newton P. Top 5 Problem Solving Tools
6. University of Arkansas at Pine Bluff, The Six Step Problem Solving Model.
7. Beaubien R, Parrish S. The Great Mental Models Volume 1: General Thinking Concepts. Ottawa: Latticework Publishing Inc.; 2018. 190 pag
8. Wealth TE. The Whole Is Greater Than the Sum of Its Parts. Strategies Newsletter 2012.
9. Von Bertalanffy L. General Systems Theory: Foundations, Development and Applications; 1969, 289 pags.
10. Definition of Ecosystem, Encyclopaedia Britannica.

11. Grant MJ, Booth A. A typology of reviews: An analysis of 14 review types and associated methodologies. Health Information and Libraries Journal. 2009;26(2):91-108
12. Kitchencham B, Pretorius R, Budgen D, Brereton P, Turner M, Niazi M, et al. Guidelines for performing Systematic Literature Reviews in Software Engineering. Information and Software Technology. 2010;52:792-805
13. Genero M, Cruz-Lemus JA, Piattini M. Métodos de investigación en ingeniería del software. Madrid: RaMa; 2014. 312 pag. ISBN 978-84-9964-507-0
14. Espona MJ, Fisher YC. Teaching information quality to professionals in intelligence government agencies. In: Proceedings of the 32th Information Systems Education Conference (ISECON). Orlando (Florida, United States): Foundation for IT Education; 2015
15. Wang RY, Strong D. Beyond accuracy: What data quality means to data consumers. Journal of Management Information Systems. 1996;12(4):5-34
16. Heuer R. Psychology of Intelligence Analysis. Washington, D.C.: Center for the Study of Intelligence; 1999.
17. Doran GT. There's a S.M.A.R.T. way to write management's goals and objectives. Management Review. 1981;70(11):35-36.
18. Espona MJ. Interdisciplinary integrated tools to problem solving: A short course. US-China education review a. 2016;6(11):633-641. DOI: 10.17265/2161-623X/2016.11.002

6

Clinical Pathway for Improving Quality Service and Cost Containment in Hospital

Boy Subirosa Sabarguna

Community Medicine Department, Faculty of Medicine, Universitas Indonesia, Indonesia

ABSTRACT

The explanation begins with the Clinical Pathway in Hospital which describes how the Clinical Pathway is used in relation to 2 things: Components-Linkages and Step-Problems-Optimal Solution, followed by Linkages Clinical Pathway with Quality Improvement and Cost Containment, which describes the relationship of each. Followed by the Clinical Pathway for Service Quality: which consists of: (1) Clinical Pathway for Service Quality, (2) Patient Safety for Service Quality Improvement, (3) The role of alogarithm, thereby clarifying the form of clinical pathways in quality improvement efforts that ensure service improvement by still maintain the quality that is maintained during the cost containment. The Clinical Pathway in Cost Containment describes the roles of: (1) Link of Components, (2) Procedure, (3) Unit Cost, so that cost containment efforts can be made in the form of cost containment optimally while maintaining quality does not need to decrease. Clinical Pathway in New Era is a newly developed algorithm related to current and future conditions. This is related to: (1) New Era in Pandemic Covid-19, (2) Clinical Pathway in Non Curative Service, (3) Clinical Pathway in Technology Services, (4) Clinical Pathway in Technological Rerelated while continuing to carry out quality improvement and cost containment simultaneously. Concluton: clinical pathway in hospital can be used as a system for Quality Improvement and Cost Containment, related to New Era in Pandemic Covid-19, Non Curative Service, Technology Services and Technological Rerelated.

Keywords: *clinical pathway, quality improvement, cost containment, pandemic covid-19, non curative service, technology services, technological rerelated*

1. INTRODUCTION

1.1 Clinical pathway in hospital

Clinical Pathway [1] is an effort made in order to:

1. Outlines the steps in detail:
2. Outlines the important steps that must be taken;
3. Describe services to patients;
4. Estimate possible clinical problems.

The description above provides directions to make it easier to discuss and try to get the same understanding, thus further formulation can be carried out to find clinical problems that may occur and provide directions for possible solutions, so that optimal conditions or the best conditions can be considered in existing conditions. This will be important for the following 3 things:

1. Provide an overview of the optimal service quality conditions;
2. Linkage with the best activity steps of cost-related services;
3. Clear activity as part of the steps that an algorithm can make, so that software can be made for computer or smartphone applicants.

Now with more advanced and superior computerization advancements, help simplify the complex problems of the Clinical Pathway, thus providing a discussion space for clinicians and hospital management to:

1. The use of the Clinical Pathway, its components and relationships that are clinically correct and in optimal management, an understanding that has often become difficult;
2. Provide steps, problems and optimal solutions, so that cost calculations can be carried out and rationally accepted.

The following are examples related to the role of clinical pathways in effectiveness [2]: clarity of admission, interventions, comparison of old and new therapies and clearer outcomes of clinical pathways. In this condition, the use of computerization makes it easier to explain and simulate events. The relationship of the above becomes clearer as described, as follows.

1. Components-relation to clinical pathway
   Components in the right and correct clinical pathway are important, because it determines the appropriate diagnosis and is associated with appropriate clinical reasoning [3], otherwise it will be very dangerous related to misdiagnosis. The existence of various components that can be replaced or substituted is a challenge to keep choosing the right and right choice, as well as linkages that remain in the right and precise order according to Clinical Resioning while still guided by the flow of diagnosis as well as the correct therapy. Any mistake in the association will be dangerous to diagnosis and therapy, which can be dangerous for the patient. In the use of algorithms in the use of information systems in the Clinical Pathway,

components and relationships play an important role in maintaining compatibility between clinical Reasioning and computational logic. The role of the fields of Information Technology, Medical and Medical Informatics is to jointly guard the condition of the components and their activities correctly and correctly.

2. Step-problem-optimal solution
   Actually the best is the ideal or maximum, this is one that is intact from the world of medicine which is classified as an art, although some things have been replaced by tools and computerization. Determination of Step-Problem-Solution requires clinical reasoning, judgment, and experience so it is necessary to have an alternative companion, including still considering any possible side effects. Again, the role of Medical, Information Technology and Medical Informatics [4] or Information System experts is important to guard not only accuracy-truth, also Step-Problem-Solution, it is also necessary to consider the existence of patient safety [5].

1.2 Linkages clinical pathway with quality improvement and cost containment

The existence of Component-Linkage and Step-Problem-Solution is a necessity that needs to be considered in order to achieve an optimal Clinical Pathway, so the importance of being considered is related to things like the following.

1. Quality Improvement [6] is the existence of service conditions related to the ideal or optimal quality that can be achieved, or meets the minimum or optimal quality standard requirements, thus it must be protected from decreasing quality or achieving low quality of service.
2. Cost Containment [7] must actually consider services that remain of quality, should not decrease below the minimum standard required, so it is important that Cost Containment can be carried out while maintaining the quality that does not decline. 3. Adequacy of Quality Improvement and Cost Containment in Clinical pathway, must be pursued with repeated simulations, which will be facilitated by the use of software or smartphone applications using appropriate and supportive algorithms.

It is important to note things like the following:

(1) It is necessary to pay attention to and select the quality that can be improved, related to examination, diagnosis and therapy as well as rehabilitation, in real terms with scientific developments, technology and community development, (2) so that components and steps that lead to costs are selected, and can be carried out without reducing the quality of service, related to science and technology, as well as the substitution and new sophisticated equipment at a higher or lower cost.

Thus the selection must be carried out by means of a formal and written review, so that the success rate can be measured. Described as follows, Figure 1.

In computerized technology, software development [8] and mobile phone applications [9] have many sophisticated technologies and procedures, but there is still a need for close cooperation between medical, information technology, hospital management and medical infromatics in order to manufacture form algorithm [10], so that it can be made faster and in accordance with the integrity and in harmony with the use of the application in the field with optimal results that can be achieved while still being used easily, simply and user friendly.

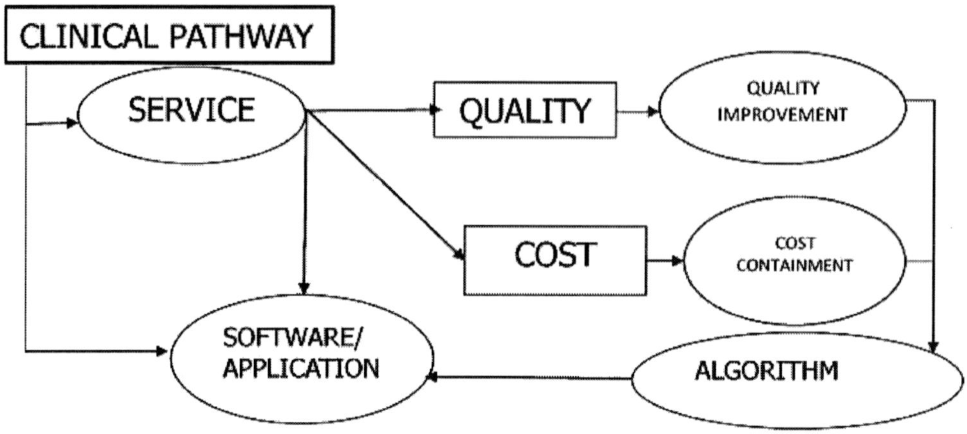

Figure 1.: *Linkages clinical pathway with quality improvement and cost Cotnaimnent.*

2. CLINICAL PATHWAY FOR SERVICES QUALITY IMPROVEMENT

2.1 Clinical pathway for service quality

The example of the Clinical Pathway algorithm for the management of malnourished patients in elderly patients, shows: clarity of steps, clarity of risk, clarity of size, clarity of time, which allows clinicians to collaborate with management; has demonstrated one quality improvement strategy [11]. Examples of the effectiveness of clinical pathways in infection disease [12], algorithms on diagnosis and therapy provide good pathways for quality improvement and also cost savings, because there are:

1. Clear and measurable steps, diagnostic steps that show a basis for the diagnosis accompanied by a measure of the likelihood of that basis;
2. Stages from beginning to end, this stage is important to develop clinical reasoning that is important in the algorithm for clinical pathways, this is important for improving service quality;
3. There are types and doses of drugs, which can be selected on the basis of the level of the type of diagnosis, in this case the therapy becomes a clear choice and can be calculated the cost burden, so at the same time cost containment efforts can be carried out.

The 3 important things above provide evidence that a Clinical Pathway can provide simultaneous direction between:

1. Quality, between components-linkages and Step-Problem-Solution, which will specifically differ for each disease diagnosis, which needs to be considered in order to maintain the quality;
2. Quality Improvement, which is the hope of the clinician, management is the patient, because it will provide improvements in the efficiency and patient satisfaction.

The relationship between Clinical Pathway and Quality Improvement [13], with its accompanying components, is illustrated as follows, Figure 2.

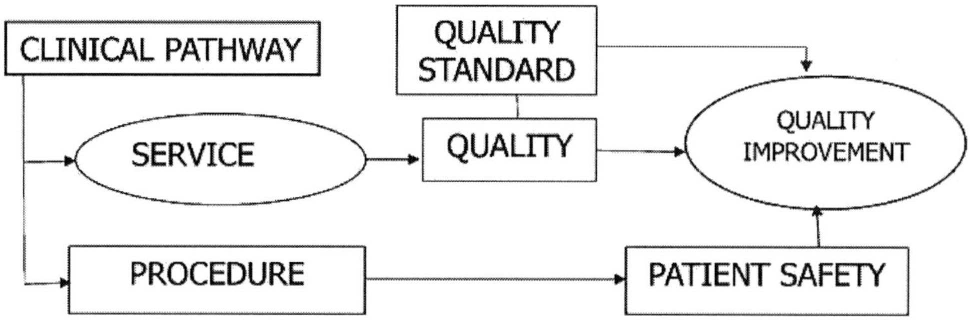

***Figure 2.:** Clinical pathway for quality improvement.*

The figure above shows:

1. Related to Quality and Quality Standard [14], which will provide an overview of the extent to which must be done and especially services that meet the minimum and optimal standards;
2. Related to procedures [15] that must be carried out and the most important thing is related to patient safety, because it will allow services that save the patient, it will include simultaneously saving doctors and hospitals;
3. Prioritization in order to improve can be done simultaneously, but the fulfillment of patient safety first and then the quality standard;
4. Quality Improvement so that it is endeavored simultaneously with different levels and simultaneously achieving an optimal level.

2.2 Patient safety for service quality improvement

One of the ways of Service Quality Improvement is to use accreditation, accreditation is an effort to periodically assess the Quality Standard as the highest reference, so that our achievement is assessed against that standard. Service Quality Improvement which is important and must be a concern is Patient Safety [16], because it is one of the main goals of health services. Patient safety which is important in the hospital is the expected outcome as follows:

1. Significantly increased patient safety;
2. There is a reduction in risk and accidents;
3. There are health outcomes that are better than before;
4. There is an improved patient experience.

The four things above are related to the Quality Improvent of the service so that it will be clear what processes, outputs and outcomes will be achieved, and this effort needs to be carried out continuously and continuously, and is always a fun daily activity.

1. Optimal cost, in connection with this the existence of Cost Containment is required, it is proposed to do the following:

2. Create a clear clinical pathway component-Linkage and Step-Problem-Optimal Solution, and can be tracked for costs;
3. Make efforts to carry out a clear and directed Quality Improvement towards the expected quality standard;
4. Work on Cost Containment which takes into account the quality of service, service procedures, unit costs which are simultaneously reviewed in order to create an optimal cost condition without reducing the specified quality.

2.3 Algorithm usage

The following is an example of an algorithm, which is the basis for making diagnosis and therapy, with this algorithm it can be used as a software or smartphone application. Like the following example, Figure 3.

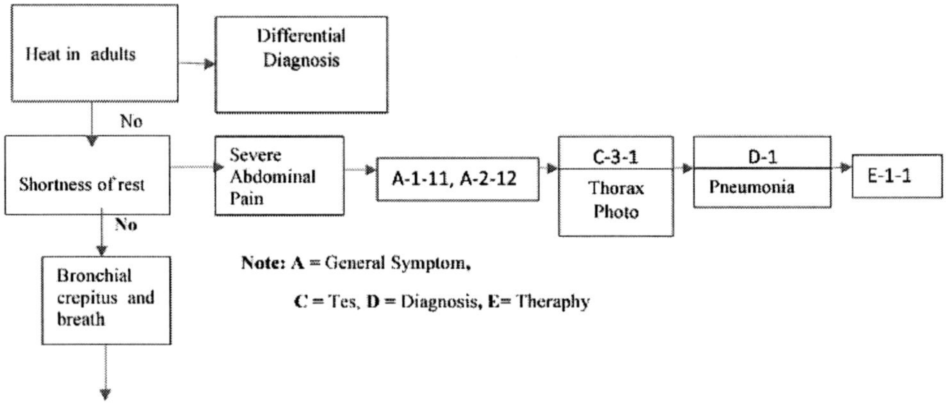

Figure 3.: *Example of algorithm [17].*

The figure below shows:
1. The existence of certain steps in accordance with the direction of the signs and symptoms, in this case Heat in Adults;
2. There is a Differential Diagnosis guide;
3. There is a flow for yes and no choices;
4. If the yes path is selected it will lead to the further path-Tets-Diagnosis-Therapy.

This simple algorithm image will provide an opportunity for programmers to create software and smartphone applications, which can then be developed to examine in each of the steps which allows for quality improvement, so that it is easier to analyze shortcomings and their relationship with other steps to be improved.

Research process in the context of making APSIS (*Aplikasi Pembelajaran Alur Diagnosis dan Terapi Kedokteran* = Learning Application Flowchart of Medical Diagnosis and Therapy) in Smartphone Application, related to algorithm development can be sown as above Figure 4.

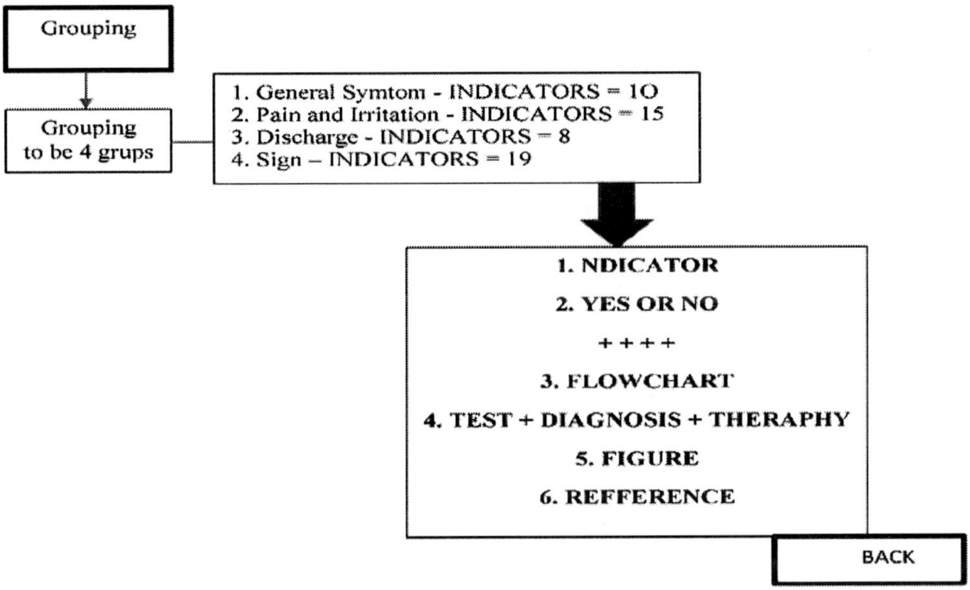

Figure 4.: *Flowchart of APSIS [17].*

The figure above shows:

1. There is direction about the beginning of the start,
2. There is a division of groups which contains relatively similar indicators,
3. There are continuous steps in the form of a flowchart,
4. Provide a final description of the series, in the form of tests, diagnosis and therapy.

3. CLINICAL PATHWAY IN COST CONTAINMENT

3.1 Link of components

Cost Containment is done by maintaining the quality of service, because that is the first and important value of medical services, so the thought of costs is the next thing to consider, not the other way around. This effort can be done in terms of: [18].

1. Rates that reflect costs, with the help of Clinical Pathway and software algorithms, will easily provide remedial options, and better still provide easy possibilities for simulations by performing simulation at various costs, so that lower costs will be found while still maintain quality;
2. On investment, tools and instruments can now be selected which results in an easier and cheaper basis for diagnosis and therapy.

Described as follows, Figure 5.

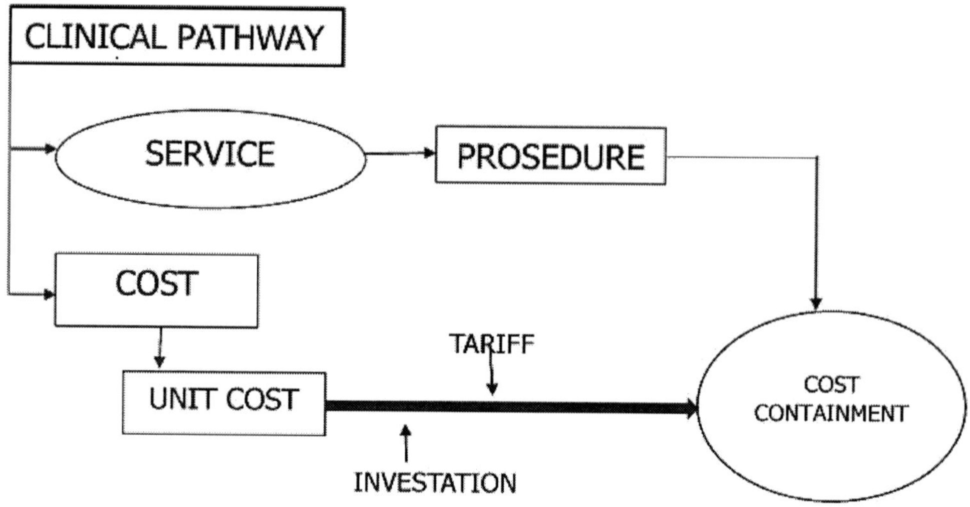

Figure 5.: *Link of component in cost containment.*

3.2 Prosedure

Procedure is a series of activities that have been directed and specific in order to carry out the service, so that the service achieves the objectives as determined, in accordance with the competence of the specified executor, as Figure 6.

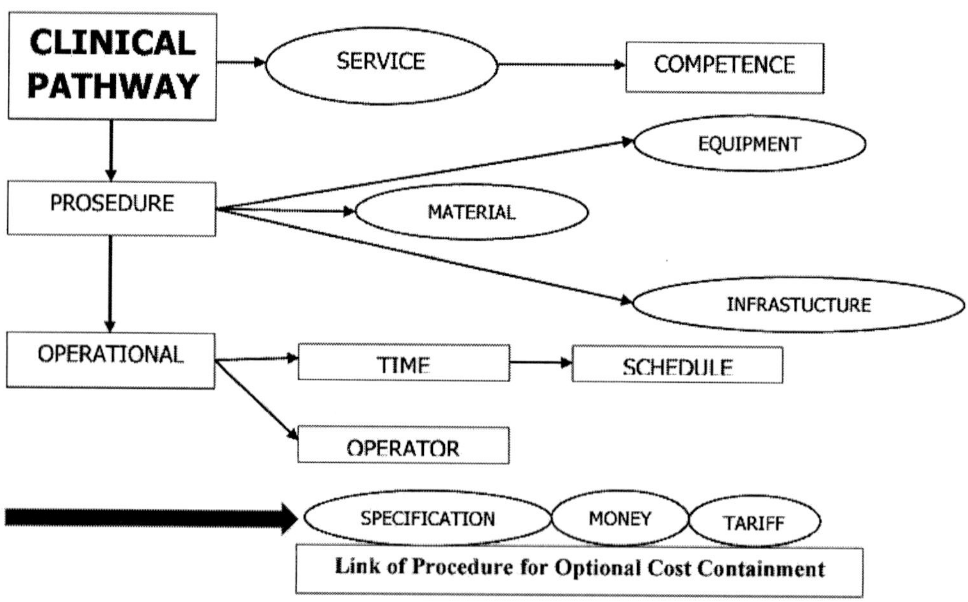

Figure 6.: *Link of procedure for cost containment.*

The figure below shows:

1. Procedure, will be related to equipment, material and infrastructure so as to enable services to run smoothly;
2. Related to operations, namely: time, schedule and service implementation, as well as operators to enable services to run according to their destination and time;
3. The existence of certain service specifications, which are related to available funds and determined service rates, are considered in the context of cost containment.

The 3 things above must be considered with the standard of optimal cost, and the quality of service still occurs without a decrease in quality, this is a characteristic of cost containment that is carried out properly.

3.3 Unit cost

Description related to Unit Cost [19] which is the basis for Cost Containment, related to Billing for existing Services in accordance with Quality Standards and Coding in Clinical Pathways. The figure is as below, Figure 7.

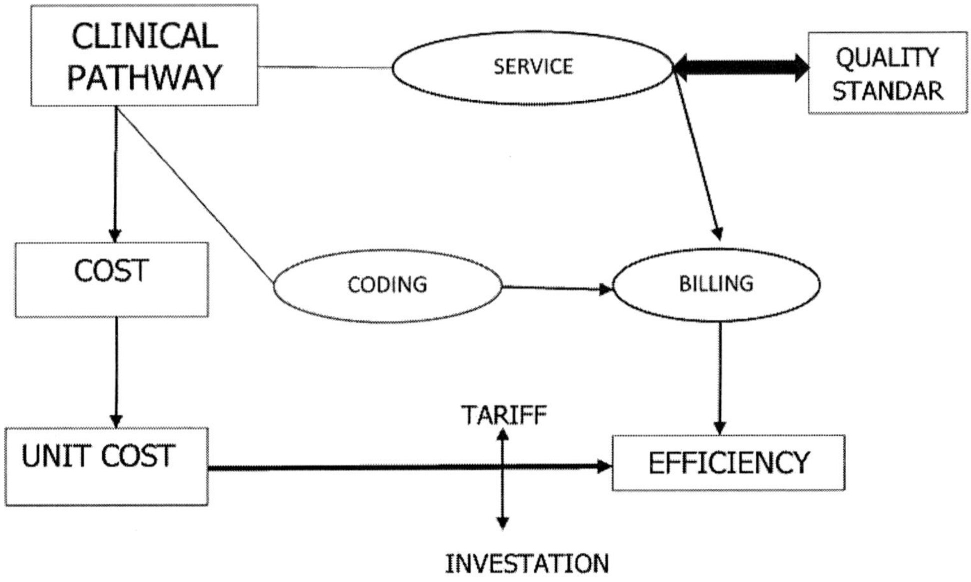

Figure 7.: *Link of unit cost for cost containment.*

Furthermore, the Unit Cost, as a breakdown of Cost in accordance with the required cost details, will be the basis for determining the tariff and the charging of investment, so that a complete loading will occur; thus the optimal efficiency conditions will be calculated. In this case, it will be a part that provides a limitation so that the Quality Standard does not decrease by keeping the Unit Cost from decreasing drastically which causes the Quality Standard also decline too.

4. CLINICAL PATHWAY IN NEW ERA

4.1 New era in pandemic Covid-19

There are 4 important things related to the Covid-19 Era Pandemic: [20]

1. Pandemic atmosphere, anxious atmosphere, lots of information circulating and often confusing, mainstay information centers are often late in reporting, so there is an atmosphere that is at least unsettled and unpleasant.
2. Daily behavior, work and trying behavior are limited and there is a health protocol, providing a new, limited atmosphere and additional rules.
3. Patients with chronic diseases, such as hypertension, diabetes, chronic lung disease and others are known as comorbid people, a label that is very susceptible to infection, so there must be special protection and treatment.
4. This is invisible to the eye, the prominent patient being treated is only limited stress [21] which can be handled alone, an iceberg phenomenon that requires special treatment which currently only focuses on physical activities. The proof is that the health protocol is very difficult to implement, it must be violent until the threat of punishment, it does not develop automatic and natural awareness.

In connection with the matters above, how is the condition of the hospital: [22]

1. Outpatient visits decreased dramatically, so admissions were reduced;
2. Additional costs for the implementation of the health protocol, required immediately and cannot be delayed,
3. Protection for medical personnel, paramedics and other personnel related to hospital services, requires extra efforts to maintain a balance of quality services with protection of health workers so that they do not become infected.

Throughout the current journey, no hospital has gone bankrupt, apart from being supported by the government with social assistance, also because the hospital can make good adjustments, or postpone the burden into the future. In this connection:

1. There is an effort to maintain quality, it remains an important task that must be carried out without adjustments that can reduce quality;
2. The existence of cost containment is an option that must be done, with all the risks and consequences, which must be done right now;
3. There is an effort to give a big role to clinical pathways and the use of computerized analysis [23] to simplify complex problems and prepare new efforts quickly and easily, in this case when normal is only an option for later, then now inevitably have to be selected and worked on now, using computerized assistance.

There are 3 important things that will immediately be used as important references in ministry in the new era, as below:

1. Clinical Pathway in Non Curative Service [24], is a service that needs attention, as part of reducing contact and cost containment, which is promoted as a service that tries to reduce curative services which are usually

more expensive, which of course can only be done at certain diseases and stages of therapy only;

2. Clinical Pathway in Technology Services [25], services designed with the support of mechanical technology and information systems, thereby reducing doctor-patient contact and providing better accuracy, which may be lacking in compassionate contact;
3. Clinical Pathway in Technological Related [26], is a service that from the beginning relied on technology as a mainstay, thus the presence of doctors will be made more efficient and on matters that are important and that are not harmful.

4.2 Clinical pathway in non curative service

The application of the Clinical Pathway now and in the future requires adjustments related to earlier approaches and prevention, not just therapy, because technological advances and awareness of healthy living are being promoted. Advance clinic and treatment to an earlier direction, such as Promotive, Preventive and Rehabilitation which is more aggressive and earlier.

An example is illustrated as follows as Figure 8.

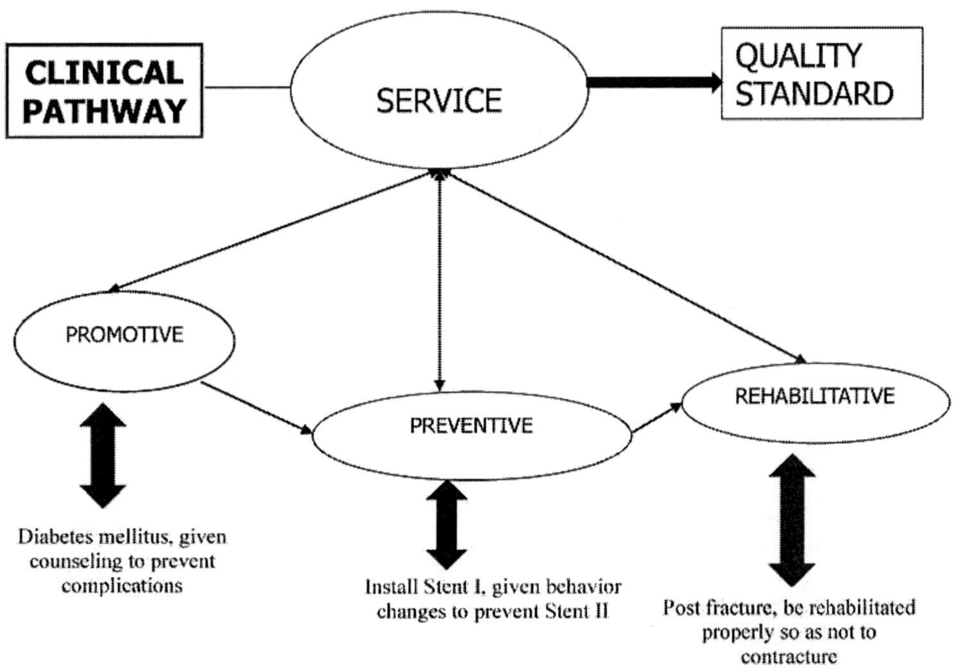

Figure 8.: *Clinical pathway in non curative service.*

The current palliative approach still needs to be developed towards older and more productive patients who can still enjoy an optimal quality of life, requiring hard work and continued development.

The next explanation is as follows.

1. Promotive [27] is an effort to increase knowledge and behavior in order to have a basic knowledge in dealing with disease with 3 main activities:
   i. Awareness, is an effort to make people aware, especially those who are still healthy or slightly ill, have an awareness of the dangers that lead to disease;
   ii. Health education, which aims to increase knowledge and society or prospective patients, or have become patients so that the prevention is more severe;
   iii. Education, is an effort to encourage the community or patients to improve their abilities that previously could not be, bad behavior becomes good;
   iv. Consulting, is an effort to help the community or patients to be able to solve existing problems, and together find solutions.

This condition is often mixed up so that efforts do not produce optimal results, the best way to suggest is to select the required picture, then adjust the handling according to need.

1. Preventive [28] is an effort to prevent the disease from occurring, not getting worse, not getting worse, a common example is the use of immunization. This effort will be calculated the value of the cost that is cheaper when compared to treatment.
2. Rehabilitation [29] is an effort to make improvements to a condition that is already damaged or there is already an abnormality, so that as much as possible it can be restored as before. The current rehabilitation, many use tools and some are computerized, what is needed is a careful study so that it is sorted according to needs and the use of cost containment can be done.

4.3 Clinical pathway in technology services

The era of Telemedicine [30], with the Covid-19 Pandemic, the need to maintain distance makes it imperative to use more massive telemedicine, it is necessary to develop algorithms that are in accordance with the following: (1) there is a standard procedure and still meets clinical reasoning, (2) services that can be carried out gradually Quality Improvement, (3) services that can be simultaneously carried out cost Contaiment optimally but reduce quality. This presents a challenge, not only for doctors, hospitals, Information Communication Technology and Medical Informatics experts, to collectively achieve the above expectations.

The robotic era [31] will be greatly stimulated by the Covid-19 Pandemic by trying to avoid contact between doctors and patients in order to prevent transmission. The differences that occur are: (1) the procedure will be relatively the same, dealing with the patient is a robot, (2) the doctor controls the robot, not the instrument, also the time and sequence will be clear and can be calculated. Increasingly sophisticated computer performance with large capacities, supported by Artificial Intelligent, provides challenges, and at the same time, care must be taken with regard to patient safety, not according to good tools, still violating the patient safety principle.

The era of the Internet of Things [32] is a challenge now in various countries with a large number of elderly people, several countries have happened, some countries are not less than 10 years old will be a heavy burden. Thus the use of: Clinical Pathway, Quality Improvement, Cost Containment and the Internet of Things will be the way out that is needed. An example illustration is as follows as Figure 9.

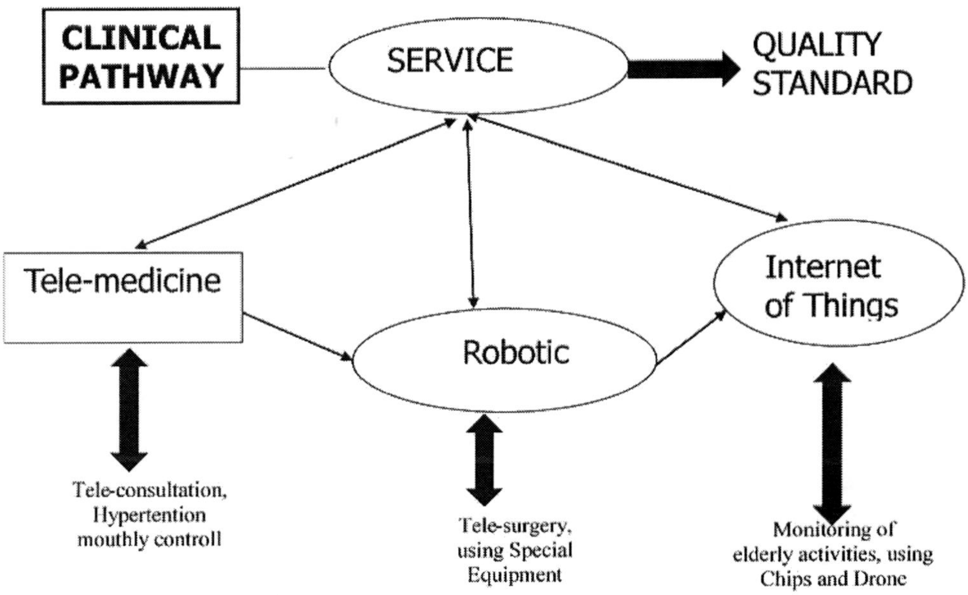

Figure 9.: *Clinical pathway in technology services.*

The description above provides options and accelerates the use of advanced technology and with large capacities more quickly and relatively forced, due to the Covid-19 Pandemic which requires maintaining distance, avoiding contact and avoiding relatively long trips. Anticipation must be developed immediately with the following standards:

1. Keep following Clinical Reasoning and Clinical Pathway which are based on service quality standards;
2. Developing Quality Improvement and Cost Containment that are relevant and balanced, so that the perspective is accepted by doctors, hospitals, patients and insurers.

4.4 Clinical pathway in technological related

1. Heath Electronic Record (HER) or Medical Record (MR) [33] related to electronic medical records, which is getting more and more advanced with regard to voice recognition which provides direct recording of the

history, and video recognition which records examination conditions using video in an integrated manner. The importance of an integrated and electronically based Medical Record (MR) provides:

i. Higher speed;
ii. Clearer accuracy, greater capacity and high access, also with completeness, will help Quality Improvement;
iii. Conditions that will impose large costs, which require Cost Containment to achieve optimal efficiency and cost load; with the Direct Consultation tool, the patient can consult a doctor or a robot, for several diseases that have been standardized first.
iv. Tele-device [34], is a device that can be controlled remotely, or performs remote inspection, so that examinations that use certain tools do not need people to come from a distant city, just at the initial place, the results of the examination can be sent including the description. This is important for reference and preparedness in the context of Covid-19.
v. Self Service [35] with a standardized algorithm, a Guidance Commission Support System can be used to make diagnosis and therapy of diseases. In this case, Quality Improvement and Cost Containment is important in giving choices, because the decision is made by the patient, it may need to be limited to chronic disease and regular control and options that are not feasible.
vi. A simple example illustration as follows as Figure 10.

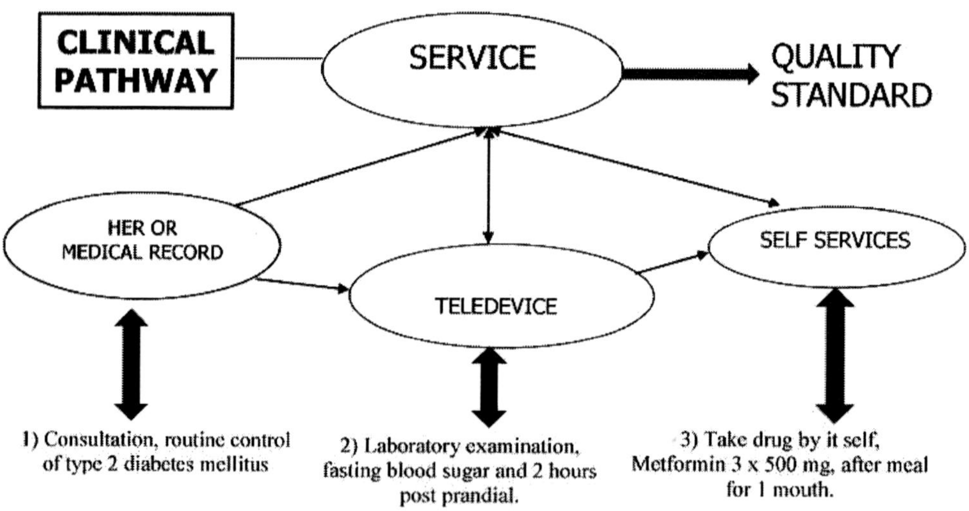

Figure 10.: *Clinical pathway in technological related.*

The above description is broader as below.

1. Consultations, with real doctors, with robots that use voice or video can be carried out, which requires an unbeatable Clinical Pathway Algorithm, so

the Quality Improvement role is very important and must be made from the time the services and software are used.

2. Examinations such as laboratories, methods, reagents and result criteria must be clear about the normal and maximum or minimum standards that apply, this is related to so that patients do not need to think a lot and do not need to learn clinical reasoning, but precisely in a safe corridor. This Cost Containment becomes important, especially in choosing a relatively cheap and safe examination.
3. Self-medicating, determining the usual diagnosis and therapy and in a safe category, can be done as long as it is normally done, without complications and there are new diagnoses and therapies. Quality Improvement and Cost Containment simultaneously to ensure high quality at optimal cost.

5. CONCLUTION

Clinical pathway in hospital is an effort made in order to: outlines the steps in detail, outlines the important steps that must be taken, describe services to patients and estimate possible clinical problems; it can be used as a system for Quality Improvement and Cost Containment. The effectiveness of clinical pathways in algorithms on diagnosis and therapy provide good pathways for quality improvement and also cost savings. Cost Containment is done by maintaining the quality of service, because that is the first and important value of medical services, so the thought of costs is the next thing to consider, not the other way around. The Cost Containment effort can be done in terms of rates that reflect costs, with the help of Clinical Pathway that lower costs will be found while still maintain quality. Clinical Pathway that is used on investment, tools and instruments can now be selected which results cheaper basis for diagnosis and therapy. There are important things that will immediately be used as references in the new era that related to New Era in Pandemic Covid-19, Non Curative Service, Technology Services and Technological Rerelated, biside that Clinical Pathway will be made more efficient and on matters that are important and that are not harmful.

REFERENCES

1. Kinsman, L, at. al, What is a clinical pathway? Development of a definition to inform the debate, May 2010, BMC Medicine 8(1):31, DOI: 10.1186/1741-7015-8-31
2. Iroth1,R.A.M., Achadi, A., The Impact of Clinical Pathway to Effectiveness of Patient Care In Current Medical Practice In Hospital:A Literature Review, Proceedings of International Conference on Applied Science and Health (No. 4, 2019), ICHSH-A111
3. Michele Groves, Peter O'Rourke, Heather Gwendoline, & Innes Alexander, The clinical reasoning characteristics of diagnostic experts, June 2003, Medical Teacher 25(3):308-13, DOI: 10.1080/0142159031000100427.
4. Emma Aspland, Daniel Gartner & Paul Harper, Clinical pathway modelling: a literature review, September 2019, Health Systems, DOI: 10.1080/20476965.2019.1652547, License CC BY 4.0

5. Danielsson, Marita; Nilsen, Per; Rutberg, Hans; Årestedt, Kristofer, A National Study of Patient Safety Culture in Hospitals in Sweden, Journal of Patient Safety: December 2019 - Volume 15 - Issue 4 - p 328-333 doi: 10.1097/PTS.0000000000000369

6. Adam Backhouse quality improvement programme lead & Fatai Ogunlayi public health specialty registrar, Quality improvement into practice, BMJ 2020;368:m865 doi: 10.1136/bmj.m865 (Published 31 March 2020)

7. Niek Stadhouders, Florien Krusea, Marit Tankea, Xander Koolmanb, Patrick Jeurissena,c Niek Stadhouders, Florien Krusea, Marit Tankea, Xander Koolmanb, Patrick Jeurissena, Effective healthcare cost-containment policies: A systematic review, '2018 The Authors. Published by Elsevier Ireland Ltd. This is an open access article under the CC BY-NC-ND license (http://creativecommons.org/licenses/by-nc-nd/4.0/)

8. M F Aarnoutse, Sjaak Brinkkemper, Marleen de Mul & Marjan Askari, Pros and Cons of Clinical Pathway Software Management: A Qualitative Study, January 2018, Studies in health technology and informatics 247:526-530

9. Aida Aalrazek, Effect of Implementing Clinical Pathway to Improve Child-Birth and Neonatal Outcomes, October 2018, American Journal of Nursing Research 6(6):454-465, DOI: 10.12691/ajnr-6-6-13

10. Emma Aspland, Daniel Gartner & Paul Harp, Clinical pathway modelling: a literature review, September 2019, Health Systems, DOI: 10.1080/20476965.2019.1652547, License CC BY 4.0

11. Thomas Rotter, Robert Baatenburg de Jong, Sara Evans Lacko, Ulrich Ronellenfitsch, and Leigh Kinsman, Improving healthcare quality in Europe: Characteristics, effectiveness and implementation of different strategies

12. Bahar Madrana, Şiran Keskeb, Soner Uzunc, Tolga Taymazc, Emine Bakırc,_Ismail Bozkurtd, Önder Ergönüle, Effectiveness of clinical pathway for upper respiratory tract-infections in emergency department, international Journal of Infectious Diseases 83 (2019) 154-159

13. Leigh Kinsman, Clinical pathway compliance and quality improvement, January 2004, Nursing standard: official newspaper of the Royal College of Nursing 18(18):33-5, DOI: 10.7748/ns.18.18.33.s51

14. American Diabetes Association, American Diabetes Association Standards of Medical Care in Diabetesd2019, Diabetes Care Volume 42, Supplement 1, January 2019

15. Elaine Mormer and Joel Stevans, Clinical Quality Improvement and Quality Improvement Research.

16. WHO, Patient Safety Making health care.

17. Sabarguna, B.S, APSIS.

18. Romeyke, T & Stummer, H., Clinical Pathways as Instruments for Risk and Cost Management in Hospitals - A Discussion Paper, Global Journal of Health Science, ol. 4, No. 2; March 2012, doi:10.5539/gjhs.v4n2p50

19. NiekStadhouders, FlorienKruse, MaritTanke, XanderKoolman, PatrickJeurissen, Effective healthcare cost-containment policies: A systematic review, Health Policy, Volume 123, Issue 1, January 2019, Pages 71-79

20. Budi Yanti , Eko Mulyadi, Wahiduddin, Revi Gama Hatta Novika, Yuliana Mahdiyah Da'at Arina, Natalia Sri Martani, & Nawan, Knowledge, Attitudes, and Behavior Towards Social Distancing Policy as A Means Community of Preventing Transmission of Covid-19 in Indonesia, Jurnal Administrasi Kesehatan Indonesia Vol 8 No 1 Special Issue 2020 Published by Universitas Airlangga Doi: 10.20473/jaki.v8i2.2020.4-14
21. WHO, Doing What Matters in Times of Stress
22. John D. Birkmeyer, Amber Barnato, Nancy Birkmeyer, Robert Bessler & Jonathan Skinner, Impact Of The COVID-19 Pandemic On Hospital Admissions The In The United States, Health Afair, September 2020
23. Raju Vaishya, Abid Haleem, Abhishek Vaish & Mohd Javaid, Emerging technologies to combat COVID-19 pandemic, May 2020, Journal of Clinical and Experimental Hepatology 10(4), DOI: 10.1016/j.jceh.2020.04.019
24. Liezl Balfour, Isabel Coetzee & Tanya Heyns, Developing a clinical pathway for non-invasive ventilation, December 2012, International Journal of Care Pathways 16(4):107-114, DOI: 10.1258/jicp.2012.012011, Project: UP - Community of Practice project
25. Jungeun Lim , Kidong Kim , Minsu Cho , Hyunyoung Baek , Seok Kim , Hee Hwang , Sooyoung Yoo , & Minseok Song, Deriving a sophisticated clinical pathway based on patient conditions from electronic health record data
26. Graham P. Martin, David Kocman, Timothy Stephens, Carol J. Peden &Rupert M. Pears, Pathways to professionalism? Quality improvement, care pathways, and the interplay of standardisation and clinical autonomy, Firest published: 21 June 2017, Sociology of Health & Illness Vol. 39 No. 8 2017 ISSN 0141-9889, pp. 1314-1329 Sociology of Health & Illness Vol. 39 No. 8 2017 ISSN 0141-9889, pp. 1314-1329, Doi: 10.1111/1467-9566.12585
27. WHO, Editor: Oliver Groene & Mila Garcia-Barbero, Health promotion in hospitals: Evidence and quality management, Country Systems, Policies and Services Division of Country Support WHO Regional Office for Europe, May 2005
28. Nathan R. Every, Judith Hochman, Richard Becker, Steve Kopecky, Christopher P. Cannon, the Committee on Acute Cardiac Care, Council on Clinical Cardiology, American Heart Association, Originally published 1 Feb 2000, doi: 10.1161/01.CIR.101.4.461, Circulation. 2000;101:461-465
29. P. Rouanet, A. Mermoud, M. Jarlier, N. Bouazza, A. Laine, H. Mathieu Daudé, Combined robotic approach and enhanced recovery after surgery pathway for optimization of costs in patients undergoing proctectomy, First published: 30 April 2020, doi:10.1002/bjs5.50281
30. Maria Victoria Concepcion P. Cruz, Policarpio B. Joves, Jr., Noel L. Espallardo, Anna Guia O. Limpoco, Jane Eflyn Lardizabal-Bunyi, Nenacia Ranali Nirena P. Mendoza, Michael Ian N. Sta. Maria, Jake Bryan S. Cortez, Mark Joseph D. Bitong, Johann Iraj H. Montemayor, Clinical Pathway for the Diagnosis and Management of Patients with COVID-19 in Family Practice

31. Zrinjka DOLIC, Rosa CASTRO & Andrei MOARCAS, IN-DEPTH ANALYSIS Requested by the ENVI committee, Robots in healthcare: a solution or a problem?, Policy Department for Economic, Scientific and Quality of Life Policies Directorate-General for Internal Policies Authors: Zrinjka DOLIC, Rosa CASTRO, Andrei MOARCAS PE 638.391 - April 2019

32. Vijayakannan Sermakani, Transforming healthcare through Internet of Things, Robert Bosch Engineering and Business Ltd

33. Yiye Zhang, Rema Padman & Larry Wasserman, Show all 6 authors, Qizhi Xie, On Clinical Pathway Discovery from Electronic Health Record Data, January 2015, Intelligent Systems, IEEE 30(1):70-75, DOI: 10.1109/MIS.2015.14

34. Abayomi Salawu, Angela Green, Michael G. Crooks, Nina Brixey, Denise H. Ross, and Manoj Sivan, A Proposal for Multidisciplinary Tele-Rehabilitation in the Assessment and Rehabilitation of COVID-19 Survivors, International Journal of Environmental Research and Public Health

35. Marc Gutenstein, John W Pickering & Martin Than, Development of a digital clinical pathway for emergency medicine: Lessons from usability testing and implementation failure, Helath Infromatics Journal, First Published June 15, 2018

7

Trends of Top IS Research by Region, Outlet, and Emergence: A Semi-Automated Literature Review

Nadine Guhr[1], **Oliver Werth**[2], **Jens Passlick**[3] **and Michael H. Breitner**[2]

[1]*Department of Business Administration and Economics, OWL University of Applied Sciences and Arts, Campusallee 12, 32657 Lemgo, Germany*

[2]*Information Systems Institute, Leibniz University Hannover, Königsworther Platz 1, 30167 Hannover, Germany*

[3]*VHV Gruppe, VHV-Platz 1, 30177 Hannover, Germany*

ABSTRACT

Global trends towards the rapidly increasing use of information systems (IS) apply to the IS research domain and related publications. Nonetheless, investigations of trends in publication behavior and emergence as well as changes in IS research are usually narrowly focused. This article contributes to the growing number of articles published in the IS domain by analyzing the evolution of trends and major research fields as well as the regional distribution of publications in the AIS Senior Scholars' Basket of Eight (AIS Bo8) and the International Conference on Information Systems (ICIS), changes in publication behavior, and the emergence of as well as changes to IS research fields and trends. Our semi-automated literature review integrates scientific methods to support the review and classification of publications. Based on 6692 articles published in the ICIS proceedings and the AIS Bo8 journals in a period of 16 years, we elaborate the key characteristics of research development. Our contribution provides and interprets a contemporaneous account of contextual factors influencing the IS research domain. Thus, our study enhances understanding of the development of the IS research domain.

Keywords: *global information systems research; research trends; research field; (semi-) automated literature review; latent semantic indexing*

1. INTRODUCTION

The Association for Information Systems (AIS) states that "the history of any academic field plays an important role in shaping the field's present state and giving the field its unique identity. [...] It is important for all involved to study its past to understand its present, and to guide" [1] and bridge it to its possible future [2]. Ref. [3], who analyzed temporal trends in four top information systems (IS) journals and identified emergent themes that have begun to gain prominence in the IS research domain encourage other researchers to broaden their conversation by including a broader set of journals. Motivated by these statements and the need to avoid focusing solely on journals and research themes, our research paper focuses on shifts in research behavior and the development of the IS research domain, including geographical distinctions, differences in research fields, and trends in research fields and outlets (journals and conferences) to "provide important input in setting directions for future research" [4] (p. xiii).

Scientific articles in the IS domain have gained increasing interest along with the rapid growth of published articles over the last several decades [5,6,7,8]. A representative example of the rising number of articles is the ICIS, where the number of the overall publications increased from 94 articles in the year 2000 to 345 in 2015 [9]. Given the variety of topics and the interdisciplinarity of the IS research domain, multiple research choices exist. The sheer dynamism of IS and information technologies (IT), the variety of topics and the interdisciplinarity of the IS research domain offer a broad range of areas for investigation.

To understand the development of the IS research domain, it is important to understand how the research landscape has changed [8] and how scientific disciplines have evolved [10]. There is a need for a strong description of the origins and the development of IS research in different regions. To the best of our knowledge, no recent research on the development of IS research includes such a large database that looks not only at the trends but also at geographical differences and publication behavior in top IS journals and conferences.

In order to fill this gap in the literature, we review all AIS Senior Scholars' Basket of Eight (AIS Bo8) publications and publications in the proceedings of the ICIS over a 16-year period to answer the following research questions:

- **RQ1:***What is the regional distribution of publications in the AIS Bo8 and the ICIS?*
- **RQ2:***How has publication behavior changed by region, and what are the greatest changes?*
- **RQ3:***Where—in terms of region and outlet—do IS research trends emerge, and how have these changed over time?*

To address these research questions, we conducted a semi-automated literature study. We generated our data by reviewing the journals of the AIS Bo8 and the Proceedings of the ICIS between 2000 and 2015 to create a massive database containing information from 6692 research papers.

In Section 2, we argue for the importance and relevance of contemporaneous reports of IS research that take into account geographical differences as well as the differences between journals and conferences as a means of developing a detailed understanding and history of the IS research domain. Section 3 describes the multistage research process. This is followed by a presentation of the results of our analysis in Section 4. Following the discussion and implications in Section 5, we conclude by identifying limitations and providing an outlook for further research (Section 6 and Section 7).

2. RELATED WORK AND GEOGRAPHICAL DIVERSITY

The comparatively young IS research domain emerged from several reference disciplines characterized by diverse research domains with regard to methods, theories, and topics (e.g., [11]). A representative example of the correlation with other disciplines was the introduction of a discussion held at the first ICIS in 1980. Keen ([12] (p. 10) stated, "Since MIS [Management Information Systems] is a fusion of behavioral, technical and managerial issues, there is no obvious or single reference discipline". With this fragmentation of the research domain, Keen [12] (p. 18) further concluded, "It would be impossible to identify a narrow set of topics that constitute MIS research". The resulting discussion has been dominated by the discourse of paradigms and diversity (e.g., [13,14]), methods used (e.g., [11]), topics and trends (e.g., [3]), and the value and identity of IS research (e.g., [15]).

Since research fields are already difficult to identify, detecting the source of such emerging research fields might be even more complex. In this context, literature reviews, meta-analyses, and scientometric analyses are useful tools for analyzing and improving the progress of research in the IS research domain. In the past few years, many researchers have published literature reviews including objective methodologies, such as text mining (e.g., [3,8,16,17]), meta-analysis (e.g., [11,18]), and scientometric analysis (e.g., [13,19,20]), to provide a periodic introspection that can show and improve the progress of research in the IS research domain. As mentioned by [21], reviews of the literature can revitalize knowledge development and can contribute to scientific progress from both the revolutionary and the cumulative perspective [4]. A first review of related work showed that the IS research community is influenced by organizational needs [22], interdisciplinary connections [23,24], outlet preferences [25,26,27,28], and geographical diversity (e.g., [6,8,13,14,29]).

Although the IS research domain is increasingly global, geographical diversity might be a source of trends given that "many US authors use no European contributions as references" [30] (p. 347), whereas "Europeans refer mostly to American literature" ([30] (p. 347)). Suomi's study was based on a citation analysis of one volume per journal (six American and six European based) from 1990. Ref. [31] similarly demonstrated that there was a strong relationship between the "nationality" of authors and the "nationality" of the journals in which the authors' articles were published. Citation patterns were also the subject of [29]. In their article, they highlight the problem of underrepresentation of researchers and institutions outside North America. A more recent editor's comment by [14] notes that American dominance is slightly decreasing. They indicate "a hopeful trend in moving toward greater parity of regional representation in our leading journals" [14] (p. iv). Their investigation was based on the geographical author affiliation of published articles in the Management Information Systems Quarterly (MISQ). Specifically, from 2000 to 2004, the share of North and South American articles was approximately 85%, while from 2005 to 2009, this share decreased to 74.4%. Another study by [13] showed that researchers agree that MISQ and Information Systems Research (ISR) are the top research journals, regardless of geographic region. However, the data of their study revealed salient differences in perceived journal quality. North American researchers tend to favor management-science- and decision-science-oriented journals (e.g., Management Science and Decision Support Systems) more than European researchers do [13]. Furthermore, as mentioned by [13], European researchers tend to prefer active participation in research, and they also tend to prefer more interpretivist- and practitioner-oriented journals than North American researchers do. Another research work with a geographical focus is the work of [32]. They developed a profile of IS research for the Mediterranean region [32]. Ref. [33] considered the paradigmatic, thematic, and geographical development of Information Systems Journal (ISJ) publications from 1991 to 2007 (see also [34]). Ref. [35] examined the European Conference on Information Systems (ECIS) proceedings from 1993 to 2002 and revealed that European research has its own profile and is not directly influenced by North American research. This point was underlined by [8], who analyzed all papers published in ECIS proceedings during a 10-year period (2003–2012). They focused on the current research profile of the European IS research community, highlighting three main characteristics and the corresponding keywords "(1) continuation of the traditional European IS research profile as developed in the first decade...; (2) convergence with aspects of the North American tradition ...; and (3) the development of a distinct perspective and approach to DS ..." [8] (p. 12). Ref. [5] focused on the context of regional diversity in their research article on German-speaking countries in the Business and Information Systems Engineering journal and proposed recommendations that represent a long-term strategic realignment of the strategic information systems community. Other studies have also shown that perceptions of journal quality can be affected by geography [31].

With regard the previously described increasing parity between different geographic regions, both journal quality and geography may be influential. Moving toward the organizational needs perspective, ref. [22] investigated the core topics of three IS journals, ISR, Journal of Management Information Systems (JMIS), and MISQ, and two journals from other domains with a high share of IS content, Management Science (MS) and Decision Sciences (DS). In terms of the diversity of these North American journals from 1995 to 1999, JMIS had the broadest diffusion/variance in terms of topics, while AAA had the smallest variety of topics. When analyzing the main topics of these five journals, organizational concepts, problem domain-specific concepts, and systems/software were most frequently discussed. Since organizational concepts were by far the strongest main topics, relevant subtopics identified were IT usage/operation, technology transfer, IT impact, and management of computing function. The fragmented IS foundation "created an interdisciplinary space that straddles the dis-courses of all these disciplines" [24] (p. 808). This growing variety of different research topics and vocabularies is seen as a weak point in the clear identification of IS subjects [36]. The interdisciplinary IS foundation mentioned by [12] was also addressed by [23]. They analyzed keyword networks in IS research journals (MISQ, JMIS, ISR, Information & Management, Decision Support Systems) over the period from 1999 to 2008 and revealed that the keyword diffusion process is a hierarchical one in which clusters are built under popular keywords. Since those clusters are strongly related, they suggest that interdisciplinary terms might have the potential to lead future research trends. Furthermore, ref. [11] conducted a meta-analysis in their research work and focused on topic and methodological trends. They indicated that there was a partial mismatch between research and business needs.

Regarding outlet preferences, top IS journals can be differentiated from conference proceedings and lower-ranked journal publications. The results of a comprehensive study by [13] showed that researchers in the IS research domain rated MISQ and ISR as the top journals. Ref. [28] stated that "conference papers can only be used as a starting point" [28] (p. 566) for the discussion of topics. This statement leads to the suggestion that instead of top IS journals, conference proceedings are the source of new IS research. Furthermore, ref. [26] suggested that researchers "may appreciate the chance to publish an innovative idea more quickly, avoiding long review rounds and the rigor required for publishing in premier journals" ([26] (p. 431) compared to lower-ranked journals. Top IS journals are not the trendsetters in IS research. Following [27], the gap between top IS research and conferences should be improved with regard to their interaction and exchange. In contrast to other research disciplines, such as computing science, the reputation of conference proceedings should improve through high-quality review procedures that are comparable to those of top IS journals [37]. The ICIS was an exception by conducting high-quality double-blinded reviews, resulting in worldwide acceptance by top IS researchers [25].

3. RESEARCH METHODOLOGY

In our research article we followed the argument by [17] that the identity construction and the core of a research discipline can be revealed by "aggregating individual research papers at a higher semantic level" [17] (p. 470). In this context our research is based on an extended latent semantic indexing (LSI)-based literature review using an LSI tool [38]. We chose the underlying LSI-based approach because the number of publications and the complex information environment would have made an extensive literature review, without the support of a tool, an incredibly time-consuming task. Furthermore, keyword-based approaches also have their shortcomings (e.g., synonymy/polysemy problems). Due to the above-mentioned limitations, we wanted to use an approach, which is not solely based on term-matching methods. In this context, it would have been possible to use LSI-based approaches that include only the abstracts in the analysis (e.g., [17]). However, since abstracts usually have clear structures, they contain only aggregate content and we wanted to include substantial longer text corpora in our article to provide the broadest possible information base and to e.g., reliable identify research papers that belong to a specific research field. To structure our research process adequately and to make it comprehensive and clear, our approach is oriented toward the approach of [39]. Since the analysis of thousands of documents is time consuming, we divided our research approach into four different phases, which enabled a structured and efficient approach (compare Figure 1).

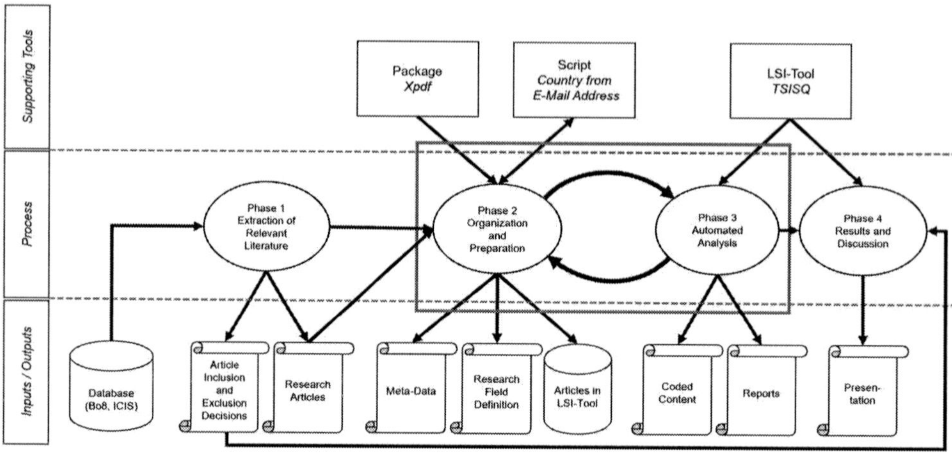

Figure 1.: *Research methodology and process model.*

Phase 1 is characterized by problem identification and formulation and subsequently by the extraction of relevant literature. As in any literature study, our study emphasizes that the selection of journals and/or conference proceedings plays a central role. Although selecting a single journal or a conference proceeding may, in some cases, provide a clear research scope, in our case, this was not expedient because we wanted to investigate how the IS domain has changed over time, how trends develop, which geographical differences exist, and how publication behavior has changed. We also wanted to discuss the differences between conference papers and journal articles, which justified the inclusion of the ICIS proceedings. Before going into more details in the selection of IS journals and conference proceedings, an overview of encountered barriers is given. (1) Multidisciplinary journals can be mentioned as a source of uncertainty. For instance, the Journal of Business Research has published a number of IS paper (e.g., [40]). (2) The IS research discipline is multidisciplinary, nonhomogeneous, and without clear boundaries. (3) The population size for our research focus (complete academic IS literature) is too large to conduct a total population study. In addition, compiling a list of relevant journals in IS research and related fields is too complex, so we attempted to narrow down the journals and conference proceedings to be studied in the most comprehensible way possible. Therefore, we used as a sample group all publications of the AIS Bo8 journals and the ICIS proceedings in the time period from 2000 to 2015. Our study integrates all journals of the AIS Bo8 and all articles of the ICIS proceedings in the previously mentioned time period because most IS scholars agree that these outlets are the most significant [7]. In addition to the Bo8 journals, we included the proceedings of the ICIS into our outlet, reflecting possible interesting trends of topics within conferences. We assume that certain topics are published within this outlet since conferences are the source of new IS research and an opportunity to acquire feedback on ideas more quickly based on the short revision times [26,28]. As mentioned, ICIS provides high-quality double-blinded reviews, resulting in worldwide acceptance by top IS researchers [25]. Consequentially, as recommended by [3], we have covered a wide range of top IS research with our included outlet that is recognized in the global IS community. We downloaded all publications from several sources and imported them into a literature management tool. We removed different elements, such as book reviews, errata notes, and editorials, which we documented in an exclusion list. Table 1 presents the number of articles per outlet.

Table 1.: *Number of articles differentiated by particular outlet.*

Outlet (Journal/Conference)	**Abbr.**	**# Articles**	**Rel. Share**
European Journal of Information Systems	EJIS	562	54.30%
Information Systems Journal	ISJ	309	
Information Systems Research	ISR	551	
Journal of the Association for Information Systems	JAIS	381	
Journal of Information Technology	JIT	345	
Journal of Management Information Systems	JMIS	619	
Journal of Strategic Information Systems	JSIS	287	
Management Information Systems Quarterly	MISQ	574	
International Conference on Information Systems	ICIS	3058	45.70%
	Σ	6692	100%

Phase 2 aimed to organize and prepare the literature. We structured and organized the articles and assigned corresponding metadata. For the determination of geographical trends, we developed an algorithm to add this information by using the country suffix of e-mail addresses to assign the corresponding author to a country. Many publishers, such as Elsevier, accept this restriction to only the first author [14]. With the aid of the package Xpdf, we converted the .pdf files to .txt files, which facilitated the further processing of the documents. Before the investigation of trends within the interdisciplinary research domain of IS can be conducted, we had to cluster topics in appropriate research fields. Specific IS research topics are covered under these research fields. Alternatively, we had way too many topics not manageable because of short interests and relevance of topics or several synonyms changing over the time. Each research field contains one or more topics equipped with a text module, which is necessary for the assignment of the articles. To group the topics into reasonable research fields, we used an inductive procedure. We tried to identify and describe similarities and patterns based on the collected data and observations (track descriptions, etc.) in order to derive descriptions of the research fields based on this. To do so, we analyzed topics of various track descriptions of the ICIS and special issues of AIS Bo8 journals. Based on this, we created a table containing different topics and corresponding descriptions. Within this iterative process, research fields were created, renamed, replaced, or consolidated along with a running adjustment of the corresponding text module. As a result, we identified 22 research fields consisting of a multiplicity of topics to cover all topics within 16 years of IS research in the mentioned outlets (see Table 2).

Table 2.: *Compilation of research fields.*

Business Process Management	IS Projects & IS Development
Contribution of Applied Science	IS Security & Privacy
Data Science & Business Analytics	IS Strategy & (Out-)Sourcing
E-Business & E-Government	IT Implementation, Adoption, & Use
Funding of Innovations	Knowledge Management
Human Behavior & Cultural Aspects	Mobile Information Systems
Impacts of IT/IS	Open Source Software & Open Innovations
IS Curriculum & Education	Research Methods & Philosophy
IS History	Service Science in IS
IS in Healthcare	Social Media & Digital Collaboration
IS in Organizations & Society	Sustainability

In Phase 3, the literature database was analyzed. Researcher's face various challenges during the literature review process. The first challenge is selecting the correct keywords, since authors use synonyms and paraphrases. The second time-consuming challenge is screening the results for relevance [41,42]. Enormous savings of time are possible through using LSI [38,41]. LSI is an automated literature analysis approach using mathematical techniques to ascertain patterns between articles. By possessing a literature database, relating articles can be identified. An input for such an analysis is a complete article or just some text modules. Therefore, more and truly relevant publications that relate to the inserted article or text module can be identified resulting in a useful method for similarity queries [38,41]. For our investigation, we inserted our database consisting of 6692 articles into an LSI-Tool, which is located on a private server due to access restrictions of the contained publications. In this regard, we extended the approach of [3] because we used not only the textual data in the abstracts but also the textual data of the entire research articles (full text). For each article, the tool conducts an LSI process while the resulting queries were stored in a separate SQLite database representing the basis for our investigation. With inserting our developed text modules (compare Phase 2), these pass through this LSI process too, were compared to contained publications of our database and related articles were presented sorted by relevance. Throughout the entire LSI process, we manually checked the results to ensure the correct assignment of articles to research fields. Table 2 presents the 22 identified research fields.

To understand the sequence of LSI, the following section briefly focusses on the mathematical functionality. In a first step and before the proper mathematical operations start, often contained terms such as "the", "it" or "and" have to be eliminated, because words were expressed as vectors. The fundamental idea of LSI is the vector-space-model, which was developed by [43]. The model constitutes words or documents as vectors $d_i = (d_{i1}, d_{i2}, \ldots, d_{ij})$ where d_{ij} represents the weight of the jth terms. As advantage for a given vector query $q = (w_{1q}, w_{2q}, \ldots, w_{nq})$, the similarity can be calculated as the angle of the document vector and the query vector. The document vectors are summarized in a term document $m \times n$ matrix called A, where m represents the number of words and n the number of documents. With this basis, a Singular Value Decomposition (SVD) as core part of LSI is conducted. The results are three new matrices U, S, and V, which will be further rated by SVD. A rank reduction with the help of an empirical factor k has the consequence that the small singular values are deleted from the matrix which removes the noise from the documents [44]. At this point, the SVD is completed. The existent document matrix V_k^T contains the eigenvector values of the considered documents of *di*. The matrices *Uk* and S_k^{-1} are multiplied with the query vector q^T to achieve a rank-reduced query vector *qk* which represents the final vector for the last operation. With the resulting vector, the actual query process can be started. Therefore, each entry of the matrix V_k^T is needed, here named as *dvi*, and the rank reduced vector *qk*. The following Equation (1) shows the cosine of the angle from the two vectors with the Euclidean dot product expressing the similarity between the input words and documents:

$$\cos\theta = \frac{d_{Vi} \times q_k}{\|q_k\| \times \|d_{Vi}\|} \tag{1}$$

The value of this comparison can take a value between "1" (identical) and "0" (orthogonal). If the vectors are orthogonal to each other, the similarity is entirely not given. If the value is 1, they are equal.

For more information on the underlying theoretical concepts and applied methods of the used LSI-approach, see [38]. In Phase 4, we present our results in terms of the regional distribution of publications in the AIS Bo8 and the ICIS, the change in publication behavior, and the emergence and change of IS research fields and trends over time. In order to carry out a meaningful analysis of the temporal change in publication behavior, and the emergence and change of IS research fields and trends over time, we divided the entire period of 16 years into four-year segments (YS). This is justified by the fact that we needed a sufficient number of publications per YS and outlet (ICIS proceedings and AIS Bo8 journal) to carry out a meaningful analysis. To ensure this, each YS describes a time span of four years. This period allows enough time for the analysis of temporal changes in publication behavior and enough time for research fields to go through a large part of its life cycle [17,45]. In order to reflect the time span in each segment equally, we limited our analysis to the time period from 2000 to 2015 because JAIS began publishing in 2000. YS1 contains the years 2000–2003, YS2 2004–2007, YS3 2008–2011, and YS4 2012–2015.

4. DEMONSTRATION OF RESULTS

4.1. Regional Distribution of Publications in the AIS Bo8 and the ICIS

In this section, the results of our investigation are presented by answering the first research question with regard to the regional distribution of publications and their corresponding outlets. As explained, the foundation for our investigation is formed by a database of 6692 articles consisting of 3061 publications in the ICIS proceedings and 3631 AIS Bo8 journal publications from 2000 to 2015. Table 3 presents a time-independent classification of articles by continent and chosen country (groups) divided into the number of published articles in total (ICIS proceedings and AIS Bo8 journals). The color-coding (e.g., North America = yellow) is intended to clarify the assignment to the groups. This assignment is also used in the following figures or tables.

***Table 3.**: Assignment of articles to geographical regions differentiated by outlet.*

Continent Country (Group)	**Total Articles**	**ICIS Articles**	**AIS Bo8 Articles**	**Continent Country (Group)**	**Total Articles**	**ICIS Articles**	**AIS Bo8 Articles**
North America	3654	1529	2125	Asia	852	476	376
Europe	1738	818	920	China	319	174	145
Germany, Austria, and Switzerland	595	454	141	Singapore	276	200	76
Great Britain	574	140	434	Korea	92	39	53
Scandinavia	278	108	170	Taiwan	63	19	44
Northern Mediterranean	155	64	91	Further Asian countries	102	44	58

Continent Country (Group)	**Total Articles**	**ICIS Arti-cles**	**AIS Bo8 Arti-cles**	**Conti-nent Country (Group)**	**Total Arti-cles**	**ICIS Articles**	**AIS Bo8 Articles**
Benelux Union	124	45	79	South America	18	10	8
Further European countries	12	7	5	Africa	14	10	4
Australia	359	188	171	No country identifi-able	57	30	27

Focusing on the overall continental distribution, in total North American researchers published approximately 55% (3654) of the worldwide articles in these IS outlets, followed by Europe with 1738 (approx. 26%), and Asian countries with 852 articles (approx. 13%). Less than 7% (448 articles) were from other regions of the world (Australia, South America, and Africa). These included 57 articles in which the country of the corresponding author was not identifiable. We merged Australia with Oceania because of the comparatively low share of Oceanian articles. Due to the small number of published articles, the South American and African regions were not subdivided into countries. Regarding Europe, most of the articles (approx. 17% in total) were published by researchers from Germany, Austria, and Switzerland (595 articles) as well as Great Britain (UK and Ireland) (574 articles). Scandinavian researchers (from Norway, Sweden, Finland, Denmark, and Island) produced 278 articles (4%), Northern Mediterranean researchers (consisting of Portugal, Spain, France, and Italy) produced 155 articles (2.3%), and researchers from the Benelux Union (Netherlands, Belgium, and Luxembourg) produced 124 articles (1.8%). The remaining publications (12 articles) were grouped as other European countries (approx. 0.1%). Analyzing Asia, researchers from China and Singapore published 319 and 276 articles, respectively, approximately 9% of the total number of publications. Researchers from Korea published 92 articles (slightly more than 1%), and researchers from Taiwan produced 63 articles (less than 1%). These are mentioned separately, while research articles from other Asian countries are grouped together.

In the next step, geographical appearance in the ICIS proceedings and the AIS Bo8 journal publications was investigated in more detail. North American publications dominated the AIS Bo8 journals with a total of 2125 articles from 2000 to 2015, representing nearly 60% of all articles within this span. In Europe and North America, there were more articles published in the AIS Bo8 journals than in the ICIS proceedings. Regarding the other continents, there were (slightly) fewer articles published in AIS Bo8 journals. Intracontinental differences were clearly visible in Europe and Asia. While researchers from Germany, Austria, and Switzerland were commonly present in the ICIS proceedings (454 articles), the majority of publications from the UK and Ireland were published in the AIS Bo8 journals (434 articles). In Asia, measured at share, China and Singapore were quite evident in the ICIS proceedings, but Singapore was less represented in the AIS Bo8 journals. On the contrary, articles by Korean and Taiwanese researchers as well as those from other Asian countries were published in the AIS Bo8 journals and comparatively less in the ICIS proceedings.

4.2. Temporal Change in Publication Behavior—A Geographical Perspective

Based on the above findings, the following investigations are focused on the detection of the temporal change in publication behavior. Figure 2 visualizes this change by application of YS with regard to ICIS proceedings and AIS Bo8 journal publication numbers. YS1 contains the years 2000–2003, YS2 2004–2007, YS3 2008–2011, and YS4 2012–2015. For visualization and comparability reasons, Figure 2 is narrowed to continental trends, while the investigation of Table 4 includes the specific country-related distribution. As previously mentioned, the number of articles in the AIS Bo8 journals is continuously rising, and ICIS proceeding articles show a rapid increase, especially from YS2 to YS3, when the number of articles more than doubled. Upon investigation, the number of articles from Europe, Australia, Asia, and the other continents (South America, Africa, and unidentifiable) nearly doubled each YS. Except for YS2 to YS3, the North American researchers are quite similarly represented by comparing the number of articles between two segments. Regarding YS4, European and North American publications are at nearly the same level, which became apparent regarding the past trend. Analyzing the AIS Bo8 journal publications from YS1 to YS3, a steady rise in all regions is observable. The development in YS4 follows the primary development except in North America. The number of North American publications is slightly decreasing, although the number of overall articles is rising. To recap, in both outlets, the number of publications is increasing, while all regions over the time period show an increase, with the exception of North America in the last YS.

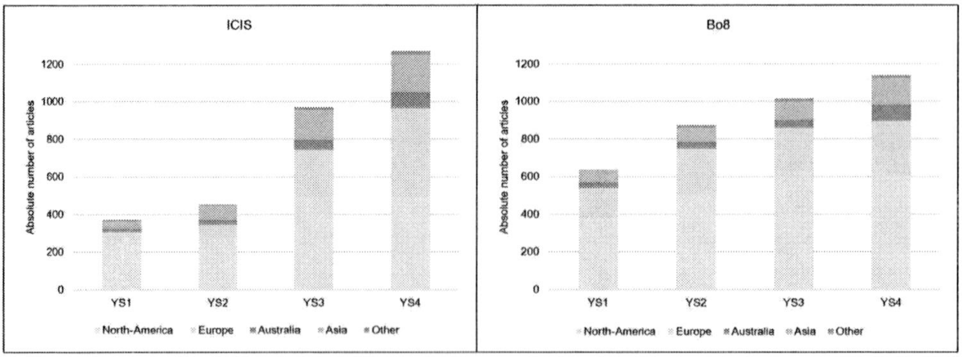

Figure 2.: *Absolute number of articles per YS and region in comparison to outlets.*

***Table 4.:** Relative share of articles in terms of regional distribution and outlet in comparison to the YS.*

Continent Country (Group)	ICIS				AIS Bo8			
	YS1 (2000–2003)	YS2 (2004–2007)	YS3 (2008–2011)	YS4 (2012–2015)	YS1 (2000–2003)	YS2 (2004–2007)	YS3 (2008–2011)	YS4 (2012–2015)
Total	100.00%	100.00%	100.00%	100.00%	100.00%	100.00%	100.00%	100.00%
North America	70.85%	61.15%	51.09%	39.09%	58.88%	57.48%	61.28%	54.16%
Europe	10.70%	15.01%	25.75%	36.72%	25.08%	27.10%	22.18%	25.60%
Germany, Austria, and Switzerland	1.07%	3.31%	11.27%	25.85%	0.78%	1.93%	3.70%	7.05%
Great Britain	4.29%	7.06%	5.69%	2.92%	16.36%	16.33%	8.27%	8.92%
Scandinavia	2.41%	1.32%	4.03%	4.33%	3.58%	4.54%	5.54%	4.37%
Northern Mediterranean	0.53%	1.55%	3.00%	2.13%	1.87%	1.81%	2.72%	3.03%
Benelux Union	1.87%	1.77%	1.76%	1.10%	2.49%	2.38%	1.95%	1.87%
Further European countries	0.53%	0%	0%	0.39%	0%	0.11%	0%	0.36%
Australia	5.35%	5.96%	5.48%	6.93%	4.67%	4.31%	4.19%	5.62%
Asia	11.23%	17.22%	16.33%	15.60%	9.65%	8.50%	9.14%	12.93%
China	2.68%	3.97%	7.14%	6.07%	2.80%	1.81%	3.79%	6.42%
Singapore	6.69%	10.15%	6.10%	5.52%	2.34%	2.61%	1.65%	1.87%
Korea	0.80%	1.55%	0.92%	1.58%	1.40%	1.47%	1.46%	1.43%
Taiwan	0.53%	0%	1.03%	0.55%	0.47%	1.25%	0.98%	1.78%
Further Asian countries	0.53%	1.55%	1.14%	1.88%	2.65%	1.36%	1.26%	1.43%
South America	0%	0.22%	0.52%	0.32%	0.16%	0.35%	0.19%	0.18%
Africa	0%	0.44%	0.21%	0.47%	0.78%	1.13%	1.56%	0.89%
No country available	1.87%	0%	0.62%	0.87%	0.78%	1.13%	1.46%	0.62%

For deeper investigation and to understand how these continental trends are composed, the relative shares for continents and countries or respective country groups are presented in Table 4. As also apparent in Figure 2, the share of North American articles decreased from YS1 to YS4 especially for the number of publications in ICIS proceedings. Regarding Europe, for ICIS proceedings, the publication number continually grew from approximately 11% to approximately 37%, while for the AIS Bo8 journals, the relative share fluctuated by approximately 25%. For Australia, this shifting trend is also obvious, with little variation of approximately 1%. Considering the Asian countries, we see an increasing trend from YS1 to YS3 with a decrease in YS4 with regard to ICIS proceeding articles and a relative steady rise from 10% to 13% in the AIS Bo8 journals. For South American, African, and other countries, no pattern is identifiable because of small publication numbers.

Focusing on intra-European researchers, the impact of Germany, Austria, and Switzerland within YS1 in both outlets was almost not existent. In the following years, the relative share of publications considerably increased. For ICIS proceeding publications, the share more than tripled from YS1 to YS3, whereas from YS3 to YS4, the share doubled. Regarding AIS Bo8 journal publications, the relative share at least doubled. If we investigate Great Britain's researcher development in the ICIS proceedings, initially (from YS1 to YS2), the relative share increased, but from YS2 to YS4, the relative share of articles decreased from approximately 7% to only 3%. In the AIS Bo8 journals, this trend is also apparent. With more than 16% in YS1 and YS2, the relative share in YS3 and YS4 was reduced by approximately half (8%). The other European countries do not follow notable trends, fluctuating approximately 1% or 2% between the YSs. In summary, the number of publications of German, Austrian, and Swiss researchers in both outlets increased over the years, which is the key factor in increasing the relative share of European articles. When investigating differences within Asia, the developments are not as distinct. For China and Singapore, which are the most represented countries, no clear trend in terms of increasing or decreasing the relative share of articles is observed. In China, the share of articles increased in both outlets, starting with approximately 2% in YS1 to more than 6% in YS4. On the contrary, the development in Singapore slightly decreased similarly in both outlets. For the other Asian countries, no generalizations about time-dependent trends are obvious, but of course, some small variations exist.

After the regional distributions of publications are presented for ICIS and the AIS Bo8, differences within the various AIS Bo8 journals can be examined. Figure 3 presents the number of articles for all AIS Bo8 journals and their continental distribution over time.

As the name suggests, EJIS is one of the leading European IS journals [46]. This is confirmed by the results. Almost half of the publications (259 out of 552) were of European origin, and 36% of the articles are published by North American researchers. When comparing these numbers with the sum total of AIS Bo8 from Table 4, it is clear that compared to the average over the years, many European articles and few North American articles were actually published in the EJIS. Asia and Australia are each represented with 9% and 7%, respectively. With regard to the temporal distribution, it is remarkable that the number of total publications in the EJIS has declined since YS2. In particular, the number of European publications decreased from YS2 to YS3, whereas the number of North American publications increased over the same period. The number of Asian and Australian articles at least doubled from YS1 to YS4. In addition to the EJIS, there was a surplus of European articles in the ISJ and JIT. Similar to MISQ, JMIS, JAIS, and ISR show a clear spatial origin focus on North America. In all these journals, however, a recognizable internationalization of the origin of the authors can be observed within the last two YSs. A special feature of the ISR is the comparatively high number of Asian articles in recent years. The JSIS cannot be assigned to either trend. Initially more North American, it is now more influenced by European researchers and their publications.

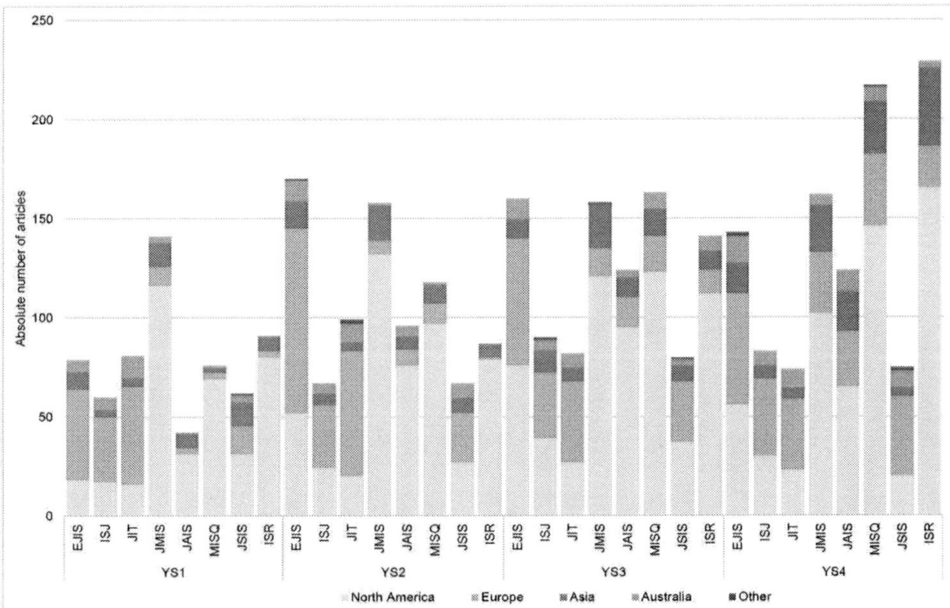

Figure 3.: Continental distribution of articles within the Bo8 journals (EJIS, ISJ, JIT, JMIS, JAIS, MISQ, JSIS, and ISR).

Both outlets (ICIS proceedings and AIS Bo8 journals) show an increasing number of articles, although the increase within ICIS proceedings is much more obvious with a tripling from YS1 to YS4. Regarding the continental distribution, North America was the leading geographic region in both outlets over the investigated period, whereas the European countries were mainly represented in the ICIS proceedings. Asian countries were quite important with comparatively high publications in China and Singapore. Australia followed the slightly increasing trend, while South American, African, and other publications remained rare in top IS research in the ICIS proceedings and the AIS Bo8 journals. When analyzing the individual AIS Bo8 journals, there are journals with a strong focus on North American research and journals with a slight European focus and vice versa (compare Figure 3). A journal dominated by Asian or Australian researchers does not exist.

4.3. Development of IS Research Fields in Terms of Region and Outlet

To further investigate trends in terms of region and outlet over time, it is necessary to conduct calculations to obtain absolute and relative shares. Table 5 serves as the foundation for the following charts and figures to identify patterns in IS research fields. Table 5 presents the number of publications per research field grouped by YS as well as by outlet and presents the absolute number of matches and the relative share. The relative shares are determined by dividing the number of absolute articles of a research field within an outlet and a YS by the number of overall publications within this research field within an outlet and a YS. These relative shares serve as input for the following investigations.

Table 5.: *Absolute and relative scientific interest by outlet, research field, and time.*

		YS1 (2000–2003)		YS2 (2004–2007)		YS3 (2008–2011)		YS4 (2012–2015)	
Overall Database of 6692 articles	AIS Bo8	637		872		1013		1114	
	ICIS	374		453		967		1269	
Research Fields (matches)	Outlet	Abs.	Rel.	Abs.	Rel.	Abs.	Rel.	Abs.	Rel.
E-Business & E-Government (842)	AIS Bo8	83	13.03%	161	18.46%	139	13.72%	144	12.93%
	ICIS	39	10.43%	54	11.92%	101	10.44%	121	9.54%
Service Science in IS (785)	AIS Bo8	65	10.20%	112	12.84%	119	11.75%	140	12.57%
	ICIS	28	7.49%	65	14.35%	94	9.72%	175	13.79%
IS in Organizations & Society (785)	AIS Bo8	54	8.48%	114	13.07%	114	11.25%	425	38.15%
	ICIS	26	6.95%	66	14.57%	103	10.65%	357	28.13%
Contribution of Applied Science (758)	AIS Bo8	96	15.07%	125	14.33%	123	12.14%	116	10.41%
	ICIS	39	10.43%	80	17.66%	94	9.72%	85	6.70%
Social Media & Digital Collaboration (713)	AIS Bo8	43	6.75%	60	6.88%	95	9.38%	118	10.59%
	ICIS	23	6.15%	42	9.27%	133	13.75%	199	15.68%
Human Behavior & Cultural Aspects (664)	AIS Bo8	90	14.13%	110	12.61%	114	11.25%	112	10.05%
	ICIS	30	8.02%	53	11.70%	77	7.96%	78	6.15%
Impacts of IT/IS (651)	AIS Bo8	84	13.19%	115	13.19%	102	10.07%	112	10.05%
	ICIS	32	8.56%	49	10.82%	77	7.96%	80	6.30%

		YS1 (2000–2003)		YS2 (2004–2007)		YS3 (2008–2011)		YS4 (2012–2015)	
Research Methods & Philosophy (433)	AIS Bo8	39	6.12%	42	4.82%	61	6.02%	80	7.18%
	ICIS	11	2.94%	20	4.42%	59	6.10%	121	9.54%
IS Security & Privacy (319)	AIS Bo8	18	2.83%	28	3.21%	82	8.09%	57	5.12%
	ICIS	11	2.94%	22	4.86%	50	5.17%	51	4.02%
Mobile Information Systems (290)	AIS Bo8	11	1.73%	35	4.01%	31	3.06%	60	5.39%
	ICIS	11	2.94%	13	2.87%	28	2.90%	101	7.96%
IS in Healthcare (259)	AIS Bo8	5	0.78%	32	3.67%	41	4.05%	50	4.49%
	ICIS	1	0.27%	7	1.55%	53	5.48%	70	5.52%
Funding of Innovations (285)	AIS Bo8	17	2.67%	32	3.67%	28	2.76%	35	3.14%
	ICIS	12	3.21%	6	1.32%	39	4.03%	89	7.01%
Knowledge Management (242)	AIS Bo8	17	2.67%	36	4.13%	37	3.65%	36	3.23%
	ICIS	19	5.08%	27	5.96%	33	3.41%	37	2.92%
IS Curriculum & Education (205)	AIS Bo8	14	2.20%	21	2.41%	25	2.47%	17	1.53%
	ICIS	9	2.41%	24	5.30%	43	4.45%	52	4.10%
Data Science & Business Analytics (160)	AIS Bo8	10	1.57%	21	2.41%	22	2.17%	23	2.06%
	ICIS	8	2.14%	14	3.09%	19	1.96%	43	3.39%
IT Implementation, Adoption, & Use (146)	AIS Bo8	9	1.41%	14	1.61%	29	2.86%	18	1.62%
	ICIS	3	0.80%	10	2.21%	27	2.79%	36	2.84%
Business Process Management (123)	AIS Bo8	21	3.30%	10	1.15%	15	1.48%	14	1.26%
	ICIS	2	0.53%	8	1.77%	18	1.86%	35	2.76%
IS Projects & IS Development (93)	AIS Bo8	13	2.04%	16	1.83%	17	1.68%	12	1.08%
	ICIS	5	1.34%	5	1.10%	11	1.14%	14	1.10%
Open Source Software & Open Innovations (90)	AIS Bo8	5	0.78%	1	0.11%	16	1.58%	8	0.72%
	ICIS	7	1.87%	6	1.32%	14	1.45%	33	2.60%
Sustainability (90)	AIS Bo8	5	0.78%	7	0.80%	19	1.88%	11	0.99%
	ICIS	5	1.34%	2	0.44%	17	1.76%	24	1.89%

		YS1 (2000–2003)		**YS2 (2004–2007)**		**YS3 (2008–2011)**		**YS4 (2012–2015)**	
IS History (87)	AIS Bo8	7	1.10%	17	1.95%	12	1.18%	21	1.89%
	ICIS	4	1.07%	11	2.43%	6	0.62%	9	0.71%
IS Strategy & (Out-)Sourcing (84)	AIS Bo8	1	0.16%	4	0.46%	24	2.37%	15	1.35%
	ICIS	0	0.00%	11	2.43%	9	0.93%	20	1.58%

It must be mentioned that it is quite possible that a publication can be classified into two or even more research fields. For example, a publication that develops a mobile application for mobility is mentioned in the fields of "Service Science", "Mobile Information Systems", and "Sustainability". On the other hand, there are articles that are not assigned to one of the 22 categories. On average, a publication was assigned to 1.21 research fields. From our analysis four different trends in research field development were revealed. These differ in terms of development over time in relation to the number of publications on specific research fields in the AIS Bo8 journals and the publications in the ICIS proceedings. These four different trends are illustrated by four research fields ("Social Media & Digital Collaboration", "Impact of IT/IS", "Service Science in IS", and "Funding of Innovations") as examples and can be categorized as follows: (a) similarly increasing, (b) similarly decreasing, (c) similarly consistent, and (d) divergent (see Figure 4). Corresponding graphics for the other 18 research fields can be found in Appendix A.

As an example of a research field with a constant increase in the number of publications over time, the research field "Social Media & Digital Collaboration" can be mentioned. There is a similar increase in publications in this research field in both the AIS Bo8 and the ICIS proceedings. It should be noted, however, that in this context, the number of publications in the ICIS proceedings increased faster than in the AIS Bo8 journals and more publications were published in the ICIS proceedings over time than in the AIS Bo8 journals. This overall development indicates that these research fields are trending research fields and that the IS community has placed an even greater focus on such research fields. The overall interest in this research field is also reflected in the total number of publications (compare Table 5) as well as in a distinct increasing trend that has interest peaks in both the AIS Bo8 and ICIS. The development of the IS research community and its research interests appear to be somewhat fluid and follow certain trends in society. For example, the number of studies on "Social Media & Digital Collaboration" has grown considerably in number (YS1, YS2) together with the rise of, for example, Twitter and Facebook in 2006 and 2004. It is obvious that researchers have noticed this trend and its relevance for research. Most AIS Bo8 publications in this field have been published in EJIS, JIT, JAIS, and MISQ (compare Table 6 and Figure A17).

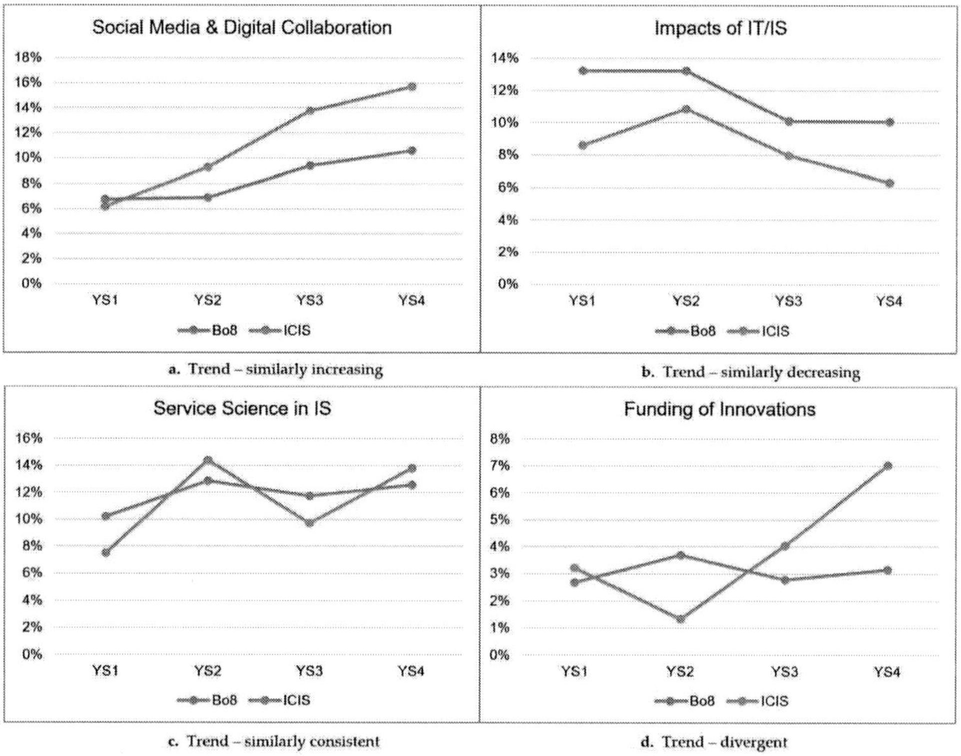

***Figure 4.**: Identified pattern regarding outlet and YS' for exemplified research.*

***Table 6.**: Share of a journal in a research field.*

Research Field	EJIS	ISJ	ISR	JIT	JMIS	JAIS	MISQ	JSIS	Total
Contribution of Applied Science	21%	9%	6%	9%	4%	27%	18%	6%	460
E-Business & E-Government	26%	9%	8%	17%	11%	7%	10%	12%	527
Funding of Innovations	16%	4%	9%	11%	11%	12%	19%	19%	112
Human Behavior & Cultural Aspects in IS	22%	13%	3%	20%	4%	15%	16%	8%	426
Impacts of IT/IS	17%	10%	3%	19%	19%	9%	14%	9%	413
IS in Healthcare	23%	2%	20%	9%	12%	13%	13%	7%	128
IS in Organizations & Society	20%	9%	4%	16%	5%	20%	16%	10%	425
IS Research Methods & Philosophy	29%	11%	5%	13%	3%	18%	15%	8%	222

Research Field	EJIS	ISJ	ISR	JIT	JMIS	JAIS	MISQ	JSIS	Total
IS Security & Privacy	17%	7%	8%	8%	12%	18%	19%	10%	185
Knowledge Management	17%	9%	6%	19%	8%	10%	20%	13%	126
Mobile Information Systems	8%	7%	11%	26%	4%	18%	18%	9%	137
Service Science in IS	20%	8%	5%	20%	3%	19%	17%	9%	436
Social Media & Digital Collaboration	18%	8%	6%	16%	6%	18%	22%	5%	316
Average	19%	8%	7%	16%	8%	16%	17%	10%	

Note: Only research fields with more than 110 publications in total were considered.

This result is in line with the findings of [8], who came to a similar conclusion in their study of developing research fields with a special focus on the European IS research community. Furthermore, we have identified areas of research (e.g., "IS in Healthcare") that are in a nascent stage with a steadily increasing tendency and that are considered equally interesting by major IS journals, especially EJIS and ISR (see Table 6), and the ICIS. Although there are a few minor differences in the evolution of other research fields that have been attributed to this category (e.g., "IS in Healthcare", "Mobile Information Systems"), a similar pattern can be observed regarding the overall increased interest of the IS community in these research fields (compare Figure A1 and Figure A2). In sum, the trends observed here suggest some interesting dynamics between society and publishing in leading IS journals and conference proceedings.

Regarding the decreasing overall interests, such trends are evident within research fields with high interest and, therefore, a comparatively high number of articles published over the years. Looking at the research field "Impact of IT/IS" (651 articles), it can be seen that the peak of scientific interest in the AIS Bo8 journals was achieved in YS1 and at the ICIS in YS2, followed by a slight decrease. This pattern can also be observed in other research fields, such as the "Contribution of Applied Science" (compare Figure A3). These findings illustrate the interesting dynamics in IS research and underline the sometimes short lifespan of research fields, as mentioned by [3]. In their analysis, these authors made a similar observation regarding the topic of virtual worlds, noting that even one of the hottest topics in research may lose importance in IS research and may wane in the top IS research outlets [3]. Most AIS Bo8 publications in this field have been published in EJIS, JIT, and JMIS (compare Table 6).

The third trend that we have identified based on our analysis is "similarly consistent". Although there are differences in the extent of development, the trends are very similar in both the AIS Bo8 and ICIS. Looking at the selected example, "Service Science in IS", it becomes clear that the number of publications initially increases, then decreases and then rises again and reaches its peak in YS4. Similar developments, which also show fluctuations in the number of publications, can be observed for other fields of research, such as "E-Business & E-Government", "IS Curriculum & Education", "Management IT Projects & Development", and "IS History" (compare Figure A4, Figure A5, Figure A6 and Figure A7).

The deviating evolution of research fields is represented by the category "divergent". In this category, very different courses of publication trends on specific topics can be observed. As an example, we have chosen the research field "Funding of Innovations". In this context, contrary development trends can be observed, which also differ according to the strength and characteristics. Research interest at the ICIS has significantly increased more in recent years than in the AIS Bo8 Journals. In the AIS Bo8, most publications in this research field were published in the EJIS, MISQ, and JSIS (compare Table 6). Other research fields that have a different development course with regard to the development in the AIS Bo8 and that of the ICIS are "IT Strategy & Outsourcing", "Business Process Management", and "Open Source & Open Innovation". This different development over time can be attributed to different reasons, such as the different times from submission until the paper is published or the perception of the importance and accuracy of individual research fields to the appropriate journal.

To show which journals have published in certain research fields above or below the average amount, we calculated the corresponding differences to the average of the respective journal (compare Table 7). The European-based journal ISJ has the lowest total deviation from the respective average value. The value varies between –6% and +5%. This broad thematic focus, without placing special focus on specific topics, has been mentioned by [34], who noted that the European-based ISJ is characterized by a methodological diversity and willingness to take on risky topics [34]. A similar characteristic can be found for the MISQ. Again, the deviations are relatively small compared to the other journals. Other journals, such as the ISR, JIT, and JAIS, have other characteristics. ISR has placed an even greater focus on the research field "IS in Healthcare", while JIT has focused on, for example, "Mobile Information Systems" and "Human Behavior & Cultural Aspects in IS", and JAIS has focused on research fields such as "Contribution of Applied Science" and "IS in Organization & Society". Of course, while it is not possible to characterize a journal only by the number of publications on a given research field, this information provides a valuable indication of the journal's focus.

Table 7.: *Deviations from the respective average value.*

Deviations from the Respective Average Value	**EJIS**	**ISJ**	**ISR**	**JIT**	**JMIS**	**JAIS**	**MISQ**	**JSIS**
Contribution of Applied Science	1%	1%	–1%	–6%	–4%	11%	1%	–3%
E-Business & E-Government	7%	1%	0%	2%	3%	–9%	–6%	3%
Funding of Innovations	–3%	–4%	2%	–5%	3%	–4%	2%	9%

Deviations from the Respective Average Value	EJIS	ISJ	ISR	JIT	JMIS	JAIS	MISQ	JSIS
Human Behavior & Cultural Aspects in IS	2%	5%	−4%	5%	−4%	−1%	−1%	−2%
Impacts of IT/IS	−3%	2%	−4%	3%	11%	−7%	−3%	−1%
IS in Healthcare	3%	−6%	13%	−6%	4%	−2%	−3%	−3%
IS in Organizations & Society	1%	1%	−3%	0%	−3%	4%	0%	0%
IS Research Methods & Philosophy	9%	3%	−3%	−3%	−5%	2%	−1%	−2%
IS Security & Privacy	−2%	−1%	1%	−8%	5%	3%	2%	0%
Knowledge Management	−3%	1%	−2%	3%	0%	−6%	3%	3%
Mobile Information Systems	−11%	−1%	4%	10%	−4%	2%	1%	0%
Service Science in IS	0%	0%	−2%	4%	−5%	3%	1%	0%
Social Media & Digital Collaboration	−1%	0%	−1%	1%	−1%	3%	5%	−4%

Note: Color coding for the percentage deviation of the number of publications from the average value: Red = Deviation down from the mean; Green = Deviation upwards from the mean.

The number of publications in the respective AIS Bo8 journals for the individual research fields can be found in Appendix B, Figure A11, Figure A12, Figure A13, Figure A14, Figure A15, Figure A16 and Figure A17.

Since thematic, paradigmatic, and geographical aspects are important when analyzing the development of a research domain [8,33], we also want to take a closer look at the development of IS research fields in different regions. In this context, we again used the four research fields "Social Media & Digital Collaboration", "Impact of IT/IS", "Service Science in IS", and "Funding of Innovations". However, the geographical assignment was not based on journals (e.g., EJIS, and ISJ–European-based and MISQ, ISR–North American-based). Instead, the origin of the authors was used to make a corresponding geographical assignment of the publications to a specific region.

As we can see in Figure 5a,b, there are regional differences in the development of the respective research fields. The research field "Impacts of IT/IS" developed differently regionally. While it has been relatively steady throughout North America and Europe with a slight increasing trend, in Asia, a relatively steep increase can be observed before the trend in YS3 starts to decline. Visible geographical trends in the second decade (YS3 and YS4) compared with the first (YS1 and YS2) include the strong rise of contributions from North America, Australia, and Asia concerning the research field "Social Media & Digital Collaboration". Overall, the number of publications in all regions, except Europe, has risen sharply in this area. In Europe, there is also an increase in the second decade, but it is not as strong as in the other regions. These findings are in line with the conclusions drawn from Table 7: the number of publications in the research field "Social Media & Digital Collaboration" in European-based journals (e.g., EJIS and ISJ) is below the respective average value in terms of the proportions of journals in a research field. In contrast, this research field is more well represented in North American-based IS Journals (e.g., JAIS and MISQ).

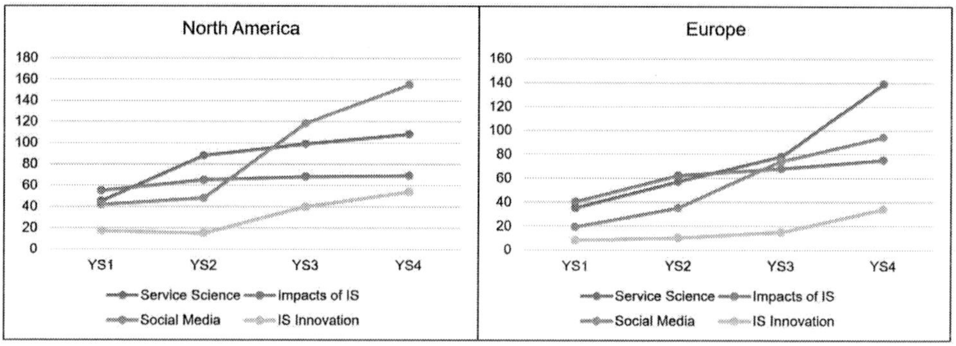

(a)

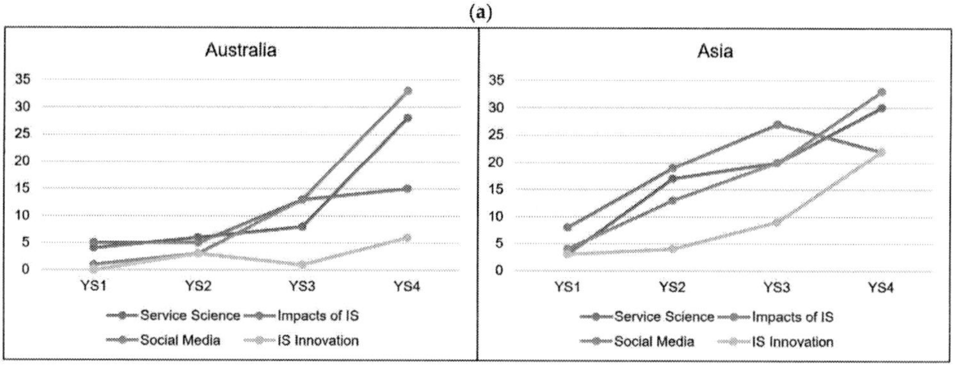

(b)

Figure 5.: *(a) Regional development of research fields—North America and Europe. (b) Regional development of research fields—Australia and Asia.*

5. DISCUSSION AND IMPLICATIONS

As mentioned by [35], some researchers developed their research papers on, for example, the evolution and state of the IS research domain or citation classics by drawing on data in earlier studies (e.g., [47]). Thus, there is a risk of path dependency because such studies normally had a tendency to analyze a limited set of ideas, approaches, and papers [35]. We argue that the use of papers published in the AIS Bo8 and in ICIS proceedings, which represent the highest quality of research in the field [48], provides a useful component for the presented longitudinal analysis because these data are less likely to suffer from problems of path dependency. The findings of our analysis, therefore, provide a useful complement to existing studies (e.g., [3,7,8]). Our study contributes to theory by following the commentary of [3] (p. 413) and examining "a much broader set of journals such as the Senior Scholar's basket of eight journals" to enhance the diversity. This was also mentioned by [17], who noted that a comparative study of North American versus European IS research identities by including journals with a higher share of European publications could be an interesting direction for further research. By additionally drawing on conference papers rather than only journals, we are able to examine to what extent current trends in society are reflected in research. Journal publications are not very well suited for this because of their sometimes very long publication times. Thus, conference proceedings may complement the analysis and provide a more up-to-date picture than can be found by analyzing journal articles alone [35].

The distribution of all publications speaks for itself. It should be noted that the majority of research contributions come from North American or European researchers. This finding is confirmed by studies by [33], who analyzed publications within the journal ISJ. They called for more internalization and cited China, India, South America, and Africa, in particular, as countries that "are hotbeds of IS practice and becoming hotbeds of IS research" [33] (p. 19). Looking at the distribution over the course of time, European research in the specific outlets has clearly adapted and caught up in terms of quantity. Ref. [29] criticize the under-representation of publications by non-North American researchers. Our results demonstrate a change in recent years. These developments have also been noted in general terms by [14]. During their investigations on MISQ, ISR, and EJIS from 2000 to 2009, they found a decrease in the publication numbers of American publications and a nearly doubling of European (and African) and of Asian and Australian publications. A decisive point for the future distribution is the number of published articles themselves. In the period under investigation, the number of ICIS publications more than tripled and almost doubled for AIS Bo8 publications. The only exception, with a decrease in published articles in this context, was the EJIS. The overall increase in publications as well as the increased interest over the past years has been identified by several authors [5,7,8].

Ultimately, it is questionable to what extent continental publication volumes will develop in the future. Under certain circumstances, European research may gain further importance within these outlets under consideration, while publication numbers from the US may stagnate or even shrink. In contrast to [8], who examined the development of European IS research based on ECIS, we did not find a leading position of the United Kingdom and Australia. However, we found an increase in the number of publications in Australia and Asia indicating that researchers from Australia and Asia may also experience an upswing in publication numbers. Despite this increasing internationalization of the IS research domain, it is still "disappointing that so few articles emanate from China and India" [33] (p. 19).

When considering journal-specific characteristics with regard to regional development, our study uncovered certain foci. While the EJIS, ISJ, and JIT have a more European focus, the majority of articles of the MISQ, JAIS, JMIS, and ISR are published by North American researchers. The JSIS was more North American at the beginning of the time periods considered here but has become a journal with a higher number of European articles, which is interesting, because the JSIS is one of the four important European IS journals in the AIS Bo8 [46]. Ref. [31] stated in their article that there is a clear connection between the origin of the author and that of the journal. Ref. [13] found that North American researchers prefer more management-science- and decision-science-oriented journals and that European researchers, in contrast, are more interpretive and practice-relevant in their research. One reason for the increase in publications in the JSIS and the overall AIS Bo8 by European researchers in the last YS may be the different publication behavior in Europe as opposed to North America. The German-speaking research community (Germany, Austria, and Switzerland) is characterized by participation in industry projects according to the engineering tradition [5] and has had a long-standing commitment to practice and business relevance [8]. Despite this close link between research and practice, Ph.D. students and junior faculty members (tenure track) are increasingly forced to publish in high-quality journals, especially while participating in doctoral or post-doctoral qualification program, and their guidelines are based on rankings. For example, the continuous increase of publications from German researchers can probably be explained by the A+ and A rating awarded to AIS Bo8 journals and ICIS papers by the Verband der Hochschullehrer für Betriebswirtschaft (VHB-JOURQUAL 3, 2015) [8]. This development, which has emerged in the German-speaking IS community over the last 15 years, leads to increased publication pressure and research performance and suggests that German-speaking Ph.D. students and junior faculty members are similar to North American researchers who are forced to publish in "elite" journals [35]. This development was also observed in a study by [8]. They examined the trends in European IS research, especially in the ECIS, and noted a large increase in publications by German researchers. On the basis of our results, we could not find a similar development for the United Kingdom, thereby contradicting the study by [8] who stated that the relative drop in yearly contributions at the ECIS "may well be because of the Research Assessment Exercise/Research Excellence Framework (RAE/REF) pressures to publish in leading journals as against conference proceedings" [8] (p. 6). We could not confirm such a development because of a decrease in the number of publications from British researchers at the ECIS and the ICIS and in the AIS Bo8 journals. This is partially confirmed by the study by [33], who noted that the number of publications from the United Kingdom in ISJ has dropped by half. The increasing pressure to compete internationally might be one reason for this development. Regions such as South America and Africa are still very rarely represented. This applies to publications in the AIS Bo8 journals as well as at conferences. Visible geographic trends in the fourth YS compared to the first YS include the rise of contributions from Asia in both the ICIS proceedings and the AIS Bo8 journals. An interesting issue here is that there is a significant increase in publications by Asian researchers in journals with a more North American tradition (e.g., MISQ, JMIS, JAIS, and ISR). In journals with a more European tradition (e.g., EJIS, ISJ, JSIS, and JIT), there are significantly fewer publications by Asian researchers and no significant increase in the number of publications.

The longitudinal analysis of papers published by the ICIS and in the AIS Bo8 journals also confirms a number of characteristics in the context of research fields considered both the European and the North American research tradition. For example, in their study of research published by the ECIS, ref. [8] show that IS organizational and strategic as well as systems development themes were the most popular. Another study by [46], in which two European Journals–EJIS and ISJ–were compared showed that in both IS journals, the most popular research topics were related to IS development and IS management. Looking at the results of these two studies, the dynamics of our research domain are visible. If these results are supplemented by the results of our study, it becomes clear that in the further course of European IS research, research fields such as "IS Research Methods & Philosophy", "Human Behavior & Cultural Aspects in IS", and "E-Business & E-Government" have become relevant. E-government was also identified in a study by [49] as one of the relevant topics in the EJIS. The growth of papers on e-business and e-government is perhaps explained by the nature of IT and the growth of the Internet and the ongoing digital transformation [35,50]. The number of publications on these topics is significantly higher than the respective average value. More limited attention is given to specific technologies and the economic sector. This was also noted for the ECIS in a study by [8] and suggests that even during times of the internationalization and dynamization of our research domain, not all characteristics of the European or North American research tradition have changed. As an example of a research field with a constant increase in the number of publications over time, the research field "Social media & Digital Collaboration" can be mentioned. There is a similar increase in publications in this research field both in AIS Bo8 and in the ICIS proceedings. The overall interest in this research field is also reflected in the total number of publications as well as in a distinct increasing trend with peaks in both the AIS Bo8 and the ICIS. The development of the IS research community and its research interests appear to be somewhat fluid and follow certain trends in society (e.g., Use of Twitter and Facebook). On the other hand, it can also be observed that topics that were of great interest in research at the end of the 1990s and the beginning of the 20th century are decreasing in terms of publication numbers at the ICIS and in the AIS Bo8 journals. This development, which represents the dynamics in our research domain, becomes very clear here. While knowledge management was considered a growing research field in the studies by [15,29,50], we observed a decreasing trend here, with other research fields becoming increasingly important.

With this overview, we hope to provide scholars with sufficient information to identify the best outlet for reporting their research with regard to the thematic fit and, as mentioned by [8] (p. 12) "to prompt individual researchers to reflect on the motivation for their research and justifications for their future research plans". A further implication is that knowledgeable researchers avoid unnecessary review cycles that occur when submitting research work to the wrong outlet [46].

6. LIMITATIONS

First, the aim of this study was to provide a more comprehensive overview of the development of research fields. One limitation is that we did not review all conference proceedings and journals in IS. For the database itself, which consisted of AIS Bo8 journals and ICIS proceeding publications, we focused on these outlets with regard to the classification and worldwide acceptance of the AIS. Certainly, there are journals at the top level and practitioner journals such as MISQ Executive [11] or Decision Support Systems and Information with a more Operation Research focus that are not part of this research due to an evident regional focus or varying reputations. For conferences and journals such as the Pacific Asia Conference on Information Systems (PACIS), Scandinavian Conference on Information Systems (SCIS), and Pacific Asia Journal of the Association for Information Systems, the regional influence is obvious. These conferences and journals can be explored in the future to examine the evolution of the regions in our IS community that are not wholly attributable to either the European or the North American IS research tradition. In addition, more (IS-)conferences could be included in the outlet, which have generally quicker revision times than academic journals, to identify and discuss short-term trends, "hot-topics", and fashion waives for specific topics in IS. Furthermore, it would be interesting to look at the development over the next 15 years. However, other papers show that the age of the sample does not necessarily affect scientific impact. For example, ref. [51] is still heavily cited today, even though their analysis of scientific practice examines the years 1997 to 1999. By including all the AIS Bo8 journals as recommended by [3], we have covered a wide range of top IS research that is recognized in the global IS community.

Regarding database preparation, the varying data provisions by the different publishers of the AIS Bo8 journals and the ICIS proceedings resulted in several challenges. The automatic identification of the reference managing software was sometimes incorrect due to different metadata pro-visions, resulting in extensive manual postprocessing. Each publisher uses a different template and varying corresponding information. In outlets, where a Digital Object Identifier (DOI) was available (EJIS, ISR, JMIS and partly ISJ, JIT, and JSIS), precise results were obtained. In cases with non-existent DOIs, we had to manually enter the metadata of each article because the journal sources are fragmented and the article layouts change over time, even if they are from the same source. Due to this extensive procedure, we cannot exclude some outliers despite a double check. Further limitations resulted from automatic country detection. Our developed algorithm was used to identify the origin of articles by using the country suffix of e-mail addresses. Therefore, we limited the investigation only to the corresponding author. However, this procedure is common, as noted in the database preparation section. In future studies, this method could be extended by an author position method. In cases where a public e-mail provider was used or no corresponding e-mail address was provided (JMIS), we had to manually determine the country of origin from the postal address. Due to different metadata and layout structures of the outlets, algorithms identifying the country, country code or zip code achieve unusable results in most instances. A further limitation on a related issue is that it was not possible to detect 57 of 6692 articles with regard to the author's origin, although this represented less than 1% of the overall database.

7. CONCLUSIONS

In the sense of cumulative research, we have expanded existing research on the understanding of the profile of IS research. This is useful because continual introspection helps any research domain as it thrives and matures [50]. Although recent studies have mentioned that there are differences in terms of the development of the IS research domain, academic research has not properly considered the role of geographical aspects and topic emergence and has not taken into account various outlets, particularly the differences between publications in conference proceedings and journals. To shed light on this issue, we aimed to answer the following research questions: What is the regional distribution of publications in the AIS Bo8 and the ICIS? How has publication behavior changed by region, and what are the greatest changes? Finally, where-in terms of outlet and region-do IS research topics and trends emerge, and how have these changed over time? Our study offers contributions valuable for the IS community and its goal of developing an impact on research and society. First, in this longitudinal study, we investigated publications of top IS research outlets (all AIS Bo8 journals and the ICIS proceedings) in terms of geographical and periodical evolution from 2000 to 2015. With the help of a semi-automated database, we were able to handle a large number of articles (6692). Through the use of an algorithm to identify geographical emergence and a LSI tool, we established the foundation for our investigation. Based on the results of our analysis of 6692 papers, we were able to identify differences in terms of the development of research topics in general and, particular, differences in the geographical context as well as the choice of outlet. This effort provides in-depth insights into the overall landscape of IS publications and the emerging body of IS-specific knowledge. Prospective authors also benefit from our work because it provides a good overview of our relatively young research domain and its growth and development. With this overview, we hope to provide scholars with sufficient information to identify the best outlet for reporting their research with regard to the thematic fit and, as mentioned by [8] (p. 12) "to prompt individual researchers to reflect on the motivation for their research and justifications for their future research plans". A further implication is that knowledgeable researchers avoid unnecessary review cycles that occur when submitting research work to the wrong outlet [46]. Overall, this study shapes the future understanding and development of the IS research domain.

Author Contributions

Conceptualization, N.G., O.W. and J.P.; methodology, N.G. and J.P.; validation, N.G., O.W. and J.P.; formal analysis, J.P., O.W. and N.G.; investigation, N.G., O.W. and J.P.; data curation, O.W. and J.P.; writing—original draft preparation, N.G., O.W. and J.P.; writing—review and editing, N.G., O.W., J.P. and M.H.B.; visualization, N.G., O.W. and J.P. All authors have read and agreed to the published version of the manuscript.

Appendix A. IS Research Fields Development Trends—Patterns in Terms of Outlet (Conference and Journal)

As mentioned in Section 4.3 four different trends in theme development revealed from our analysis. These differ in terms of development over time in relation to the number of publications on specific topics in the Bo8 journals and the publications in the ICIS proceedings. These trends can be categorized as follows: (1) similarly increasing, (2) similarly decreasing, (3) similarly consistent, and (4) divergent (see Figure A1, Figure A2, Figure A3, Figure A4, Figure A5, Figure A6, Figure A7, Figure A8, Figure A9 and Figure A10).

Trend—Similarly Increasing

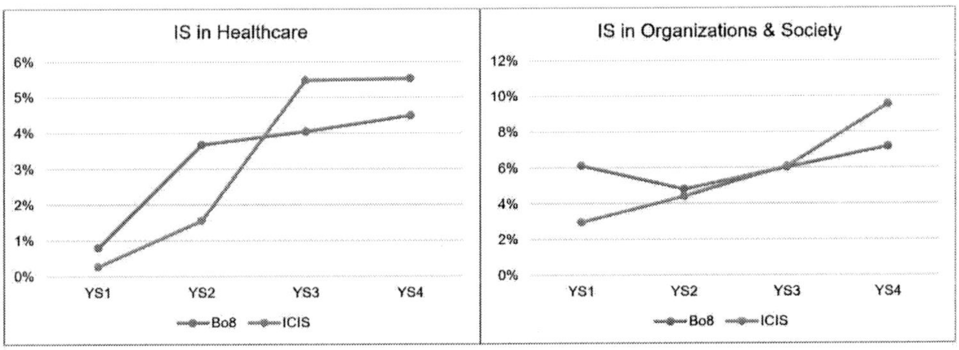

Figure A1.: Development of research fields "IS in Healthcare" and "IS in Organizations & Society" in the Bo8 and the ICIS Proceedings.

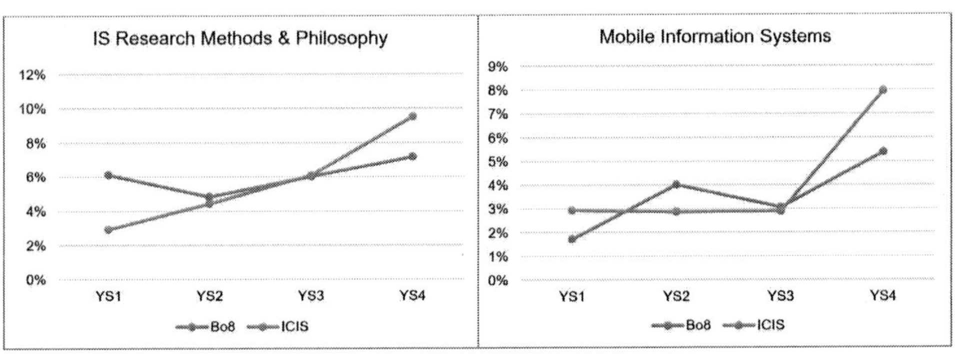

Figure A2.: Development of research fields "IS Research Methods & Philosophy" and "Mobile Information Systems" in the Bo8 and the ICIS Proceedings.

Trend—Similarly Decreasing

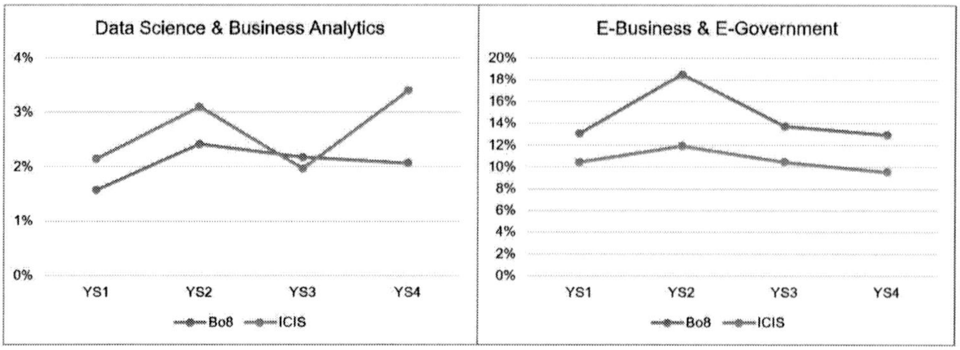

Figure A3.: *Development of research fields "Contribution of Applied Science" and "Human Behavior & Cultural Aspects in IS" in the Bo8 and the ICIS Proceedings.*

Trend—Similarly Consistent

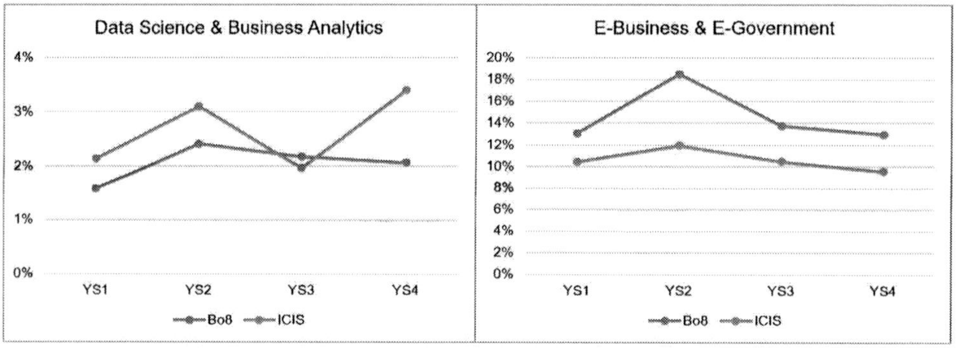

Figure A4.: *Development of research fields "Data Science & Business Analytics" and "E-Business & E-Government" in the Bo8 and the ICIS Proceedings.*

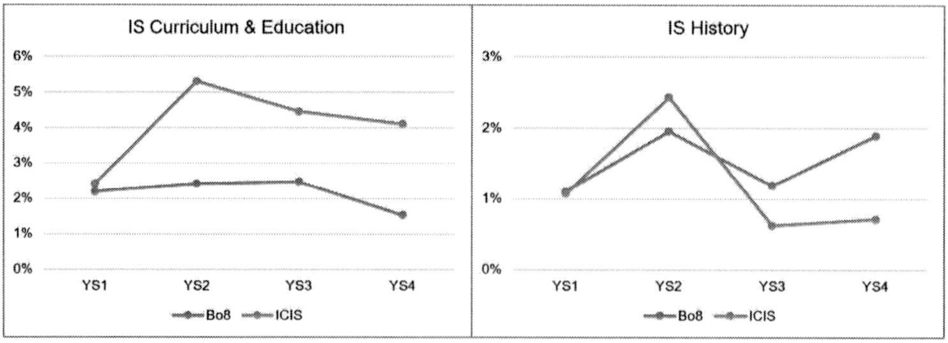

Figure A5.: *Development of research fields "IS Curriculum & Education" and "IS History" in the Bo8 and the ICIS Proceedings.*

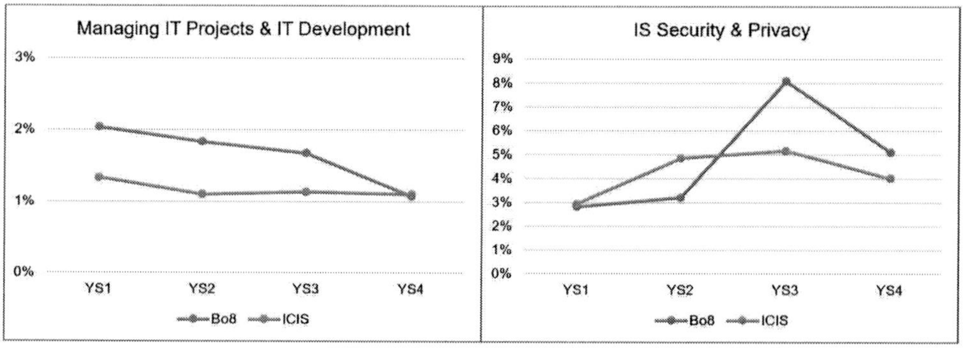

Figure A6.: *Development of research fields "Managing IT Projects & IT Development" and "IS Security & Privacy" in the Bo8 and the ICIS Proceedings.*

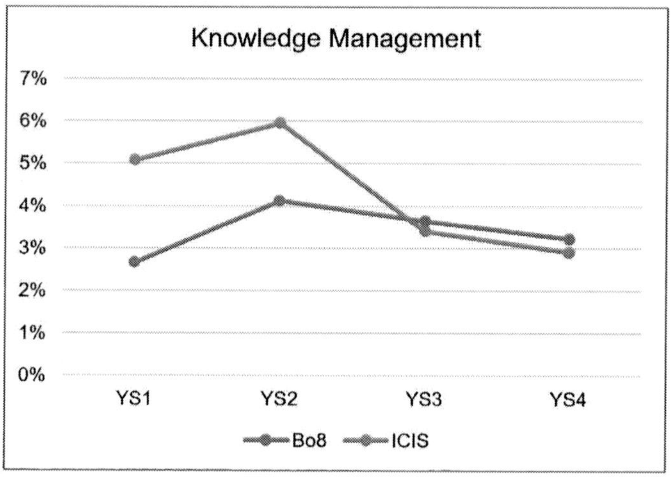

Figure A7.: *Development of the research field "Knowledge Management" in the Bo8 and the ICIS Proceedings.*

Trend—Divergent

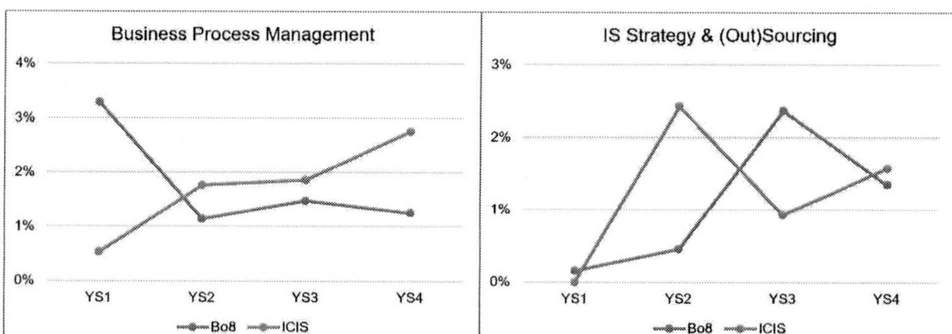

Figure A8.: *Development of research fields "Business Process Management" and "IS Strategy & (Out)Sourcing" in the Bo8 and the ICIS Proceedings.*

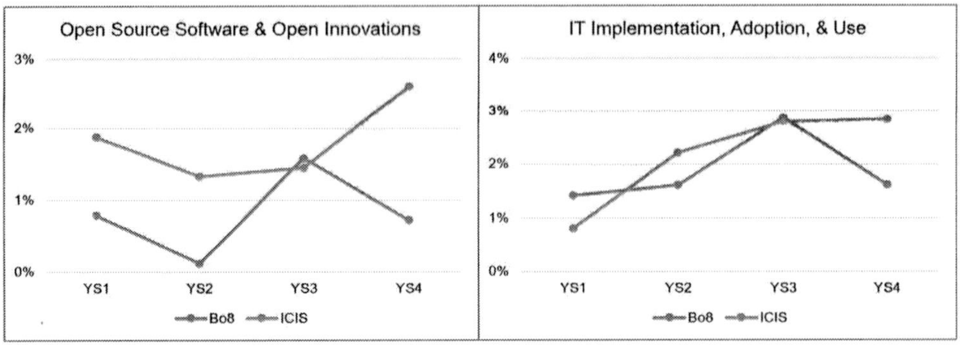

Figure A9.: Development of research fields "Open Source Software" and "IT Implementation, Adoption, & Use" in the Bo8 and the ICIS Proceedings.

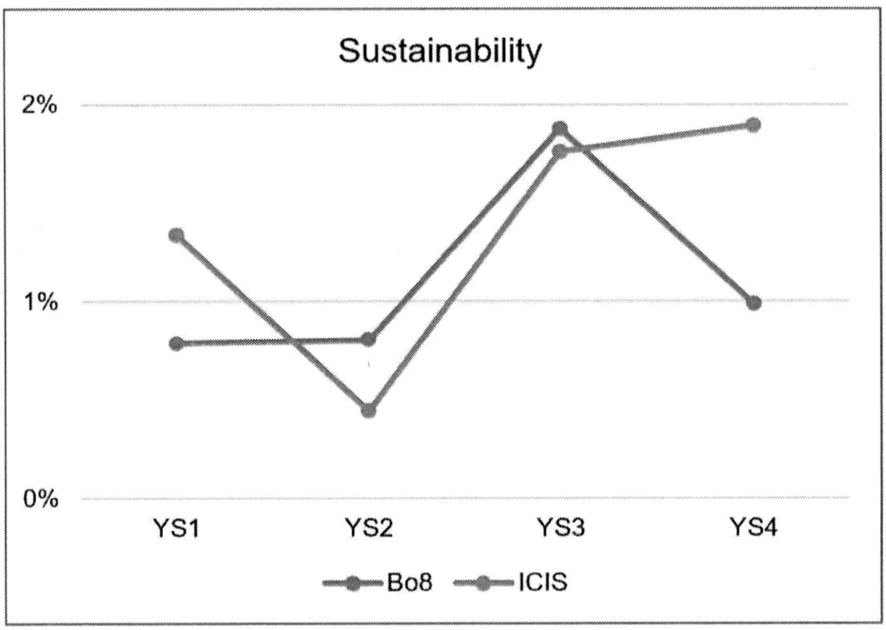

Figure A10.: Development of the research field "Sustainability" in the Bo8 and the ICIS Proceedings.

Appendix B. Number of Publications on Individual Topics in the Bo8 Journals

As additional information intended to support the discussion and to clarify the distribution accordingly, in this part of the appendix we have separately depicted the respective number of publications in the individual journals in graphics for each research field. Only those topics were considered where the total number of publications in the Bo8 exceeds 110 publications.

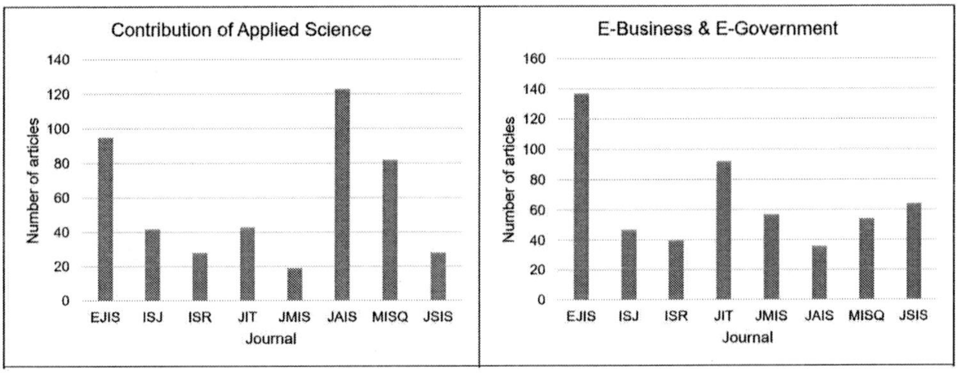

Figure A11.: *Number of publications in research fields "Contribution of Applied Science" and "E-Business & E-Government" in the respective Bo8 journals.*

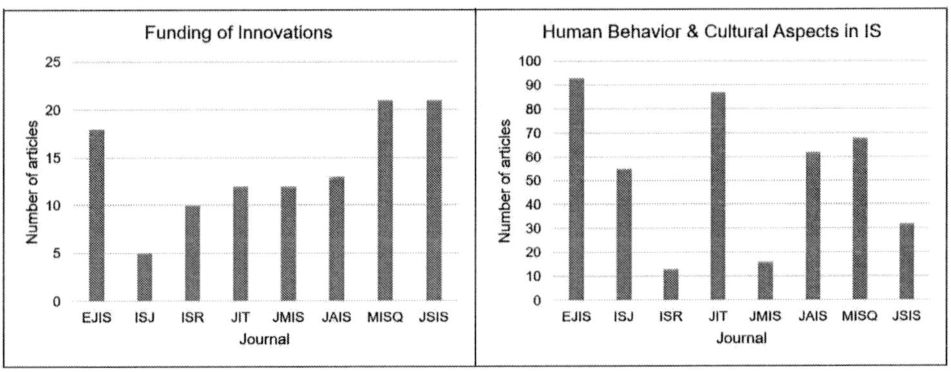

Figure A12.: *Number of publications in research fields "Funding of Innovations" and "Human Behavior & Cultural Aspects in IS" in the respective Bo8 journals.*

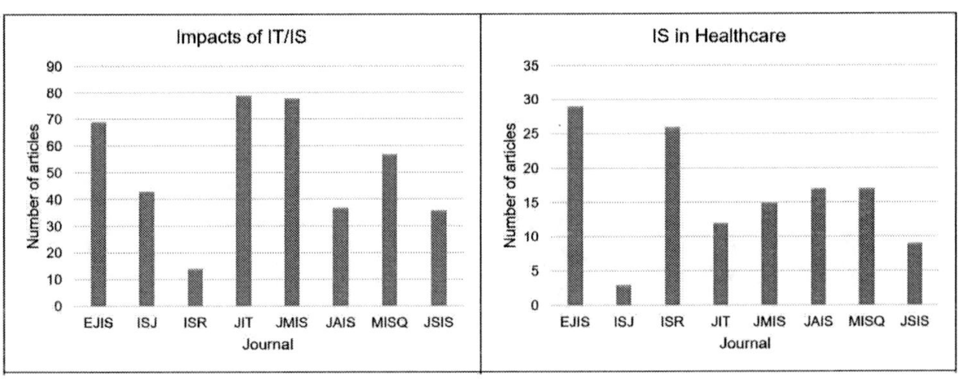

Figure A13.: *Number of publications in research fields "Impact of IT/IS" and "IS in Healthcare" in the respective Bo8 journals.*

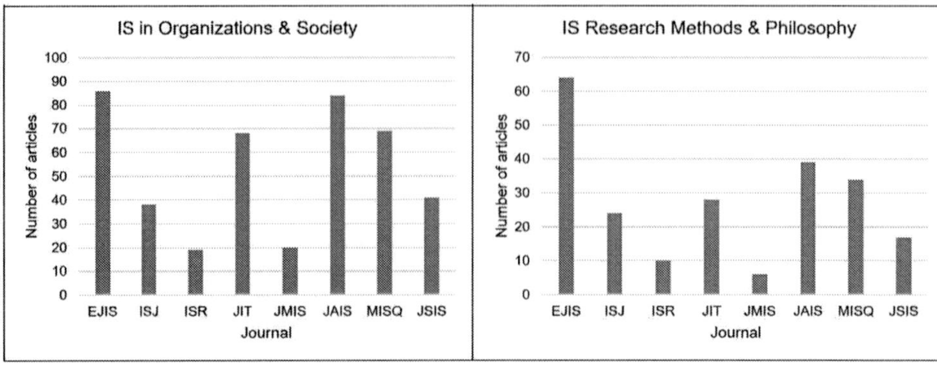

Figure A14.: *Number of publications in research fields "IS in Organizations & Society" and "IS Research Methods & Philosophy" in the respective Bo8 journals.*

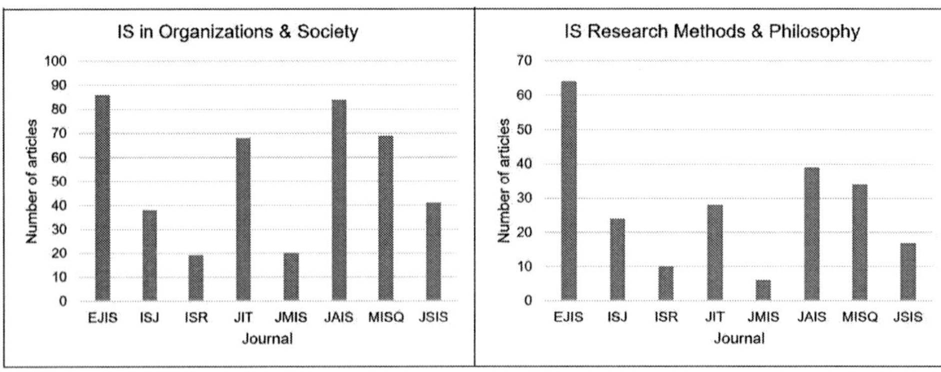

Figure A15.: *Number of publications in research fields "IS Security & Privacy" and "Knowledge Management" in the respective Bo8 journals.*

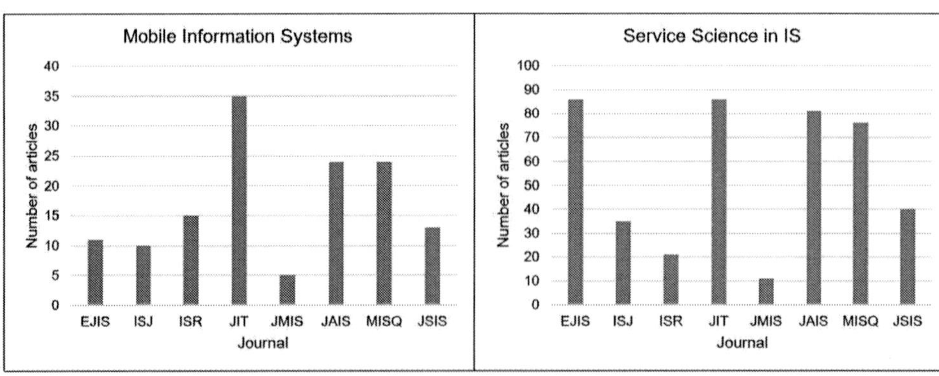

Figure A16.: *Number of publications in research fields "Mobile Information Systems" and "Service Science in IS" in the respective Bo8 journals.*

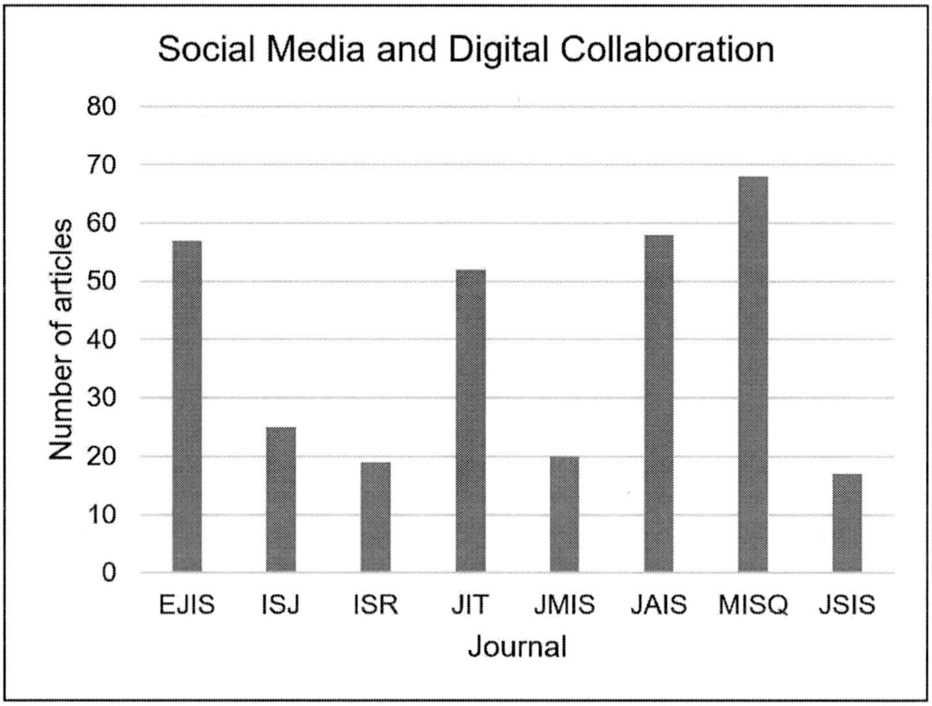

Figure A17.: *Number of publications in the research field "Social Media & Digital Collaboration" in the respective Bo8 journals.*

REFERENCES

1. AIS. About IS History. 2020.
2. Bjørn-Andersen, N.; Clemmensen, T. The Shaping of the Scandinavian Socio-Technical IS Research Tradition. Confession of an accomplice. Scand. J. Inf. Syst. 2017, 1, 4.
3. Goyal, S.; Ahuja, M.; Guan, J. Information Systems Research themes: A seventeen-year data-driven temporal analysis. Commun. Assoc. Inf. Syst. 2018, 43, 404–431.
4. Webster, J.; Watson, R.T. Analyzing the past to prepare for the future: Writing a literature review. MIS Q. 2002, 26, xiii–xxiii.
5. Buhl, H.U.; Fridgen, G.; König, W.; Röglinger, M.; Wagner, C. Where's the competitive advantage in strategic Information Systems Research? Making the case for boundary-spanning research based on the German business and information systems engineering tradition. J. Strateg. Inf. Syst. 2012, 21, 172–178.
6. Galliers, R.D.; Whitley, E.A. Vive les differences? Developing a profile of European Information Systems Research as a basis for international comparisons. Eur. J. Inf. Syst. 2007, 16, 20–35.

7. Hassan, N.R.; Mathiassen, L. Distilling a body of knowledge for Information Systems development. Inf. Syst. Res. 2018, 28, 175–226.
8. Stein, M.-K.; Galliers, R.D.; Whitley, E.A. Twenty years of the European information systems academy at ECIS: Emergent trends and research topics. Eur. J. Inf. Syst. 2016, 25, 1–15.
9. AIS. Advanced Search. 2020.
10. Straub, D. The value of scientometric studies: An introduction to a debate on IS as a reference discipline. J. Assoc. Inf. Syst. 2006, 7, 241–245.
11. Palvia, P.; Kakhki, M.D.; Ghoshal, T.; Uppala, V.; Wang, W. Methodological and topic trends in Information Systems research: A meta-analysis of IS journals. Commun. Assoc. Inf. Syst. 2015, 37, 630–650.
12. Keen, P.G.W. MIS research: Reference disciplines and a cumulative tradition. In Proceedings of the International Conference on Information Systems, Philadelphia, PA, USA, 8–10 December 1980.
13. Lowry, P.; Romans, D.; Curtis, A. Global journal prestige and supporting disciplines: A scientometric study of Information Systems journals. J. Assoc. Inf. Syst. 2004, 5, 29–77.
14. Straub, D.; Anderson, C. Authorship from 2000 through 2009. MIS Q. 2010, 34, iii–vi.
15. Neufeld, D.; Fang, Y.; Huff, S. The IS identity crisis. Commun. Assoc. Inf. Syst. 2007, 19, 447–464.
16. Hirschheim, R.; Klein, H.K. A glorious and not-so-short history of the Information Systems field. J. Assoc. Inf. Syst. 2012, 13, 188–235.
17. Sidorova, A.; Evangelopoulos, N.; Valacich, J.S.; Ramakrishan, T. Uncovering the intellectual core of the Information Systems discipline. MIS Q. 2008, 32, 467–482.
18. Everard, A.; Pierre, K.S.; Heck, J.L. Contributors to the high-impact IS journals (1977–2014): An aid for setting research standards. Commun. Assoc. Inf. Syst. 2017, 40, 53–81.
19. Fleischmann, M.; Miglena, A.; Benlian, A.; Hess, T. Cognitive biases in Information Systems research: A scientometric analysis. In Proceedings of the European Conference on Information Systems, Tel Aviv, Israel, 9–11 June 2014.
20. Wagner, G.; Prester, J.; Schryen, G. Exploring the scientific impact of Information Systems Design Science Research: A scientometric study. In Proceedings of the International Conference on Information Systems, Seoul, Republic of Korea, 10–13 December 2017.
21. Schryen, G.; Wagner, G.; Benlian, A. Theory of knowledge for literature reviews: An epistemological model, taxonomy and empirical analysis of IS literature. In Proceedings of the International Conference on Information Systems, Fort Worth, TX, USA, 13–16 December 2015.
22. Vessey, I.; Ramesh, V.; Glass, R. Research in Information Systems: An empirical study of diversity in the discipline and its journals. J. Manag. Inf. Syst. 2002, 19, 129–174.
23. Choi, J.; Yi, S.; Lee, K.C. Analysis of keyword networks in MIS research and implications for predicting knowledge evolution. Inf. Manag. 2011, 48, 371–381.
24. Hassan, N.R. Value of IS research: Is there a crisis? Commun. Assoc. Inf. Syst. 2014, 34, 801–816.

25. Chen, W.; Hirschheim, R. A paradigmatic and methodological examination of Information Systems Research from 1991 to 2001. Inf. Syst. J. 2004, 14, 197–235.
26. Loebbecke, C.; Leidner, D. The contribution of top IS publications to subsequent research: A citation analysis. Commun. Assoc. Inf. Syst. 2012, 30, 423–438.
27. Te'eni, D. Journals and conferences in discourse. Eur. J. Inf. Syst. 2013, 22, 589–591.
28. Te'eni, D.; Rowe, F.; Ågerfalk, P.J.; Lee, J.S. Publishing and getting published in EJIS: Marshaling contributions for a diversity of genres. Eur. J. Inf. Syst. 2015, 24, 559–568.
29. Lowry, P.B.; Karuga, G.G.; Richardson, V.J. Assessing leading institutions, faculty, and articles in premier Information Systems research journals. Commun. Assoc. Inf. Syst. 2007, 20, 142–203.
30. Suomi, R. On the nationality balance of authors and references in selected MIS journals. Inf. Manag. 1993, 24, 339–347.
31. Galliers, R.D.; Meadows, M. A discipline divided: Globalization and parochialism in Information Systems Research. Commun. Assoc. Inf. Syst. 2003, 11, 108–117.
32. Pouloudi, N.; Poulymenakou, A.; Pramatari, K. A profile of information systems research in the Mediterranean region. Eur. J. Inf. Syst. 2012, 21, 345–357.
33. Avison, D.; Dwivedi, Y.K.; Fitzgerald, G.; Powell, P. The beginnings of a new era: Time to reflect on 17 years of the ISJ. Inf. Syst. J. 2008, 18, 5–21.
34. Avison, D.; Fitzgerald, G. Reflections and opinions on 25 years with the ISJ. Inf. Syst. J. 2012, 22, 179–193.
35. Whitley, E.A.; Galliers, R.D. An alternative perspective on citation classics: Evidence from the first 10 years of the European Conference on Information Systems. Inf. Manag. 2007, 44, 441–455.
36. Barki, H.; Rivard, S.; Talbot, J. A keyword classification scheme for IS research literature: An update. MIS Q. 1993, 17, 209–226.
37. Chen, J.; Konstan, J.A. Conference paper selectivity and impact. Commun. ACM 2010, 53, 79–83.
38. Koukal, A.; Gleue, C.; Breitner, M.H. Enhancing literature review methods—Evaluation of Literature Search Approach based on Latent Semantic Indexing. In Proceedings of the International Conference on Information Systems, Auckland, New Zealand, 14–17 December 2014.
39. Bandara, W.; Furtmueller, E.; Gorbacheva, E.; Miskon, S.; Beekhuyzen, J. Achieving rigor in literature reviews: Insights from qualitative data analysis and tool-support. Commun. Assoc. Inf. Syst. 2015, 37, 154–204.
40. Tian, M. Turning a technology into many solutions: A case study of embedding an information system. J. Bus. Res. 2019, 101, 23–39.
41. Dumais, S.T. Improving the retrieval of information from external sources. Behav. Res. Methods Instrum. Comput. 1991, 23, 229–236.
42. Foltz, P. Using Latent Semantic Indexing for information filtering. In Proceedings of the ACM SIGOIS and IEEE CS TC-OA Conference on Office Information Systems, Cambridge, MA, USA, 25–27 April 1990.

43. Salton, G.; Wong, A.; Yang, C.-S. A vector space model for automatic indexing. Commun. Assoc. Inf. Syst. 1975, 18, 613–620.
44. Deerwester, S.; Dumais, S.T.; Furnas, G.W.; Landauer, T.K.; Harshman, R. Indexing by Latent Semantic Analysis. J. Am. Soc. Inf. Sci. 1990, 41, 391–407.
45. Merali, Y.; Papadopoulos, T.; Nadkarni, T. Information systems strategy: Past, present, future? J. Strateg. Inf. Syst. 2012, 21, 125–153.
46. Dwivedi, Y.K.; Kuljis, J. Profile of IS research published in the European Journal of Information Systems. Eur. J. Inf. Syst. 2008, 17, 678–693.
47. Walstrom, K.A.; Leonard, L. Citation classics from the information systems literature. Inf. Manag. 2000, 38, 59–72.
48. Lowry, P.B.; Moody, G.D.; Gaskin, J. Evaluating journal quality and the Association for Information Systems (AIS) Senior Scholars' Journal Basket via bibliometric measures: Do expert journal assessments add value? MIS Q. 2013, 37, 993–1012.
49. Mustafee, N. Evolution of IS research based on literature published in two leading is journals—EJIS and MISQ. In Proceedings of the European Conference on Information Systems, Helsinki, Finland, 9–11 June 2011.
50. Palvia, P. A profile of Information Systems research published in Information & Management. Inf. Manag. 2007, 44, 1–11.
51. Boudreau, M.C.; Gefen, D.; Straub, D.W. Validation in information systems research: A state-of-the-art assessment. MIS Q. 2001, 25, 1–16.

8

Does an Information System Security Notice Format Influence Users' Compliance Willingness from the Perspective of the Framing Effect?

Linhui Sun [1], **Xun Li** [1], **Jie Gao** [2], **and Fangming Cheng** [3]

[1]*School of Management, Xi'an University of Science and Technology, Xi'an 710054, China*

[2]*School of Management, Xi'an Jiao Tong University, Xi'an 710049, China*

[3]*School of Safety Science and Engineering, Xi'an University of Science and Technology, Xi'an 710054, China*

ABSTRACT

Information security issues have triggered both academic and practical circles to think about operation management and the sustainable development of information systems. Based on the theory of framing effect, this study constructs a theoretical model of the presentation framework of security notice information on users' compliance willingness and empirically tests the proposed research hypotheses using a combination of behavioral experiments and questionnaires to analyze the mechanism of the information presentation framework on compliance willingness. The results show that (1) the information presentation framework has a significant effect on users' decision to comply, but it varies according to specific frameworks. While the attribute and risk frameworks have a significant effect on users' decision to comply, the goal framework does not have a significant effect on users' decision to comply. (2) The security notice situation moderates the relationship between the security notice information presentation frame and users' compliance willingness, but this varies according to the specific situation of the specific framework. The security notice situation moderates the relationship between the attribute framework, the risk framework, and users' compliance willingness but not the relationship between the goal framework and users' compliance willingness. (3) Information security cognition has a moderating effect on the relationship between the security notice presentation framework and users' compliance willingness, but it varies by the specific frameworks. Information security cognition moderates the relationship between attribute frames, risk frames, and users' compliance willingness but not the relationship between goal frames and users' compliance willingness.

Keywords: *framing effect; security notice; compliance willingness; notice format; information system*

1. INTRODUCTION

Information systems are frequently used by a variety of businesses and organizations to support their own operational management, to conduct enterprise resource planning, and to view information systems as playing a crucial part in the management of production activities. Systems for handling the collection, processing, transfer, storing, and utilization of information are known as information systems. Today, information systems are a crucial and advantageous tool for organizational management and enterprise resource management. Indeed, various information systems have merged with communication and computer technologies, and the term "information system" now most often refers to the system that enables human and computer coexistence.

System equipment will continuously provide users with a variety of feedback prompts in a variety of methods during the functioning of the information system. When a user performs a job within the system, the system responds to their actions by sending feedback prompts. These prompts include requests for personal information, security notices regarding the system's operational state, etc. Of these, security notices are one of the most common categories of feedback prompts.

The purpose of security notices is to inform users of the implications of their current actions, including the preservation of system identification numbers (IDs) or passwords, the backup of key customer data, and the encryption of classified files. Generally speaking, compliance and confirmation are the decision content required from users in the face of these security notices, which include users' determination of whether some user privileges are available to the system, whether users' current operations are in line with their actual intentions, whether they will choose to comply with the system specifications required by the security notices, and whether they will choose to share key information. Security notices often play a guiding role in users' information security behaviors and have been shown to have an impact on the effective and stable operation of information systems [1].

In the case of information systems, security notices can provide good information feedback to users by making the user more aware of the system's operations, reducing waiting anxiety, improving users' experience, and increasing users' compliance willingness. By creating psychological expectations, security notices help users form compliance expectations by letting them know whether their operations have been executed, if they have been undone, what impact they will have after execution, where the execution results could be checked, and how to resolve current system problems, all of which will increase users' compliance willingness with the next system operation. Meanwhile, the user's compliance willingness influence information security, personal property protection, and privacy assurances if they are willing to comply with the system requirements. Clearly, security notices and compliance willingness are interrelated, and the importance of security notices and compliance willingness for information systems is self-evident.

It has been demonstrated that the notice format (textual description) of information system security notices has an impact on individuals' behavioral willingness [2]. In other words, different methods of presenting information would affect people's behavior choices. However, the influence of information descriptions on users' behavioral choices in real life has often been neglected, leading to the development of hidden issues relating to information security behavior and the development of security issues. Considering this, it is highly useful to investigate the impact of notice formats on compliance willingness of users regarding security notices, in order to enhance users' compliance willingness with information system security notices, as well as to improve users' attitudes toward security notices. For reference, the security notice interface of the information system used in the actual situation in the current study is shown in Figure 1.

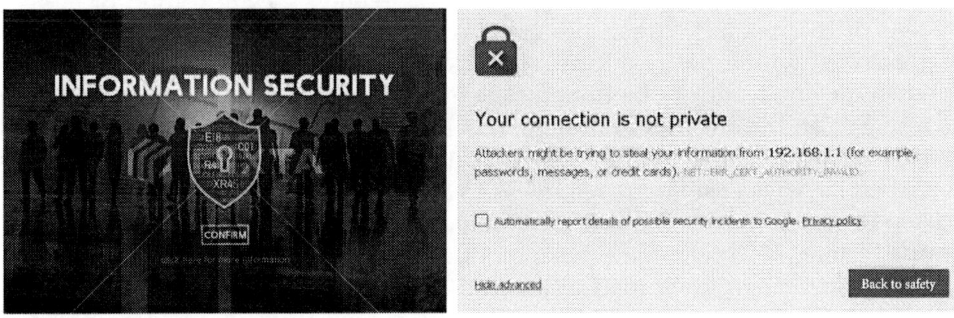

***Figure 1.:** Security Notice Interface.*

2. LITERATURE REVIEW

The framing effect refers to the possibility that alternative formulations of the same issue may influence people's choices [3]. Its existence was discovered by Tversky and Kahneman in their "Asian Disease Problems" study. Furthermore, after an interdisciplinary meta-analysis, Levin et al. (1998) found that there are three distinct categories into which framing effects can be subdivided: risk framing effects, attribute framing effects, and goal framing effects. Each of these categories has a different information description focus [4].

Numerous studies have shown that the framing effect has two division dimensions: the external framing effect and the internal framing effect. The internal framing effect is also known as the self-framing effect, as used by Levin (1998) and Wang (2004) [4,5]. Additionally, Wang (1996) also proved the existence of the two-way and one-way framing effects as further dimensional divisions [6].

The framing effect phenomenon has attracted the attention of numerous scholars, and it continues to be discussed and explored in a variety of different research fields, including the real estate market [7], purchase intention [8], donor decision [9], perceived credibility [10], public attitude [11], and more. A framing effect has also been found in the area of information security [12]. As the information security of a system is often reflected in the specific results brought by the user after the operation or the online security behavior of the user, a framing effect may also exist in the compliance decisions in response to security notices. It is worth noting that after clarifying the classification of the framing effect, subsequent scholars have jointly or separately discussed its influence or application in specific scenes or situations based on either three types or a single type in different research fields based on this classification.

2.1. Research on the Attribute Framing Effect

The attribute framing effect affects evaluations about the characteristics of an object or event, and a positive attribute framing effect occurs when a key characteristic of a thing or event is placed in a positive light. In general, people prefer things described with positive framing in the attribute framing effect. For instance, when Levin and Gaeth (1998) classified beef as having a composition of either 75% lean or 25% fat, individuals preferred beef with a 75% lean composition (i.e., beef described with a positive format) [4]. Negative attribute framing effects occur when the key features of a thing or event are placed under negative framing. The research on the attribute framing effect is concentrated primarily in the field of marketing. According to the research by Wen et al. (2021), a negative framing format can increase customers' readiness to acquire and spend while making the decision to purchase personalized vacation packages when compared to a positive framing format [13]. Meanwhile, customers are more likely to pay a higher stated price when prices are presented in a positive format, according to Dixit (2014), than when prices are presented in an unframed or a negative framing format [14].

In the debate of attribute framing effect and individual willingness, Gasteiger (2020) discovered that framing strongly influenced participants' desire to convert to biosimilar drugs, with positive framing being more likely to do so than negative framing [15]. It can be seen that there is a correlation between the attribute framing effect and individual willingness. In view of this, in the process of designing information systems, system developers should pay attention to the security notices of different notice formats so that they might develop and utilize security notices with particular attribute frameworks to better guide the users' compliance decisions.

2.2. Research on the Goal Framing Effect

The goal framing effect refers to the ability to change the decision-making behavior of individuals by affecting the persuasiveness of communicated information. When persuasive messages focus on the positive consequences of an action, or when they focus on negative consequences, the messages will have a different level of attractiveness, resulting in the goal framing effect. The goal framing effect can be divided into a framework that may achieve gains (i.e., gain framework) and a framework that may face losses (i.e., loss framework). Meyerowits and Chaiken's (1987) Breast Self-Examination study, which encouraged women to voluntarily submit to breast examinations, is one particularly known example of goal framing effect research [16]. Although research on the goal framing effect has also been concentrated in the field of marketing, it has also been discussed in other fields. For instance, Yang (2020) discovered that media persuasion influenced residents' green buying behavior by simultaneously activating a three-dimensional goal framework [17]. Wang (2022) observed that individuals with high (vs. poor) self-esteem had increased destination visit intent in response to gain-framework (vs. loss-framework) statements [18].

Tanford (2019) integrated framing and anchoring effects to evaluate the relationship between price anchoring, framing, and metric compatibility on one's willingness to pay for holiday accommodations when examining the goal framing impact on individual willingness [19]. When presented with reading materials that focused on the advantages for everyone in society rather than only those of the individual, Ceylan (2021) discovered that citizens considered the information more persuasive and were more motivated to help others [20]. DeGolia (2019) discovered that in order to acquire political and public support for environmental management, communicating within a loss framework was more effective than communicating within a gain framework [21]. Meanwhile, participants' opinions regarding vaccination were more favorable when the topic was framed in a positive format, according to a study by Altay (2020) [22]. Furthermore, punitive framing was shown to diminish information sharing willingness and affective commitment while enhancing effort-related commitment, according to the findings of Fehrenbacher (2019) [23].

In view of this, to return to the process of information systems, security notices encountered by users may have different goal frameworks, and users may also have different information security cognition levels. It is therefore worthwhile to draw on existing research paradigms to analyze and test the combination of the above variables in the field of information security to determine what influence mechanisms exist between the users' information security cognition level and their compliance willingness under the goal framework and whether similar differences in influence exist in other types of notice formats.

2.3. Research on the Risk Framing Effect

The risk framing effect refers to the framing effect first proposed by Tversky and Kahneman in 1979. The study of risk framing effects has a long history, and is connected to numerous research fields. The risk framing effect shows how the value function affects risk preferences, and suggests that different risk preferences emerge according to whether the outcome of a risky action is framed positively or negatively, as was demonstrated in the "Asian disease problem" study, which showed that a preference for either benefit or loss avoidance depends on how the question is framed and phrased. More specifically, when presented information with a beneficial framework, people tend to be risk-averse, and when presented information with a loss framework, they tend to be risk-seeking.

Channa (2021) discovered that people with higher levels of risk aversion were marginally more prepared to pay for risk-reducing devices when making risk-based decisions [24]. Li et al. (2020) found that farmers' perceived risk had a substantial negative effect on agricultural green production intentions [25]. Through research into event-related potential, Xu et al. (2020) discovered that, while making risky decisions in the face of uncertainty, gain framing improved behavioral and brain sensitivity to decision failure [26]. In addition, some scholars have discussed the framing effect of risk decision-making within the fields of medicine [27], economics [28], sports science [29], and college students' income control [30,31] and have verified the impact of the risk framing effect on behavioral decision-making in a wide variety of fields.

In the situation of an information system, when a security notice is delivered in a "gain" or a "loss" framework, users are informed of what they stand to gain or lose by obeying the security notice. The aforementioned studies into the impact of framing effects in various domains and the question of whether types of notification formats increase compliance willingness serve as theoretical benchmarks for research on information system security notices.

2.4. Research on Information Security Cognition

Research on information security cognition in recent years has primarily analyzed and discussed from the aspect of information security cognition. By considering the roles of the design and implementation of information security cognition, for instance, Ki-Aries (2017) developed a method for identifying security-related human elements [32]. Meanwhile, Hadlington (2019) demonstrated that job control position has a significant predictive role in calculating the overall information security cognition score [33]. Lh (2020) discovered that moral disengagement tendencies, particularly in the distribution of duty, play a significant influence in information security cognition [34]. Through case studies and questionnaires, Jaeger (2020) found that situational information security cognition improves the perception of risk and one's sense of reaction efficacy, which thereby increases actual behavioral response to phishing assaults [35]. To improve the level of information security cognition among employees in both private and public sector firms, Kk (2021) conducted a thorough assessment of the literature on the topic of information security cognition and recommended a set of advanced information security cognition methods and criteria [36]. Kvds (2021) investigated the role of information security cognition on some users' intentions to review their Facebook privacy settings, or, more specifically, how the Big Five personality qualities interacted with the desire to examine these settings, as mediated by information security cognition [37]. Overall, the introduction of the notion of information security cognition has allowed this study to delve deeper into the influential mechanisms and underlying mechanisms that influence users' willingness to make compliance decisions in the face of security notices.

2.5. Individuals Compliance Willingness Related Research

Social, organizational and individual elements have been shown to make up the three main contributing factors of compliance willingness [38]. Gurses (2018) examined the primary causes of non-compliance in the nursing sector and came to the conclusion that following evidence-based recommendations is essential for providing safe nursing care [39]. Enwereuzor (2020) investigated the relationship between moral leadership and safety compliance, finding that trust in the leader was a moderating component [40]. Meanwhile, Kilbane (2020) examined how staff members felt about using surgical safety checklists in small animal operating rooms, shedding light on the challenges to their utilization [41]. The existing studies are not comprehensive enough to discuss the analysis of information system users' compliance willingness with security notices and their influencing mechanisms.

2.6. Theoretical Analysis Framework

In summary, regardless of the information presentation framework (i.e., risk framework, attribute framework, or goal framework), each information presentation framework can be divided into two categories of positive and negative frameworks. Furthermore, in the situation of security notices, the content of security notices presented by these positive and negative frameworks are both positive and negative aspects of the same information description. Based on the implications of these three frame effects, framing effect theory was deemed to be a suitable theoretical paradigm to utilize to explore information descriptions, making this a reasonable and practical basis on which to build our theoretical model and experimental protocol design for the current study. Therefore, the information presentation framework based on the framing effect theory was used as the independent variable for the conceptual model of this study.

Information processing theory identifies two different systems and modes by which individuals can make decisions: intuitive inspiration and rational analysis. Specifically, when users make compliance decisions under different conditions and in the face of security notices in various situations, they may be influenced by their own information security cognitive level–that is, when a user has a high information security cognitive level, they will more often adopt the rational analysis mode when facing security notices, and make compliance decisions only after fully weighing the pros and cons. In contrast, when a user has a low information security cognitive level, they will more often adopt the intuitive inspiration mode when facing security notices and make compliance decisions based on their intuitive experience, rather than thinking rationally. One's degree of cognition, or users' understanding and attention to information systems and security notices, will to some degree influence their desire to comply. The introduction of the idea of information security cognition facilitates the investigation of the influence mechanism and inner mechanism of users' readiness to make compliance decisions in the face of security notices.

In information security management, the willingness of users of information systems to comply with security notices may be influenced by the security notice situation. The security notice situation can be understood as a security notice or description with different information content, which appears within the operating environment of an information system, depending on the immediate operating status of the system. In reality, security notices are immediate, multiple, and flexible, and they are important feedback prompts that users are often exposed to when using information systems. In the situation of information system security notices, the content of a security notice is specialized and complex. The decision to comply to a security notice is closely related to the situation of the security notice. In the situation of a security notice that may involve the users' property security, users may have a strong compliance willingness regardless of the nature of the framework in which the system presents the information because they attach special importance to their property security; however, in the situation of security notices that do not involve property security, the users' compliance willingness is more likely to be influenced by the different frameworks in which the information is presented. Therefore, differences in users' compliance willingness in various security notice situations merit further investigation. As such, the concept of the security notice situation was used as a moderating variable in the conceptual model of this study.

Regarding users' compliance willingness, generally speaking, willingness is a prerequisite for behavior formation. One study on policy shaping and behavior compliance noted that the compliance willingness of grassroots cadres to take charge of policy compliance was influenced by individuals' personal characteristics and psychological factors, and this willingness determined their choice of actual compliance behavior. In the field of information security, information security compliance behavior can be understood as the implementation compliance of system users or organization employees in the face of information security policies or information security systems, which is often premised on one's compliance willingness with information security. The individual human will of system users is therefore an important research concern in terms of information security compliance behavior. By analyzing users' compliance willingness in the face of security notices, the laws of user information security compliance behavior can be better understood, and the correlation and consistency between willingness and behavior can also be discussed, thereby enriching the research scope of compliance willingness and information security behavior. We therefore used the concept of users' compliance willingness as the dependent variable in the conceptual model used in this study.

The conceptual model of "information presentation framework–security notice situation–information security cognition–user's compliance willingness" was constructed in this study by synthesizing the above-mentioned theoretical derivation. The model used the security notice information presentation framework as the independent variable, security notice situation and information security cognition as the moderating variables, and users' compliance willingness as the dependent variable, reflecting the correlation and influence mechanisms between the security notice information presentation framework and users' compliance willingness. The conceptual model of this study is shown in Figure 2.

2.7. Experimental Hypothesis

The question of whether users' compliance willingness regarding security notices differs across various situations depending on the information presentation framework used, current research is not thorough enough to analyze this issue, but this question has already received the attention of scholars in related fields (e.g., information system, human-computer interaction, and cybersecurity). The content of security notices can greatly influence the understanding and judgment of users in the lead-up to making operational decisions. System users tend to make compliance decisions based on the text headings and content of security notices, so there may be a causal relationship between the information presentation framework and users' compliance willingness.

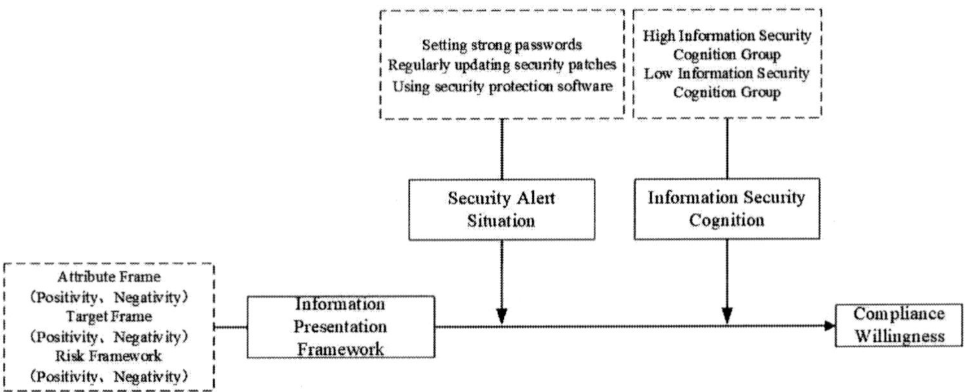

Figure 2.: *Theoretical Analysis Framework.*

In the closed loop of "human–machine–environment" management, users are the key detail that can affect the trend of information system security issues, and their compliance willingness with security notices involves a process that begins with a psychological reaction and leads to a behavioral choice, which requires the invoking of their individual information security cognition. Faced with an information system security notice, users will go through the process of weighing pros and cons to make a judgment based on the content of the security notice information presented by the system. Therefore, users' information security cognition level may affect their compliance willingness. To ensure the effective operation of information systems, then, it is necessary to explore the impact of users' information security cognition on the compliance willingness with security notices in order to understand users' cognition and its impact on their evaluation of information security and information systems.

According to the technology–organization–environment framework, an individual's adoption or acceptance of information technology is influenced by both internal forces and the external environment. The security notice is an important environmental factor in information systems. Studies have been conducted in the field of marketing to investigate the moderating effect of purchasing in green advertising appeals and green purchase intentions, confirming the moderating role of the situation in the relationship between appeals and intentions. As a system appeal format, variations in information presentation frameworks in security notices can be integrated with known understandings of their impacts to affect compliance willingness, with consideration of information security cognition. Therefore, this study proposes the following hypotheses, as shown in Table 1.

***Table 1.**: Research Hypothesis.*

Experimental Hypotheses for the Attribute Framework
H1: Subjects experience framing effects for all three attribute frameworks when presented with security notice situations.
H1-1: Participants' compliance willingness choices in the positive and negative format conditions differ significantly when prompted to set up a strong password.
H1-2: Participants' compliance willingness choices within the positive and negative format conditions differ significantly when prompted to update security patches regularly.
H1-3: Participants' compliance willingness choices in the positive and negative format conditions differ significantly when prompted to use security protection software.
Experimental Hypotheses for the Goal Framework
H2: Information security notices presented in all three goal-framed situations demonstrate framing effects.
H2-1: Participants' compliance willingness differs significantly according to whether a positive or negative format is used to prompt them to set up a strong password.
H2-2: Participants' compliance willingness differs significantly according to whether a positive or negative format is used to prompt them to regularly update their security patches.
H2-3: Participants' compliance willingness differs significantly according to whether a positive or negative format is used to prompt them to use security protection software.
Experimental Hypotheses for the Risk Framework
H3: Participants demonstrate framing effects when confronted with security notice situations across all three risk frameworks.
H3-1: Participants' choice in deterministic and uncertain scenarios differ significantly according to whether a positive or negative format is used to prompt them to set up a strong password.
H3-2: Participants' choice in deterministic and uncertain scenarios differ significantly according to whether a positive or negative format is used to prompt them to regularly update their security patches.
H3-3: Participants' choice in deterministic and uncertain scenarios differ significantly according to whether a positive or negative format I used to prompt them to use security protection software.
Information Security Cognition Hypotheses
H4: Subjects with different levels of information security cognition differ in their compliance willingness with different types of security notice situations according to the different attribute framework used.
H4-1: Participants with high information security cognition differ in their compliance willingness with security notices depending on the attribute frameworks condition.

H4-2: Participants with low information security cognition differ in their compliance willingness with security notices depending on the attribute frameworks condition.
H5: The compliance willingness of participants with different information security cognitive levels differs when presented with different goal frameworks of security notice situations.
H5-1: Participants with high information security cognition differ in their compliance willingness when presented different goal frameworks of security notice situations.
H5-2: Participants with low information security cognition differ in their compliance willingness when presented different goal frameworks of security notice situations.
H6: Participants with different cognitive levels of information security demonstrate different levels of compliance willingness when presented with security notice situations of different risk frameworks.
H6-1: When faced with security notices of different risk frameworks, users in the high information security cognition group exhibit a different level of compliance willingness.
H6-2: When faced with security notices of different risk frameworks, users in the low information security cognition group exhibit a different level of compliance willingness.

3. METHODS

Through three experimental studies that explored the attribute framework, the goal framework, and the risk framework, respectively, this paper explored the influence of different security notice formats on user compliance willingness. To analyse of the various information system situations, the E-prime program was used to present a simulated security notice. The program is designed to carry out behavioral experiments, and it is able to record and measure the system users' compliance decisions and reaction times within the specific attribute, goal, and risk frameworks.

3.1. Participants

Kühberger (1998) found no appreciable difference between the findings of framing effect research that used a student group as the experimental sample compared to a sample comprised of adults with job experience [42]. Therefore, we chose a student group as the experimental sample.

A laboratory study was conducted in which undergraduate and graduate students from general colleges and universities in China participated in the experiment. Empirical studies have shown that the number of participants in E-prime behavioral experiments should generally be within the range of 80 to 200, and the number of participants in framing effect experiment should generally be above 100. For our formal experiment, 180 subjects were recruited and the sample size passed the effect size test, and each subject was required to complete three E-prime experimental procedures, comprising either three positive framework procedures (i.e., positive attribute framework, goal framework, and risk framework) or three negative framework procedures (i.e., negative attribute framework, goal framework, and risk framework). All participants were between the ages of 20 and 30 years. All were familiar with enterprise information systems and had experience in using them. According to the empirical criteria, the experimental subjects all had experience using or hearing information system information prompts. The participants were all in good physical condition, had normal vision, and were right-handed. The experiment of the study was approved by the IRB of university organization.

This study adopted a between-groups design, with participants divided into two groups of 30 each, in accordance with the classification of frameworks. In the attribute framework experiment, the first group completed the positive attribute framework experimental task while the second group completed the negative attribute framework experimental task. In the goal framework experiment, the first group completed the positive goal framework experimental task while the second group completed the negative-goal framework experimental task. In the risk framework experiment, the first group completed the positive risk framework experimental task and the second group completed the negative risk framework experimental task. A pre-experiment had been conducted for all three frameworks to ensure that validity was maintained both internally and externally, leading to an adjustment in the order in which the framework stimulus materials and security notice messages were presented. All participants in the study met the following criteria:

(1) To ensure that visual fatigue did not occur during the experiment, participants were given regular pauses and rest breaks.
(2) Participants had not taken part in similar framework effect experiments prior to participating in the attribute framework experiment, the goal framework experiment, and the risk framework experiment.

3.2. Experimental Procedure

The overall experimental procedure of the framing effect situational experiment is shown in Figure 3.

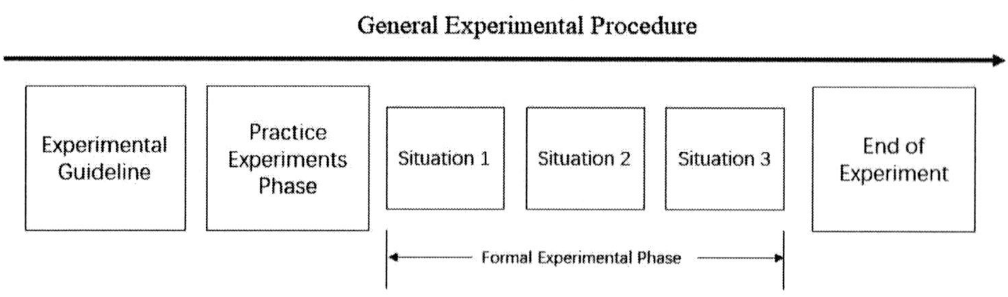

***Figure 3.**: General Experimental Procedure.*

(1) Attribute Framework Experiment Process

The attribute framework experiment used a 2framework properties (positive frame, negative frame) × 3situations (setting strong passwords, regularly updating security patches, using security protection software) three-factor mixed design, where the information presentation framework and its corresponding frame properties were between-group variables and the security notice situation was a within-group variable. There were three situations: Situation I was to set a strong password, Situation II was to regularly update security patches, and Situation III was for using security protection software. The framework properties of the two security notice situations of the attribute framework were presented randomly, and each experimental subject participated in only one condition (i.e., either positive or negative attribute framework). The attribute framework experiment was divided into a practice experiment phase followed by a formal experiment phase. The content of the experimental stimulus materials for the attribute framework of the setting strong passwords situation is described in detail as an example, and the content of the stimulus materials for the using security protection software situation and the regularly updated security patches situation are detailed in the Appendix A. Situational experiment practice session stage flow and steps are detailed in the Appendix B.

(1) Attribute Framework: (The strong and weak properties of the password-the level of complexity)

【Positivity】 When you first register your account for password setting, the confidentiality of your system account depends on the strength of your password, so be sure to set a strong password with high complexity when designing your password. In this case you will set a strong password of your choice.

【Negativity】 When you first register your account for password setting, the confidentiality of your system account depends on the strength of the password, so do not set a weak password with low complexity when designing your password. In this case you will set a strong password of your choice.

(2) Formal Phase: The formal experiment was a keystroke response experiment. Before seeing the security notice design, the situational instructions appeared on the screen:

"Suppose you are an information system user and you and the following security notice pops up onscreen while you are at work, how likely would you be to comply? Rate your compliance willingness by choosing a number from 1 to 7 for the given situation, with 1 representing "definitely would not" and 7 representing "definitely yes". The larger the number, the stronger your willingness to comply with the security notices. Please reply honestly." After this screen, the situational experiment began.

In the situational experimental phase, each participant was asked to browse through the attribute formats of the three security notice situations and make a decision about their compliance willingness, regardless of whether the respondent was in the positive or negative attribute framework experiment. Participants were first presented with the attribute framework for Situation 1 (i.e., setting strong passwords), after which they responded to the four measures of compliance willingness using keystroke responses. Once their answers were recorded, the experiment continued following the same procedure for Situation 2 (i.e., regularly updating security patches) and Situation 3 (i.e., using security protection software). The compliance questions used in all three security notice situations were identical in presentation style and wording. The experiment was concluded after the scoring was completed. Participants were then required to complete a post-test questionnaire regarding their information security cognition. The experimental procedure of the attribute framework for the positive–negative framework is shown in Figure 4.

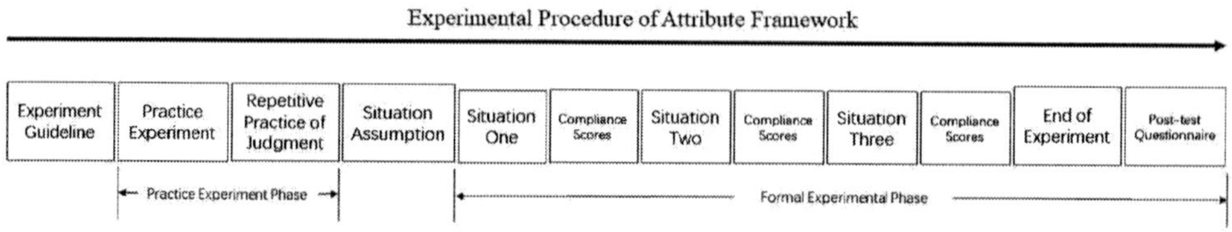

***Figure 4.**: Experimental Procedure for Attribute Framework Effects.*

(2) Goal Framework Experiment Process

The goal framework experiment used a 2framework properties (positive frame, negative frame) × 3situations (setting strong passwords, regularly updating security patches, using security protection software) three-factor mixed design, where the information presentation framework and its corresponding frame properties were between-group variables and the security notice situation was a within-group variable. The three situations were the same as in the previous part of the experiment, with Situation 1 addressing setting strong passwords, Situation 2 asking the user to regularly update security patches, and Situation 3 for using security protection software. The framework nature of the two security notice situations (i.e., positive or negative goal framework) was presented randomly, and each experimental subject participated in only one goal framework condition. The experiment was divided into a practice experiment phase, followed by a formal experiment phase. The content of the experimental stimulus materials for the goal framework of the setting strong passwords situation is described in detail as an example, and the content of the stimulus materials for the using security protection software situation and the regularly updated security patches situation are detailed in the Appendix A.

(1) Goal Framework: (The degree of security of strong passwords for system accounts)

【Positivity】 When you first register your account to log in, you will need to set your password, at which point you will be prompted to pay attention to how strong or weak your password is. If you set a strong password, there is an 80% chance that the system account you are using for work will be secured. At this point you will set a strong password of your choice.

【Negativity】 When you first register for an account to log in, you will need to set your password, and you will be prompted to pay attention to how strong or weak your password is. If you set a strong password, there is a 20% chance that the system account you are using for work will be stolen. At this point you will set a strong password of your choice.

(2) Formal Phase: The formal experiment was a keystroke response experiment which followed the same procedure and instructions of the previous part of the experiment.

In the situational experimental phase, regardless of whether the respondents were placed in the positive or the negative goal framework experiment, each participant was asked to look at the goal formats of the three security notice situations and report their willingness to comply with the request. Respondents were first exposed to the goal framework for Situation 1 (i.e., strong password setting) and then asked to rate their responses to this situation using the four measures of compliance willingness according to situation 1. They then followed the same instructions and procedure for Situation 2 (i.e., regularly updating security patches) and Situation 3 (i.e., using security protection software). The compliance questions used in all three security notice situations used the same wording and presentation style, and the experiment was concluded after scoring was complete. Afterwards, participants completed a post-test questionnaire regarding their information security cognition.

(3)`Risk Framework Experiment Process

The risk framework experiment used a 2framework properties (positive frame, negative frame) × 3situations (setting strong passwords, regularly updating security patches, using security protection software) three-factor mixed design, where the information presentation framework and its corresponding framework properties were between-group variables and the security notice situation was a within-group variable. The three situations were the same as in the previous two parts of the experiment, with Situation 1 regarding setting strong passwords, Situation 2 addressing regularly updating security patches, and Situation 3 for using security protection software. The framework properties of the two security notice situations of the risk framework were presented randomly, and each participant responded to only one goal framework condition (i.e., positive or negative risk framework). The risk framework experiment was divided into a practice experiment phase and a formal experiment phase. The content of the experimental stimulus materials for the risk framework of the setting strong passwords situation is described in detail as an example, and the content of the stimulus materials for the using security protection software situation and the regularly updated security patches situation are detailed in the Appendix A.

(1) Risk Framework: (The probability of strong passwords to protect system accounts)

【Positivity】 The account password of the information system may encounter 600 hacking attacks in a year, and it is necessary to reset the account password to ensure the security of the system account. Below are two options for you to choose from, please select the one you are most likely to comply with.

Option A: Setting a strong password can protect the system account from 400 attacks.

Option B: Setting a strong password has a 2/3 probability of protecting the system account from attacks and a 1/3 probability of not protecting the system account from 600 attacks.

【Negativity】 The account password of the information system may encounter 600 hacking attacks in a year, and it is necessary to reset the account password to ensure the security of the system account. Below are two options for you to choose from, please select the one you are most likely to comply with.

Option C: Setting a strong password will expose the system account to 200 attacks.

Option D: Setting a strong password has a 2/3 probability of keeping the system account safe from attacks and a 1/3 probability that the system account will be attacked 600 times.

(2) Formal Phase:

The formal experiment was a keystroke response experiment. Before being shown the security notice, the situation instructions appeared on the screen: "Suppose you are an information system user and you and the following security notice pops up onscreen while you are at work, which choice would you make? Two possible choices are presented for each situation in response to the information system security notices. There is no advantage nor disadvantage between Option A and Option B for each situation. The letters are used only to distinguish between the situations. Please reply honestly." The situational experiment then began.

Respondents were placed in either the positive or negative risk framework condition, and each participant was asked to look at the risk formats of the three security notice situations and to choose a response to the risk situation. Respondents were first presented with the risk format of Situation 1 (i.e., setting strong passwords) and, after seeing it, they chose between two risky situations by choosing the appropriate key. Situation 2 (i.e., regularly updating security patches) and 3 (i.e., using security protection software) were then presented, both following the same presentation style and procedure. The experiment was concluded after the final choice was made. Participants then completed a post-test questionnaire regarding their information security cognition.

3.3. Variable Measurement

The study's independent variables were the three framework formats (i.e., attribute, goal, and risk) that corresponded to the security notice situations. There were six subcategories, as each of the three formats had its own content of positive and negative frameworks.

The users' compliance willingness was set as the dependent variable and was determined by the E-prime program's keystroke response value, which was a score between 1 and 7; higher scores indicated a stronger compliance willingness with the security notifications. There were six subcategories of compliance willingness as well, due to the positive and negative conditions of each of the three frameworks.

The moderating variables in this study were the security notice situation and the information security cognition. Information security cognition can also be understood as security information cognition and refers to the process of individuals receiving and processing system security information and generating relevant cognitive information [43]. Information security cognition is described in the realm of information security as the user's total cognition and judgment of the importance of security notice compliance decisions when making decisions regarding information system operations.

In relation to the security notice situation, Chen (2016) noted the following three examples of information system security policy compliance behavior: utilizing security protection software, setting strong passwords, and keeping up with security patch updates [44]. In this experiment, these three examples were used as the moderating variables. In terms of experimental stimulus materials, following the results of existing studies examining framework effects, we chose to translate and use the "Different beef components purchase willingness problem" and the "Asian disease problem". This experiment controlled the word count of the security notice situation of the attribute framework at 75 ± 10 words, the word count of the security notice situation of the goal framework at 85 ± 10 words, and the word count of the security notice situation of the risk framework at 155 ± 20 words to ensure relative consistency in the reading difficulty across the positive and negative conditions and to control the length of the experiment. No substantial differences existed between the sample groups participating in the different experimental groups.

4. RESULTS

4.1. Testing the Relationship between Attribute Framework and Compliance Willingness

The scale items of the attribute framework situation experiment all passed the reliability and validity tests, as shown in Table 2.

***Table 2.**: Reliability and Validity Analysis Results.*

Notice Format	**Variants**	**Item Number**	**KMO**	**Approximate Cardinality**	**df**	p	**Cronbach's α Coefficient**
Attribute Framework	Information security cognition	11	0.838	921.675	55	0	0.884
	User compliance	4	0.839	546.509	6	0	0.917

(1) Hypothetical Test

A two-way analysis of variance was used to test the influence of the situation and framework nature on participants' compliance willingness (see **Table 3**). The results show that the situation did not show a significant relationship with compliance willingness ($F = 1.276$, $p = 0.282 > 0.05$), indicating that the situation had no differential effect on compliance willingness. The framework properties were significant ($F = 11.746$, $p = 0.001 < 0.05$), indicating a main effect and that the different framework properties had differing relationships with compliance willingness. Neither situation nor framework properties showed a significant correlation ($F = 0.050$, $p = 0.951 > 0.05$), indicating that there was no second-order relationship between the two variables. Comparison of means for situation and framework properties shown in Table 4.

Table 3.: *Two-Way ANOVA Results.*

Source of Difference	Sum of Squares	*df*	Mean Square	*F*	*p*
Intercept	5740.401	1	5740.401	4403.445	0.000 ***
Situation	3.326	2	1.663	1.276	0.282
Framework nature	15.313	1	15.313	11.746	0.001 ***
Situation × framework nature	0.131	2	0.066	0.050	0.951
Residual	226.829	174	1.304		

Note: *** $p < 0.001$.

Table 4.: *Comparison of Means for Situation and Framework Properties (Mean ± SD).*

Situation	Positivity ($n = 90$)	Negativity ($n = 90$)
Using security protection software	5.18 ± 1.19	5.84 ± 1.06
Regularly updating security patches	5.32 ± 1.16	5.88 ± 1.10
Setting strong passwords	5.57 ± 1.31	6.10 ± 0.99

As shown in Table 5, the positive format compliance willingness score of the attribute framework was significantly lower than the negative condition compliance willingness score ($p < 0.05$) in the security protection software situation, thus supporting Hypothesis H1-3. A lower positive condition compliance willingness score was found for the attribute framework while a lower negative condition compliance willingness score was found for the security patch update situation; however, these were statistically not significant ($p > 0.05$). Our Hypothesis H1-2 was not validated. The positive compliance willingness score of the attribute framework was lower than the negative compliance willingness score, but the difference was not statistically significant ($p > 0.05$), indicating that Hypothesis H1-1 was invalid. Mean comparisons of framework properties and situations shown in Figure 5.

A two-way analysis of variance was used to test the relationship between information security cognition and framework nature on compliance willingness (see Table 6). According to the data analysis results, information security cognition showed significant results ($F = 13.373, p = 0.000 < 0.05$), indicating that information security cognition showed an association with compliance willingness in a differential manner. The framework properties were significant ($F = 11.986$, $p = 0.001 < 0.05$), suggesting that a main effect was present and that framework properties would influence compliance differently. No significant association was found between information security cognition and framework properties ($F = 0.998$, $p = 0.319 > 0.05$), indicating that there was no second-order effect. Mean comparison of information security cognition and nature shown in Table 7.

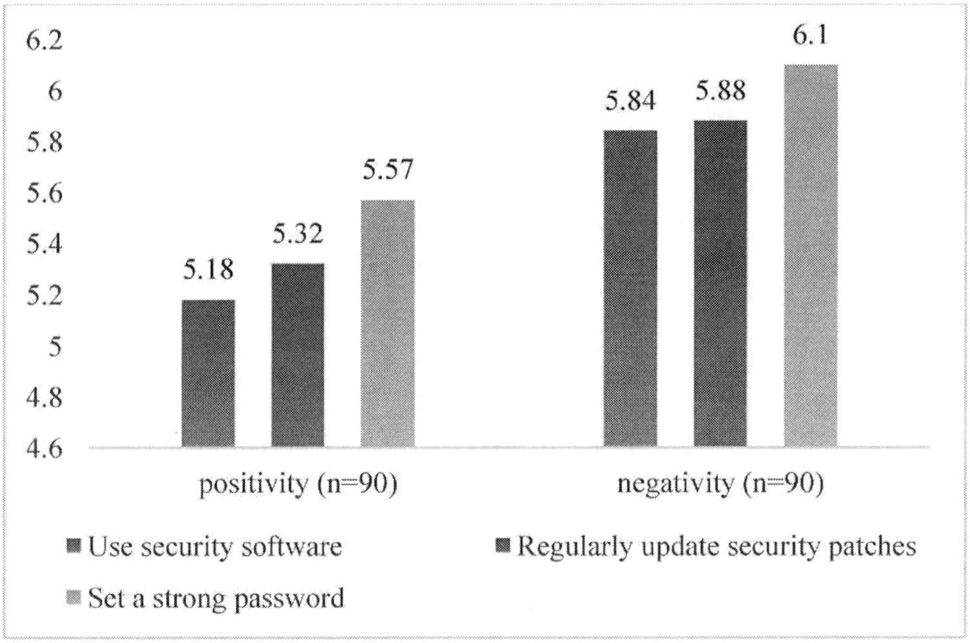

Figure 5.: *Mean Comparisons of Framework Properties and Situations.*

Table 5.: *Simple Effects (Situation and Framework Nature).*

Situation	Framework Nature	Mean Difference	*SE*	*t*	*p*
Using security protection software	positivity–negativity	−0.658	0.295	−2.233	0.027
Regularly updating security patches	positivity–negativity	−0.558	0.295	−1.894	0.060
Setting strong passwords	positivity–negativity	−0.533	0.295	−1.809	0.072

Table 8 shows that the positive condition compliance willingness score of attribute framework did not differ significantly from the negative condition compliance willingness score in the low information security cognition group ($p > 0.05$). Thus, Hypothesis H4-2 is not valid. As expected, however, the high information security cognition group had a significantly lower score for the positive condition compliance willingness within the attribute framework compared to the score for negative condition compliance willingness for the same framework ($p < 0.05$), confirming Hypothesis H4-1. Comparison of the mean value of the nature of the framework and the information security cognition shown in Figure 6.

***Table 6.:** Results of Two-Way ANOVA.*

Source of Difference	Sum of Squares	*df*	Mean Square	*F*	*p*
Intercept	5479.638	1	5479.638	4531.888	0.000 ***
Information security cognition	16.169	1	16.169	13.373	0.000 ***
Framework nature	14.492	1	14.492	11.986	0.001 ***
Information security cognition × framework nature	1.207	1	1.207	0.998	0.319
Residual	212.807	176	1.209		

Note: *** $p < 0.001$.

***Table 7.:** Mean Comparison of Information Security Cognition and Nature (Mean ± Standard Deviation).*

Information Security Cognition	Positivity ($n = 90$)	Negativity ($n = 90$)
Low information security cognition	5.09 ± 1.02	5.50 ± 1.08
High information security cognition	5.53 ± 1.32	6.27 ± 0.90

4.2. Testing of the Relationship between Goal Framework and Compliance Willingness

The scale items of the goal framework situation experiment all passed the reliability and validity tests, as shown in Table 9.

(1) Hypothetical Test

The impact of situation and framework nature on willingness compliance was tested using a two-way analysis of variance, with the results presented in Table 10. These results showed significant differences between the situations ($F = 8.055$, $p = 0.000 < 0.05$), indicating that the main effect existed and that the situation affected willingness compliance. A significant difference was not found according to the nature of the framework ($F = 0.035$, $p = 0.851 > 0.05$), suggesting that the nature of the framework did not affect compliance willingness. Neither situation nor framework properties were significantly correlated ($F = 0.197$, $p = 0.821 >$

0.05), indicating no second-order effect. Comparison of Means for Situation and Framework Properties shown in Table 11.

No significant difference was found between the positive condition compliance willingness score in the goal framework and the negative condition compliance willingness score when security protection software is used ($p > 0.05$; see Table 12). Hypothesis H2-3 was thus not supported. In accordance with Hypothesis 2-2, no significant difference was found between positive and negative condition compliance willingness in the goal framework ($p > 0.05$) when it came to regularly updating security patches. However, no significant difference was found between the positive and negative condition compliance willingness scores in the goal framework when it comes to setting strong passwords ($p > 0.05$), so Hypothesis H2-1 could not be verified. Mean comparison plot of framework nature and situation shown in Figure 7.

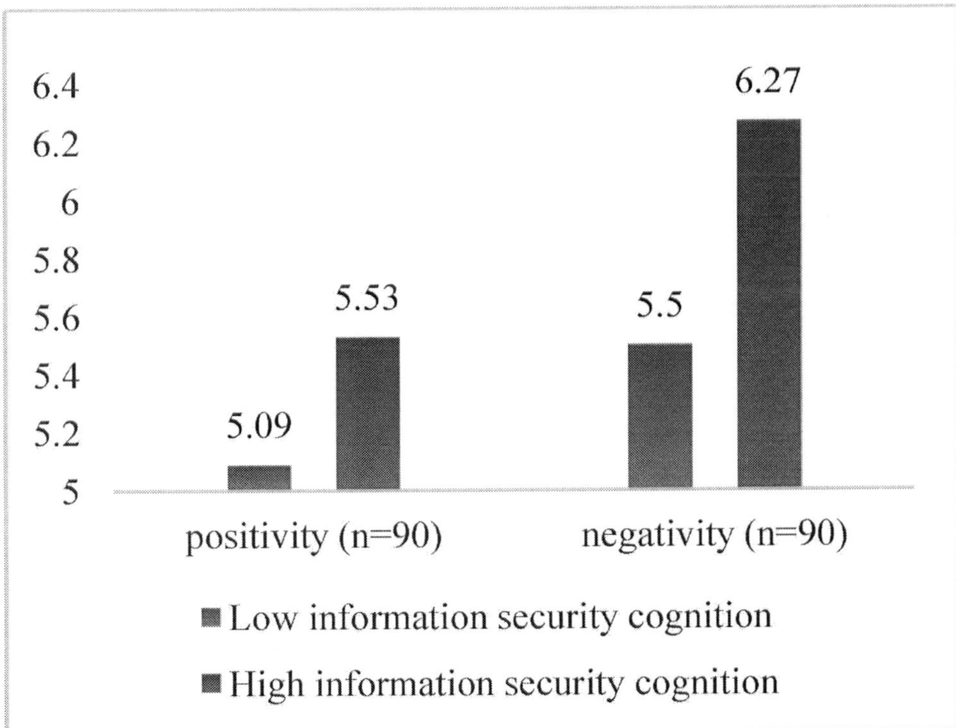

Figure 6.: *Comparison of the Mean Value of the Nature of the Framework and the Information Security Cognition.*

Table 8.: *Simple Effects (Information Security Cognition and Framework Properties).*

Information Security Cognition	Nature	Mean Difference	*SE*	*t*	*p*
Low information security cognition	positivity–negativity	–0.410	0.254	–1.612	0.109

Information Security Cognition	Nature	Mean Difference	*SE*	*t*	*p*
High information security cognition	positivity–negativity	−0.742	0.215	−3.456	0.001

Table 9.: *Reliability and Validity Analysis Results.*

Notice Format	Variants	Item Number	KMO	Approximate Cardinality	df	*p*	Cronbach's α Coefficient
Goal Framework	Information security cognition	11	0.838	921.675	55	0	0.884
	User compliance	4	0.843	622.443	6	0	0.935

Table 10.: *Two-Way ANOVA Results.*

Source of Difference	Sum of Squares	*df*	Mean Square	*F*	*p*
Intercept	5811.209	1	5811.209	4883.654	0.000 ***
Situation	19.169	2	9.585	8.055	0.000 ***
Framework nature	0.042	1	0.042	0.035	0.851
Situation × framework nature	0.469	2	0.235	0.197	0.821
Residual	207.048	174	1.190		

Note: *** $p < 0.001$.

Table 11.: *Comparison of Means for Situation and Framework Properties (Mean ± Standard Deviation).*

Situation	Positivity ($n = 90$)	Negativity ($n = 90$)
Using security protection software	5.13 ± 1.10	5.31 ± 1.29
Regularly updating security patches	5.92 ± 0.85	5.88 ± 1.08
Setting strong passwords	5.95 ± 0.83	5.91 ± 1.30

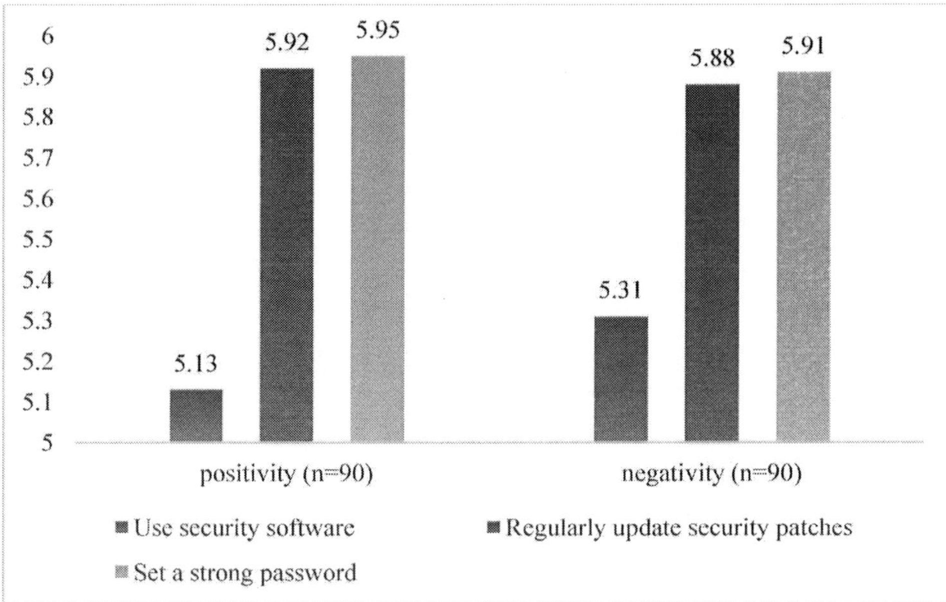

Figure 7.: *Mean Comparison Plot of Framework Nature and Situation.*

Table 12.: *Simple Effects (Situation and Framework Nature).*

Situation	Framework Nature	Mean Difference	*SE*	*t*	*p*
Using security protection software	positivity–negativity	−0.175	0.282	−0.621	0.535
Regularly updating security patches	positivity–negativity	0.042	0.282	0.148	0.883
Setting strong passwords	positivity–negativity	0.042	0.282	0.148	0.883

This table(Table 13) presents the results of the two-way analysis of variance used to test the influence of information security cognition and nature on willingness compliance. Information security cognition did not appear to have a significant linear relationship with willingness compliance ($F = 2.263$, $p = 0.134 > 0.05$). As a result, there was no significant difference was found between the frameworks ($F = 0.074$, $p = 0.785 > 0.05$), indicating no relevant relationship between the frameworks and compliance willingness. A significant relationship was also not found between information security cognition and framework properties ($F = 0.068$, $p = 0.795 > 0.05$), suggesting that there was no second-order effect between them. Mean comparison of information security cognition and nature shown in Table 14.

Table 13.: Results of Two-Way ANOVA.

Source of Difference	Sum of Squares	*df*	Mean Square	*F*	*p*
Intercept	5598.737	1	5598.737	4404.222	0.000 ***
Information security cognition	2.877	1	2.877	2.263	0.134
Framework nature	0.094	1	0.094	0.074	0.785
Information security cognition × framework nature	0.086	1	0.086	0.068	0.795
Residual	223.735	176	1.271		

Note: *** $p < 0.001$.

Table 14.: Mean Comparison of Information Security Cognition and Nature. (Mean ± Standard Deviation).

Information Security Cognition	Positivity ($n = 90$)	Negativity ($n = 90$)
Low information security cognition	5.49 ± 0.99	5.58 ± 1.02
High information security cognition	5.79 ± 0.99	5.79 ± 1.39

As shown in Table 15, there was no significant difference between the positive condition compliance willingness scores of the goal framework and the negative condition compliance willingness scores in the low information security cognition group ($p > 0.05$), so Hypothesis H5-2 was validated. In the high information security cognition group, there was no significant difference between the positive condition compliance willingness scores of the goal framework and the negative condition compliance willingness scores ($p > 0.05$), so Hypothesis H5-1 was also not validated. Comparison of the mean values of the nature of the framework and information security cognition shown in Figure 8.

Table 15.: Simple Effects (Information Security Cognition and Framework Properties).

Information Security Cognition	Nature	Mean Difference	*SE*	*t*	*p*
Low information security cognition	positivity–negativity	−0.091	0.261	−0.348	0.728
High information security cognition	positivity–negativity	−0.002	0.220	−0.010	0.992

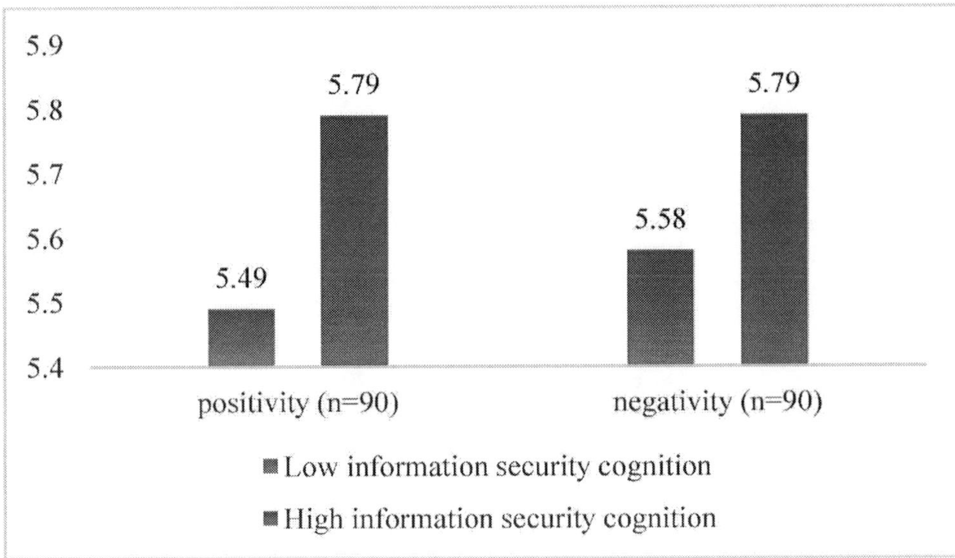

Figure 8.: *Comparison of the Mean Values of the Nature of the Framework and Information Security Cognition.*

4.3. Testing the Relationship between Risk Framework and Compliance Willingness

The scale items of the risk framework situation experiment all passed the reliability and validity tests, as shown in Table 16.

Table 16.: *Reliability and Validity Analysis Results.*

Notice Format	**Variants**	**Item Number**	**KMO**	**Approximate Cardinality**	**df**	***p***	**Cronbach's α Coefficient**
Risk Frame-work	Information security cog-nition	11	0.838	921.675	55	0	0.884

(1) Hypothetical Test

Table 17 shows that the nature of the framework showed a 0.05 level of significance (chi = 5.554, $p = 0.018 < 0.05$) for the risky scenario selection in the security protection software situation. Meanwhile, 73.33% of users selected uncertainty scenarios in the negative condition, which is significantly higher than the percentage of uncertainty scenarios selected in the positive condition (43.33%). There was a significant increase in the percentage of users selecting the deterministic scenario in the positive condition, with 56.67% compared to 26.67% in the negative condition.

Table 17.: *Results of Cross-Tabulation (Chi-Square) Analysis.*

Situation	Program Nature	Framework Nature (%)		Grand Total	χ^2	p
		Positivity	Negativity			
Using security protection software	Uncertainty scenarios	13 (43.33)	22 (73.33)	35 (58.33)	5.554	0.018 *
	Deterministic scenarios	17 (56.67)	8 (26.67)	25 (41.67)		
Regularly updating security patches	Uncertainty scenarios	7 (23.33)	20 (66.67)	27 (45.00)	11.38	0.001 ***
	Deterministic scenarios	23 (76.67)	10 (33.33)	33 (55.00)		
Setting strong passwords	Uncertainty scenarios	11 (36.67)	19 (63.33)	30 (50.00)	4.267	0.039 *
	Deterministic scenarios	19 (63.33)	11 (36.67)	30 (50.00)		

* $p < 0.05$, *** $p < 0.001$.

In the security patch update situation, the nature of the framework showed a 0.001 level of significance (chi = 11.380, $p = 0.001 < 0.01$) for the risky solution selection, with 66.67% of users choosing the uncertainty scenarios in the negative condition, which was significantly higher than the percentage of users who chose the uncertainty scenarios for the positive condition (23.33%). The percentage of users who chose the deterministic scenarios in the positive condition was 76.67%, which was significantly higher than the percentage of those who chose the deterministic scenarios in the negative condition (33.33%).

In the strong password situation, the nature of the framework showed a 0.05 level of significance (chi = 4.267, $p = 0.039 < 0.05$) for the risky solution selection. There was a significant difference between the percentages of users who chose uncertainty scenarios under the negative format (63.33%) and those who chose uncertainty scenarios under the positive condition (50.00%). It is noteworthy that the percentage of users who chose the deterministic scenarios in the positive condition was 63.33%, which is significantly higher than that of the users who chose the deterministic scenarios in the negative condition, which was 36.67%. Thus, hypotheses H3-3, H3-2, and H3-1 are all valid.

Table 18 shows that, in the low information security cognition group, the nature of the framework presents a 0.01 level of significance for the risky solution selection (chi = 7.090, $p = 0.008 < 0.01$), and the percentage of users who chose the uncertainty scenarios in the negative condition was 64.10%, which is significantly higher than the percentage of users who chose the uncertainty scenarios in the positive condition, which was 33.33%. It was found that 66.67% of users chose the deterministic scenarios in the positive condition, which was significantly higher than the 34.90% who chose them in the negative condition.

***Table 18.**: Results of Cross-Sectional (Chi-Square) Analysis.*

Classification Items	Program Nature	Framework Nature (%)		Grand Total	χ^2	*p*
		Positivity	Negativity			
Low information security cognition	Uncertainty scenarios	12 (33.33)	25 (64.10)	37 (49.33)	7.09	0.008 **
	Deterministic scenarios	24 (66.67)	14 (35.90)	38 (50.67)		
High information security cognition	Uncertainty scenarios	19 (35.19)	36 (70.59)	55 (52.38)	13.18	0.000 ***
	Deterministic scenarios	35 (64.81)	15 (29.41)	50 (47.62)		

** $p < 0.01$, *** $p < 0.001$.

In the high information security cognition group, the nature of the framework showed a 0.001 level of significance (chi = 13.180, $p = 0.000 < 0.001$) for the choice of risky scenarios, and a percentage comparison of the differences showed a 70.59% percent choice of uncertainty scenarios in the negative condition compared with the 35.19% who choose the uncertainty scenarios in the positive condition. It is significant that 64.81% of users chose the deterministic scenario in the positive condition, which was significantly higher than the 29.41% who chose it in the negative condition. As such, Hypotheses H6-2 and H6-1 are supported.

5. DISCUSSION

5.1. Discussion on the Experimental Results of the Attribute Framework

A user's compliance willingness was shown to be stronger in the negative format of the attribute framework, regardless of which security notice situation they were in. The situations of regularly updating security patches and setting strong passwords had no significance in terms of users' compliance in the attribute framework; that is, the p-value is not significant, although the use of security protection software showed an indistinctive effect. Despite the fact that users may make different compliance decisions when it comes to setting strong passwords and updating security patches, the situational effects of these two situations may be less apparent than those associated with using security protection software, which can lead to the problems described by the other two situations. We would propose that an insufficient amount of attention has been put on the specific situation when developing security notices, and strong situational cognition has not been developed in users, resulting in no significant changes made in users' decision-making process regarding compliance.

5.2. Discussion on the Experimental Results of the Goal Framework

Users' compliance willingness in the positive condition in the goal framework was more than in the negative condition when it came to updating security patches and creating strong passwords. In situations where security protection software is used, compliance willingness with the negative condition was significantly higher than in the positive condition. There was a greater compliance willingness with this framework than there was in the positive condition. Therefore, the p value was not significant in any of the above three situations, which indicates that there was no significant user compliance willingness. As a result, while users tended to make various compliance judgments in response to the various situations in the positive and negative conditions, the goal framework itself may accentuate the positive or negative effects of a particular action, creating further encouragement for users to act a certain way. Additionally, in the attribute framework situation, it is possible for cognitive dissonance to have arisen in relation to situational factors, for example, thinking that the goal framework situation may result in irreversible commitments that may ultimately result in insignificant differences in compliance decision-making.

5.3. Discussion on the Experimental Results of the Risk Framework

In the risk framework experiment, significant differences were found between users' choices of deterministic and uncertain solutions in both the positive and negative condition in all three situations (i.e., setting strong passwords, regularly updating security patches, and using security protection software). Meanwhile, in both the high and low information security cognition groups, differences were found in users' compliance willingness with security notices when faced with different risk framework nature.

In the risk framework, regardless of the security notice situation, users preferred the uncertain risk option in the negative condition while they preferred the deterministic risk option in the positive condition. This result is consistent with those of Tversky and Kahneman (1981) in response to their Asian disease problem study, finding that individuals tended to be risk-averse (i.e., choosing deterministic options) when faced with a benefit framework and risk-seeking (i.e., choosing uncertain options) when faced with a loss framework. This is also similar to the results of other existing studies on risk frameworks. Meanwhile, the results of the data analysis showed that there were significant differences, that is, significant p-values in users' risky scenario decisions in all three security notice situations. This shows that the individual risk preference phenomenon also exists in the information security domain.

Generally speaking, users showed strong compliance willingness or risk preference in the negative conditions of all three frameworks (i.e., attribute, goal, and risk frameworks) while their compliance willingness and risk preference in the positive conditions of all three frameworks were not strong. The intensity of users' compliance willingness or risk preference in both the positive and negative conditions was limited by their own information security cognition; that is, users showed similar compliance willingness and risk appetite in all positive or all negative conditions, regardless of the framework. The performance indicates that users' compliance willingness is the result of the interaction between the individual and the situational factors.

5.4. Practical Inspiration

With regard to security notices in information systems, no new frameworks were explored in this study, only the three frameworks mentioned in this study. This study proposes recommendations for the design and management of security notices for system users and information system platforms, respectively, in order to improve the degree of users' compliance willingness with security notices and reduce the possibility of system information security problems. For system users, the following aspects should be emphasized in terms of compliance willingness.

(1) In terms of behavioral will, users should regulate their own information security behavior. Users should pay attention to the decision of compliance with information system security warnings, set strong passwords for system accounts, update security patches regularly, and use security protection software according to the recommended operation settings of security warnings, so as to comply with the prompt requirements of security notices. Users also need to develop a good awareness of information system security notice compliance to avoid risks such as information leakage due to violation of the norms of security warnings. At the same time, users should pay attention to the security notices presented by the information system in a timely manner, especially the security notice situations involving the security of users' property, and should not ignore the security notices presented by the information system but should always pay attention to them to ensure the security of personal and system information.

(2) In information security cognition, users should strengthen their personal information security awareness. Users need to pay attention to various forms and types of information security training and education to enhance their own information security cognition. Only by realizing the importance of information security at the cognitive level can we control the occurrence of security threats such as information leakage from the root. Users can actively participate in the information security lectures or education training organized by their own organizations to enrich the theoretical knowledge of relevant information security, enrich the knowledge accumulation of personal information security, and avoid unnecessary losses due to certain fake and deceptive nature of security notice links.

The findings of this paper can also provide organizations or enterprises with theoretical support in information security management, which can be used to guide users to protect system information security more reasonably and effectively, and it can also help system developers to adopt effective, appropriate, and reasonable security notice design plans and measures. Specific aspects can be carried out as follows:

(1) Design and use a framework for presenting security notice information that facilitates user compliance. Guiding users' information security behavior and making users' compliance with security notices a normal behavior. Security notices are an important part of information system development and design; system developers should avoid complicating the design of security notices and should not abuse security notices. It is better to come from and go to the actual situations of information systems, design suitable security notices according to different situations, and pay attention to the design of the information presentation framework of security notices while complying with different design specifications and summarize the personalized information presentation framework suitable for each situation. The personalized information presentation framework for each situation is summarized, and if necessary, "one situation, one design" is achieved.

(2) Optimize the visual design of security notices. While focusing on the information presentation framework of security notices, attention should also be paid to the graphical design of security notices. Studies have pointed out that window size, button order change, window inverse color, window background color, text background color, and font color are the style design elements of the graphical design of the warning pop-up window. System developers can optimize one or all of these elements according to the specific information system and the characteristics of the information presentation framework of security notices.

(3) It has been shown that, compared to "security tips", "security warnings" are more attractive to users' attention when they appear, causing them to devote more cognitive resources to read the warnings carefully, and they are more likely to act in compliance with the text message of the security warning. They are also more likely to comply with the text message.

It can be seen that, as a type of warning that brings new stimuli to users and arouses their awareness, security warnings can achieve better warning effects and promote stronger compliance behaviors. In view of this, system developers should design more warning-type security notices in information systems, especially in interfaces involving the confirmation of important information, such as the entry of critical personal information, property amount entry, or payment, because users will rely more on the content of security notices in these interfaces to indicate cautious decision making. In other information system interfaces of relatively minor importance, security warnings can be replaced by security tips to reduce the cognitive load of users. In addition, in the process of designing security warnings, attention should be paid to the customary expression of textual information (i.e., to achieve the expression of warning alerts while conforming to the reading habits of the warning language).

6. CONCLUSIONS AND LIMITATIONS

6.1. Limitations

Our findings shed new light on users' compliance willingness in an information security situation with consideration of framing effect theory. However, it should be noted that there are some limitations to the current study. First, the E-prime platform was used to collect behavioral experimental data in this study. This platform provides simulated security notices and provides users with a fair amount of control over their design and presentation; however, due to the limitations of the platform, specific notice content and the content related to the real environment can still be vague or unspecific. In the future, better experimental tools should be adopted to develop improved schemes for selecting risk frameworks for the three security notice situations that would better reflect real-world situations.

Second, all three experiments in the current study used the seven numeric keys of the E-prime keyboard to indicate users' degree of compliance willingness. In real-life situations, the user may also be required to use touch screens, electronic pens, or other devices in addition to a keypad. Simultaneous needs to respond to notices, perform repeated operations, or face task operation decisions in addition to making a decision regarding a given security notice may result in further uncertainty due to social facilitation effects in real-life situations, which alters users' actual decision-making environment in comparison to the simulated decision-making situation.

6.2. Conclusions

Using framing effect theory as its foundation, this study examined the impact of information formats (in terms of positive or negative presentations) on users' compliance willingness when making decisions instigated by information system security notices. Our findings verified that users will respond differently to different types of security notices. Furthermore, system users with varying information security cognition levels demonstrated different compliance willingness. However, different formats of security notices are associated with different security notice situations. In turn, they can have an effect on one's level of information security cognition and, subsequently, on their level of compliance. Our findings suggest the following conclusions:

(1) Within the attribute framework experiment, a significant difference was found between users' compliance willingness with the positive condition compared to the negative condition in the security protection software situation. However, when faced with security notice situations with different attribute framework properties, users with high information security cognition exhibited different compliance willingness. Compliance willingness was not affected by the situation or nor information security cognition in the remaining situations.

(2) In the goal framework experiment, neither the positive nor the negative conditions were associated with significant differences in user compliance willingness in any of the three situations (i.e., strong passwords, securi-

ty patches, and security protection software). Furthermore, no difference was seen in users' compliance willingness across the various security notice situations with different goal framework properties in either the high or low information security cognition groups.

(3) In the risk framework experiment, users showed significant differences in their choices of deterministic or uncertain schemes across the various tested situations (i.e., setting strong passwords, updating security patches, and using security protection software). Furthermore, differences were seen in users' compliance willingness in the high and low information security cognition groups in response to the security notices with different risk framework properties.

(4) Compliance willingness varied according to the framework in which information security cognition was applied.

6.3. Prospects and Future Work

The current study focused on the independent element design of the information system security notice in order to explore user compliance willingness. Three common security notice situations, which corresponded with the experimental design requirements, were used to assess design frameworks, specifically the attribute framework, the goal framework, and the risk framework. Future research should consider and test more security notice situations, and a format for presenting information should be designed to provide users with a better understanding regarding the impacts of their security notice compliance decisions.

Future research should also consider combining the graphic framing effect with graphic representation to determine whether graphic representations influence users' compliance willingness under the same conditions as when the security notice expression information remains the same, as well as to better understand the mechanisms involved in users' judgment and decision-making.

APPENDIX A

Table A1. Situational stimulus materials on information system security notices.

1. Strong Password Setting
Attribute Framework: (The strong and weak properties of the password-the level of complexity) 【Positivity】 When you first register your account for password setting, the confidentiality of your system account depends on the strength of your password, so be sure to set a strong password with high complexity when designing your password. In this case you will set a strong password of your choice. 【Negativity】 When you first register your account for password setting, the confidentiality of your system account depends on the strength of the password, so do not set a weak password with low complexity when designing your password. In this case you will set a strong password of your choice.

Goal Framework: (The degree of security of strong passwords for system accounts) 【Positivity】 When you first register your account to log in, you will need to set your password, at which point you will be prompted to pay attention to how strong or weak your password is. If you set a strong password, there is an 80% chance that the system account you are using for work will be secured. At this point you will set a strong password of your choice. 【Negativity】 When you first register for an account to log in, you will need to set your password, and you will be prompted to pay attention to how strong or weak your password is. If you set a strong password, there is a 20% chance that the system account you are using for work will be stolen. At this point you will set a strong password of your choice.
Risk Framework: (The probability of strong passwords to protect system accounts) 【Positivity】 The account password of the information system may encounter 600 hacking attacks in a year, and it is necessary to reset the account password to ensure the security of the system account. Below are two options for you to choose from, please select the one you are most likely to comply with. Option A: Setting a strong password can protect the system account from 400 attacks. Option B: Setting a strong password has a 2/3 probability of protecting the system account from attacks and a 1/3 probability of not protecting the system account from 600 attacks. 【Negativity】 The account password of the information system may encounter 600 hacking attacks in a year, and it is necessary to reset the account password to ensure the security of the system account. Below are two options for you to choose from, please select the one you are most likely to comply with. Option C: Setting a strong password will expose the system account to 200 attacks. Option D: Setting a strong password has a 2/3 probability of keeping the system account safe from attacks and a 1/3 probability that the system account will be attacked 600 times.
2. Regularly Updating Security Patches
Attribute Framework: (Timeliness and relevance of patch installation) 【Positivity】 In the process of using the system, the system prompts you to update the patch, because the security patch in the system is time-sensitive and targeted, be sure to install the patch package in time, and select all the security patch content. At this time you will update the security patch will choose. 【Negativity】 In the process of using the system, the system prompts you to update the patch, because the security patch in the system is time-sensitive and targeted, do not install the patch package out of date, do not miss the security patch content. At this time, you will update the security patch will choose.

Goal Framework: (The extent of patching on system data recovery) 【Positivity】 In the process of using the system, the system prompts you to update the patch, because the security patch in the system is time-sensitive and targeted, if the patch package is installed in time, there is an 80% possibility to get restored in case of information loss. At this time you will update the security patch will choose. 【Negativity】 In the process of using the system, the system prompts you to update the patch, because the security patch in the system is time-sensitive and targeted, if the patch package is installed in time, there is a 20% chance of permanent loss in the event of information loss. At this time you will update the security patch will choose.
Risk Framework: (Probability of success / failure of software updates) 【Positivity】 During the period of using the information system, the system prompts you that there are 20 security patches for your device software that need to be updated in a timely manner. Below are two options for you to choose from, please select the one you are most likely to comply with. Option A: This update will have 15 patches updated successfully. Option B: There is a 3 / 4 chance that 20 patches will be updated successfully with this update, and a 1 / 4 chance that no patches will be updated successfully. 【Negativity】 During the period of using the information system, the system prompts you that there are 20 security patches for your device software that need to be updated in a timely manner. Below are two options for you to choose from, please select the one you are most likely to comply with. Option C: This update will have 5 patch updates fail. Option D: There is a 3 / 4 chance that this update will fail without a patch, and a 1 / 4 chance that the 20-patch update will fail.
3. Using Security Protection Software
Attribute Framework: (Versions of Software-Genuine and Pirated) 【Positivity】 For security maintenance needs, the system prompts you to use security protection software to ensure the stable operation of the system, as the protection function on the software depends on the system's data services, it is important to apply genuine security protection software. At this time you will use the security protection software will choose. 【Negativity】 For security maintenance needs, the system prompts you to use security protection software to ensure the stable operation of the system, as the protection function on the software depends on the system's data services, do not use pirated security protection software. At this time you will use the security protection software will choose.

Goal Framework: (Software prevention against hacking and theft) 【Positivity】 For security maintenance purposes, you are prompted to use security protection software to ensure stable system operation. If you use security protection software, you have a 60% chance of being protected from hacker attacks and theft. At this time you will use the security protection software will choose. 【Negativity】 For security maintenance purposes, you are prompted to use security protection software to ensure stable system operation. If you use security protection software, there is a 40% possibility of hacking and theft. At this time you will use the security protection software will choose.
Risk Framework: (The probability of protection of the system by protection software 【Positivity】 The security protection software of the information system may encounter 600 attacks in a year. To ensure the stable operation of the system, it is necessary to download and install the security protection software. The download and installation of the security protection software needs to be done on the system website. There are two options for you to choose from, please select the one you are most likely to follow. Option A: The security protection software protects the system from 400 attacks. Option B: The security protection software has a 2/3 probability of protecting the information system from attacks and a 1/3 probability of not protecting the information system from 600 attacks. 【Negativity】 The security protection software of the information system may encounter 600 attacks in a year. To ensure the stable operation of the system, it is necessary to download and install the security protection software. The download and installation of the security protection software needs to be done on the system website. There are two options for you to choose from, please select the one you are most likely to follow. Option C: The security protection software will make the information system suffer from 200 attacks. Option D: There is a 2/3 probability that the security protection software will protect the information system from attacks and a 1/3 probability that the information system will be attacked 600 times.

APPENDIX B

***Table A2.**: Situational experiment practice session stage flow and steps.*

Attribute Framework Situational Experimentation Practice Session Flow

The exercise phase: The stimulus material for the exercise phase of the attribute framing experiment was Levin and Gaeth's (1998) purchase decision problem for different compositions of beef. In the positive attribute framework experimental exercise phase, the situation was described as follows: "Suppose you go to the supermarket to buy beef and the label indicates that 70% of this beef is lean meat. How willing are you to buy this beef?" Respondents responded by pressing a numbered key, ranging from 1 to 7 to indicate their willingness to purchase the meat, with 1 representing "definitely not" and 7 representing "definitely yes". The larger the number, the stronger the respondent's willingness to make the purchase.

In the negative attribute framework experimental exercise phase, the situation was described as follows: "Suppose you go to the supermarket to buy beef and the label indicates that 30% of this beef is fatty meat. How willing are you to buy this beef?" Respondents responded by pressing a numbered key ranging from 1 to 7 to indicate their willingness to purchase the meat, with 1 representing "definitely not" and 7 representing "definitely yes". The larger the number, the stronger the respondent's willingness to make the purchase.

Goal Framework Situational Experimentation Practice Session Flow

The exercise phase: The purchase decision problem regarding beef of various compositions, as developed by Levin and Gaeth (1998), again served as the stimulus material for the goal framework experiment's exercise phase. The positive goal framework experimental exercise phase was described as follows: "Suppose you go to the supermarket to buy beef and the label indicates that 70% of this beef is lean meat. How likely would you be to buy this beef?"

In the negative condition, the material was described as follows: "Suppose you go to the supermarket to buy beef and the label indicates that 30% of this beef is fatty meat. How likely would you be to buy this beef?" Subjects responded by pressing a key corresponding a number from 1 to 7 to indicate how likely they would be to purchase the meat, where 1 represents "definitely not" and 7 represents "definitely yes". The larger the number, the stronger the respondent's willingness to purchase the meat.

Risk Framework Situational Experimentation Practice Session Flow

The exercise phase: The stimulus material for the risk framework experiment exercise phase was Tversky and Kahneman's (1981) "Asian Disease" problem, regarding disease treatment options. The manner in which the material for the positive–negative risk framework experiment exercise phase was described varied depending on the specific nature of the problem. The material in the positive risk framework condition was described as follows: "Suppose a country is preparing to face a rare epidemic, the onset of which is expected to result in 600 possible deaths. Two responses are possible:

Scenario Q, in which 200 people will survive, or

Scenario P, in which there is a one in three chance that everyone will survive, but a two in three chance that no one will survive".

The negative condition of the exercise phase is worded as follows: "Suppose a country is preparing to face a rare epidemic, the onset of which is expected to result in 600 possible deaths. Two responses options are possible:

Scenario W, in which 400 people will die, or

Scenario O, in which there is a one in three chance that no one will die, but a two in three chance that everyone will die."

REFERENCES

1. Ali, R.F.; Dominic, P.; Ali, S.E.A.; Rehman, M.; Sohail, A. Information security behavior and information security policy compliance: A systematic literature review for identifying the transformation process from noncompliance to compliance. Appl. Sci. 2021, 11, 3383.
2. Bornschein, R.; Schmidt, L.; Maier, E. The effect of consumers' perceived power and risk in digital information privacy: The example of cookie notices. J. Public Policy Mark. 2020, 39, 135–154.
3. Tversky, A.; Kahneman, D. The framing of decisions and the psychology of choice. Science 1981, 211, 453–458.
4. Levin, I.P.; Schneider, S.L.; Gaeth, G.J. All frames are not created equal: A typology and critical analysis of framing effects. Organ. Behav. Hum. Decis. Process. 1998, 76, 149–188.
5. Wang, X.T. Self-framing of risky choice. J. Behav. Decis. Mak. 2004, 17, 1–16.
6. Wang, X.T. Framing effects: Dynamics and task domains. Organ. Behav. Hum. Decis. Process. 1996, 68, 145–157.
7. Levy, D.S.; Frethey-Bentham, C.; Cheung, W.K.S. Asymmetric framing effects and market familiarity: Experimental evidence from the real estate market. J. Prop. Res. 2020, 37, 85–104.
8. Shan, L.; Diao, H.; Wu, L. Influence of the framing effect, anchoring effect, and knowledge on consumers' attitude and purchase intention of organic food. Front. Psychol. 2020, 11, 02022.
9. Qu, H.; Daniel, J.L. Is "overhead" a tainted word? A survey experiment exploring framing effects of nonprofit overhead on donor decision. Nonprofit Volunt. Sect. Q. 2021, 50, 397–419.
10. Zhang, B.; Ritchie, B.; Mair, J.; Driml, S. Can message framings influence air passengers' perceived credibility of aviation voluntary carbon offsetting messages? J. Sustain. Tour. 2019, 27, 1416–1437.
11. Liu, P.; Fei, Q.; Liu, J.; Wang, J. Naming is framing: The framing effect of technology name on public attitude toward automated vehicles. Public Underst. Sci. 2021, 30, 691–707.
12. Nuria, R.; van Bavel, R.; José, V.; Briggs, P. Framing effects on online security behavior. Front. Psychol. 2020, 11, 527886.
13. Wen, T.; Xi, Y.L.; Li, B.; Hu, L. Examining framing effect in travel package purchase: An application of double-entry mental accounting theory. Ann. Tour. Res. 2021, 90, 103265.
14. Dixit, A.; Hall, K.D.; Dutta, S. Psychological influences on customer willingness to pay and choice in automated retail settings: Context effects, attribute framing, and perceptions of fairness. Am. J. Bus. 2014, 29, 237–260.
15. Gasteiger, C.; Jones, A.S.; Kleinstäuber, M.; Lobo, M.; Horne, R.; Dalbeth, N.; Petrie, K.J. Effects of message framing on patients' perceptions and willingness to change to a biosimilar in a hypothetical drug switch. Arthritis Care Res. 2020, 72, 1323–1330.

16. Meyerowitz, B.E.; Chaiken, S. The effect of message framing on breast self-examination attitudes, intentions, and behavior. J. Personal. Soc. Psychol. 1987, 52, 500–510.
17. Yang, X.; Chen, S.C.; Zhang, L. Promoting sustainable development: A research on residents' green purchasing behavior from a perspective of the goal-framing theory. Sustain. Dev. 2020, 28, 1208–1219.
18. Wang, L.; Guo, Z.; Zhang, G. Effective destination user-generated advertising: Matching effect between goal framing and self-esteem. Tour. Manag. 2022, 92, 104557.
19. Tanford, S.; Choi, C.; Joe, S.J. The influence of pricing strategies on willingness to pay for accommodations: Anchoring, framing, and metric compatibility. J. Travel Res. 2019, 58, 932–944.
20. Ceylan, M.; Hayran, C. Message framing effects on individuals' social distancing and helping behavior during the COVID-19 pandemic. Front. Psychol. 2021, 12, 579164.
21. Degolia, A.H.; Hiroyasu, E.; Anderson, S.E. Economic losses or environmental gains? Framing effects on public support for environmental management. PLoS ONE 2019, 14, e0220320.
22. Altay, S.; Mercier, H. Framing messages for vaccination supporters. J. Exp. Psychol. Appl. 2020, 26, 567.
23. Fehrenbacher, D.D.; Wiener, M. The dual role of penalty: The effects of IT outsourcing contract framing on knowledge-sharing willingness and commitment. Decis. Support Syst. 2019, 121, 62–71.
24. Channa, H.; Ricker Gilbert, J.; De Groote, H.; Bauchet, J. Willingness to pay for a new farm technology given risk preferences: Evidence from an experimental auction in Kenya. Agric. Econ. 2021, 52, 733–748.
25. Li, M.; Wang, J.; Zhao, P.; Chen, K.; Wu, L. Factors affecting the willingness of agricultural green production from the perspective of farmers' perceptions. Sci. Total Environ. 2020, 738, 140289.
26. Xu, S.; Wang, M.; Liu, Q.; Wang, C.; Zhang, C. Exploring the valence-framing effect: Gain frame enhances behavioral and brain sensitivity to the failure of decision-making under uncertainty. Int. J. Psychophysiol. 2020, 153, 166–172.
27. Zhou, W.; Ning, N.; Zhou, Y.; Qiao, J.; Su, Y.; Zhang, X. Influence of framing effect on risk decision-making behavior of medical students in a university in Harbin under the emergency situation. Med. Soc. 2022, 35, 23–26.
28. Xu, H.; Li, M.; Peng, H. The influence of eye gaze cues on risk decision-making in the economic field: Based on the framing effect paradigm. Psychol. Behav. Res. 2022, 20, 37–44.
29. Chang, S.; Sun, Y. Influence of cognitive load and emotion on the risk decision frame effect of basketball players. J. Tianjin Inst. Phys. Educ. 2021, 36, 569–573.
30. Lin, J.; Chen, Y. The frame effect of college students' risk decision-making in different task areas. J. Guizhou Norm. Univ. 2019, 35, 44–51.
31. Zheng, M.; Chen, Y.; Chi, X. The influence of college students' disposable income on risk decision-making under the framework effect. Bus. Econ. 2018, 36, 175–179.

32. Ki-Aries, D.; Faily, S. Persona-centred information security awareness. Comput. Secur. 2017, 70, 663–674.

33. Hadlington, L.; Popavac, M.; Janicke, H.; Yevseyeva, I.; Jones, K. Exploring the role of work identity and work locus of control in information security awareness. Comput. Secur. 2019, 81, 41–48.

34. Hadlington, L.; Binder, J.; Stanulewicz, N. Exploring role of moral disengagement and counterproductive work behaviours in information security awareness. Comput. Hum. Behav. 2021, 114, 106557.

35. Jaeger, L.; Eckhardt, A. Eyes wide open: The role of situational information security awareness for security-related behaviour. Inf. Syst. J. 2020, 3, 429–472.

36. Khando, K.; Shang, G.; Islam, S.M.; Salman, A. Enhancing employees information security awareness in private and public organisations: A systematic literature review-ScienceDirect. Comput. Secur. 2021, 106, 102267.

37. van der Schyff, K.; Flowerday, S. Mediating effects of information security awareness. Comput. Secur. 2021, 106, 102313.

38. Song, G. The new theory of conformity. Psychol. Sci. 2005, 41, 1174–1178.

39. Gurses, A.P.; Rosen, M.A.; Pronovost, P.J. Improving guideline compliance and healthcare safety using human factors engineering: The case of Ebola. J. Patient Saf. Risk Manag. 2018, 23, 251604351876283.

40. Enwereuzor, I.K.; Adeyemi, B.A.; Onyishi, I.E. Trust in leader as a pathway between ethical leadership and safety compliance. Leadersh. Health Serv. 2020, 33, 201–219.

41. Kilbane, H.; Oxtoby, C.; Tivers, M.S. Staff attitudes to and compliance with the use of a surgical safety checklist. J. Small Anim. Pract. 2020, 61, 332–337.

42. Kühberger, A. The influence of framing on risky decisions: A meta-analysis. Organ. Behav. Hum. Deci. Process 1998, 75, 23–55.

43. Chen, Y.; Wang, Y.; Feng, W. The discipline construction of security information cognition. Sci. Technol. Manag. Res. 2021, 41, 204–210.

44. Chen, H.; Li, W.; Ke, Y. Research progress on security behavior of organizational employee information system. J. Inf. Syst. 2016, 9, 118–134.

9

Tracking Unauthorized Access Using Machine Learning and PCA for Face Recognition Developments

Vasile-Daniel Păvăloaia and George Husac

Department of Accounting, Business Information Systems and Statistics, Faculty of Economics and Business Administration, Alexandru Ioan Cuza University of Iasi, 700506 Iaşi, Romania

ABSTRACT

In the last two decades there has been obtained tremendous improvements in the field of artificial intelligence (AI) especially in the sector of face/facial recognition (FR). Over the years, the world obtained remarkable progress in the technology that enhanced the face detection techniques use on common PCs and smartphones. Moreover, the steadily progress of programming languages, libraries, frameworks, and tools combined with the great passion of developers and researchers worldwide contribute substantially to open-source AI materials that produced machine learning (ML) algorithms available to any scholar with the will to build the software of tomorrow. The study aims to analyze the specialized literature starting from the first prototype delivered by Cambridge University until the most recent discoveries in FR. The purpose is to identify the most proficient algorithms, and the existing gap in the specialized literature. The research builds a FR application based on simplicity and efficiency of code that facilitates a person's face detection using a real time photo and validate the access by querying a given database. The paper brings contribution to the field throughout the literature review analysis as well as by the customized code in Phyton, using ML with Principal Component Analysis (PCA), AdaBoost and MySQL for a myriad of application's development in a variety of domains.

Keywords: *face detection; machine learning algorithms; principal component analysis; AdaBoost*

1. INTRODUCTION

Individual survival in a socially complex environment is heavily reliant on the capacity to understand visual information about a person's age, gender, ethnicity, identity, and emotional state based on that person's face. Despite a range of challenging settings (numerous facial expressions and postures, alterations in light and appearance), human beings can execute face identification with astonishing consistency without conscious effort. FR problem is considered one of the most proficient and profitable application of ML and computer vision [1]. Although FR research utilizing automated or semi-automatic algorithms began in the 1960s [2], has gotten considerable interest in the last 20 years. FR algorithms have a wide range of conceivable applications, which is one reason for its current rising popularity. Another factor is the widespread availability of inexpensive hardware, including digital cameras and video cameras, which has made capturing high-quality, high-resolution photographs in a considerably facile manner. Despite the increased interest, existing state-of-the-art FR algorithms function effectively when facial photographs are taken in consistent and controlled situations. FR systems that perform reliably in uncontrolled conditions, on the other hand, are still a topic of research.

Even though there are a variety of viable biometric techniques that work well today, such as fingerprint analysis as well as iris scans, these techniques require person's participation and adhere to a rather rigorous data collecting process. FR allows for greater flexibility because participants are not needed to collaborate or even be aware that they are being examined and recognized. As a result, FR is a less invasive and perhaps more successful identifying tool. With the advancement of information technology, the desire for an accurate personal identification system based on detecting biological traits is rising, rather than traditional systems that employ ID cards or PINs. The face is the most recognized and identifiable of all bodily features, therefore utilizing it for identification reduces the necessity for direct contact, as well as any psychological or physical opposition, such as that faced while trying to acquire fingerprints.

Within the current research, in the next subchapters, will be performed a literature review that analyzes the body of literature published, starting from the first prototype delivered by Cambridge University [3,4] until the most recent discoveries for identifying the ML algorithms for FR as well as the programming languages and environments that are mostly used (Section 1, Section 1.1 and Section 1.2).

Furthermore, the research aims to build a FR application that facilitates a person's face detection using a photo and validate access by querying a given database. The applicability is immense as it can be integrated in any domain that requires facial identification. While similar applications may require purchase and maintenance, the source of the current one is free and available online: https://github.com/GeorgeHg98/Facial-Recognition-Software (accessed on 8 December 2022).

This article's guiding concepts are simplicity and efficiency. Among others, the research contributes through a clear and succinct guideline on how to build a FR system. It also employs generally available and free development technologies, while the hardware requirements are minimal. This is making it an ideal alternative for academics and/or developers interested in this area. Thus, the solution brings a less costly, efficient, and secure way of authorizing employees' access (Section 2).

The research emphasizes (in Section 3 and Section 4) that, notwithstanding the ethical concerns associated with the widespread use of AI technology, FR systems' capabilities are limitless, and their potential is genuinely immense.

1.1. Literature Review on ML Algorithms for FR

In order to investigate on the existing knowledge, studies, and debates relevant to FR research, as well as the architecture, technology, applications, and the limitations of the software it has been pursued a literature review within the latest research using the Clarivate Web of Science database of articles.

The main research questions that we have addressed throughout the literature review, are:

RQ1. What are technologies (algorithms and programming environment) mostly used for developing a FR application?

RQ2. What are the areas where FR applications are mostly seek?

1.1.1. Methodology Approach

For the purposes of undertaking the literature analysis, the Clarivate Web of Science was used, and the period was from anytime until the current year. The keywords search within Topic (TS), Title (TI), and Abstract (AB) returned 61 articles (Figure 1). After filtering the results (open access-only) a total of 44 reliable results were retained.

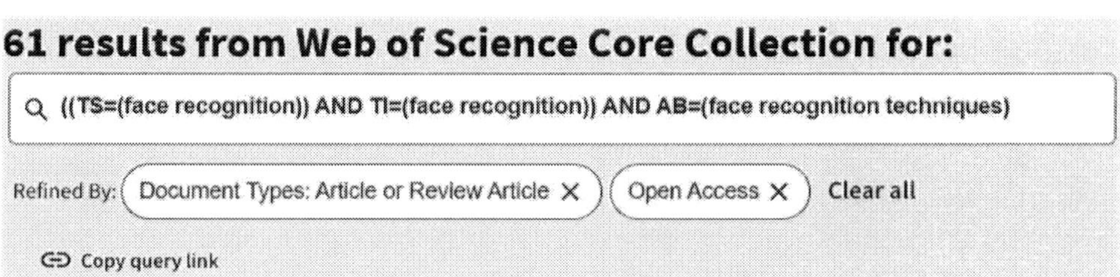

Figure 1.: *The keywords used on Web of Knowledge database platform.*

Furthermore, we have benefited from using Monkeylearn data science platform [5]. Within the platform, the articles have been classified by domains and the content was summarized for a more facile reading and processing.

Monkeylearn platform [6] classified the article's domain into the followings: Security, Services, Computers & Internet, Education, Health & Medicine, Science & Mathematics, Society.

VOS Viewer network visualization (Figure 2) highlights the main words of the selected body of literature, using as input the Abstract, Title and Keywords of the papers included in the analysis. Figure 2 depicts several clusters based on the normalization method used: Association strengths.

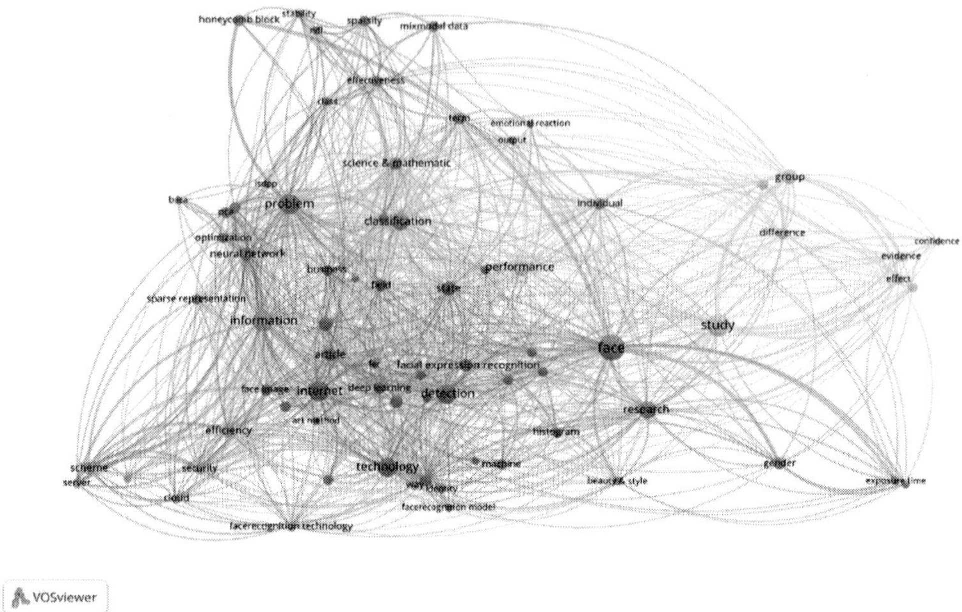

Figure 2.: *VOS Viewer representation of Title, Keywords and Abstract.*

The main four clusters depicted from VOS Viewer representation within Figure 2, are:

Blue—illustrating key features of FR such as face, gender, identity, exposure time, face image, FR model;

Red—referring to technologies specific to FR: deep learning (DL), machine (learning) ML, facial expression recognition, Internet;

Green—highlighting the FR technology's properties: effectiveness, optimization, stability, sparsity, classification;

Light blue—enlist the link between the infrastructure related terms, such as cloud, server, scheme, security, FR technology.

The literature review on FR techniques highlights several ML algorithms for FR that are being proficient in many domains. In the following paragraphs the literature review aims to illustrate the trajectory of FR research in a chronological order, paying a particular attention to finding the answer to the first research question RQ1.

In the beginning of FR era, the researchers [7,8,9] investigating this technique highlight some of the most important results and research trends in 3D and multi-modal FR in their study demonstrating that "the variety and sophistication of algorithmic approaches explored are expanding". The key problems in FR algorithms include improving identification accuracy, increasing resilience to expressions, and, more recently, enhancing algorithm effectiveness [1,9,10,11].

Majority of approaches [1] in FR rely upon Principal Component Analysis (PCA), including [11,12] who investigated the capabilities and limitations of PCA [13] by adjusting the number of eigenvectors and the size of range pictures [14,15,16] use PCA to create a new mapping of 3-D information to a spectrum, or depth, picture and also to partition the face into sub-regions that use the nose as an anchor, PCA to minimize feature space dimensionality, and the shortest distance for matching. Another important research trend is focused on the Iterative Closest Point (ICP) method, which has been used in a variety of ways for 3D form alignment, matching, or both. [17] introduced the very first insight into this type of approach to FR, after which [18] created an extended model to adapt to expressive variations, and [19] recommended to implement ICP to a set of relevant sub-areas rather than the entire face. Since a genuine face 3D form and texture completely represents it, we can consider appropriate to use both types of data (geometry and color or intensity) to boost identification accuracy: Multi-Modal (3D + 2D) biometric authentication is based on this principle.

The academic research conducted by [20] focuses on PCA to evaluate the picture's range and the intensity/color of the picture to the gallery. [21] introduced a four-dimensional (4-D) registration approach based on Iterative Closest Point (ICP) and texture while [22] suggest Eigen decomposition of flattened textures and canonical pictures for multi-modal 3D + 2D identification. Other researchers combine 3D and 2D resemblance scores derived from matching 3D and 2D profiles [23] or derive a feature representation based on Gabor filter responses in 2D and point signatures in 3D [24,25].

More recent attention has focused on the use of PCA but in combination with Python (and less with C++) programming language, as the PCA package is widely available, we will further present the concept of PCA and the mathematical basis of it that mainly relies on eigenvectors, eigenvalue, and eigenfaces.

1.1.2. PCA

In 2002, in the beginning of FR era, PCA was referred to by [26] as the karhunen-loeve transformation. The same authors [26] and others [27,28] initially defined it as the conventional method for data reduction and extraction of features in statistical pattern recognition and signal processing. Since the pattern frequently contains redundant data, mapping it to a feature vector can eliminate this redundancy while preserving most of the pattern's intrinsic relevant information [29]. These selected features play a key role in differentiating input patterns. Figure 3 consists in a visual representation of the PCA approach for FR model.

A 2-D face image of size N*N can also be thought of as a one-dimensional vector of dimension N2. For instance, a face image from the ORL (Olivetti Research Labs) repository with the size 112*92 could be thought of as a vector with the dimension 10,304, or a point in a 10,304-dimensional space. A picture ensemble corresponds to a set of points in this vast space. Face images, because of their pretty much identical arrangement, will not be distributed randomly in this massive image space and can therefore be characterized by a relatively low dimensional subspace. The fundamental concept behind the PCA is to locate the vectors that effectively account for the distribution of face pictures across the full image space. These vectors constitute the "facial space", and it is the subspace of pictures of faces. Every one of those vectors is N2 in length, represents an N*N picture, and stands for a linear model of the original facial images. Researchers call such vectors "eigenfaces" since they are the eigenvectors of the covariance matrix associated with the original face pictures and have a face-like look [29,30].

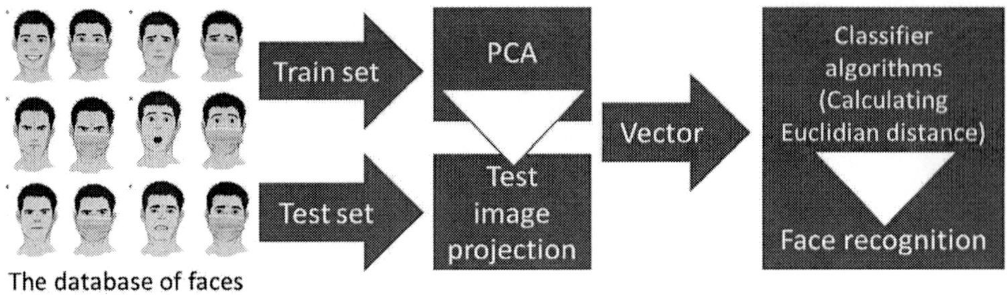

Figure 3.: *PCA approach for FR development.*

The related eigenvalues facilitate the prioritization of the eigenvectors based on their utility in defining picture variance. The eigenface pictures generated by L's eigenvectors span a basis set that may be utilized to characterize the facial image. [31,32,33,34] assessed a restricted implementation of this architecture on 115 pictures (M = 115) of Caucasian men processed in a controlled manner and discovered that 40 eigenfaces (M' = 40) were adequate for a very acceptable description of the facial image. Consequently, a smaller M' can suffice for recognition because a perfect reconstruction of the picture is not required. The procedure is a pattern-matching task rather than an image reconstruction challenge in the context of FR software. The eigenfaces cover an M' dimensional subspace of the initial N2 image space, and therefore the M' significant eigenvectors of the L matrix with the biggest corresponding eigenvalues are adequate for trustworthy representation of the faces in the eigenfaces' face space.

Our Database of Faces (ORL) [35] will be used as a source of images for the following example because it was developed and successfully applied by the Speech, Vision, and Robotics group of Cambridge University [4] in one of the most renowned and respected FR software projects ever made. In addition, this project was one of the first face detection research study of this dimension and one of the pioneers for this technology.

1.1.3. AdaBoost

This academic paper will make use of Python programming language with the Open-Source Computer Vision Library (OpenCV) for developing a FR application. Furthermore, the FR package, the ML algorithms and FR features of Python rely on AdaBoost classifiers [36]. From the above reason, the AdaBoost algorithm will be briefly presented in the next paragraphs.

The main concept of AdaBoost resides in the fact that from the same training set there will be produced two categories of classifiers [36,37]: weak and strong, and then they will be combined. This approach is implemented by altering data distribution. Each sample weight is validated based on whether the categorization of each sample in the training set is correct, as well as whether or not the previous overall classification was correct. The next classifier will train the new dataset and ultimately, all the classifiers will eventually be merged to form a final classification conclusion [38].

AdaBoost's multiple training images are performed by altering all sample weights [3,39,40]. Originally, each sample is assigned the same weight (the weight indicates the probability that the sample will be accepted into the testing phase by the classifier), and training a weak classifier is dependent on this. If the sample is successfully categorized, the weight is decreased. Alternatively, the weight is enhanced. As a result, the incorrectly classified sample will be noted, resulting in a new sample set. The next weak classifier in row, will be constructed by training the new sample set, which will adjust the weight. In an iterative loop, for example, it can obtain a certain number of weak classifiers.

Finally, the strong classifier will be constructed by overlaying the weak classifiers based on a predetermined weight. In order to use the algorithm of AdaBoost [41,42] it assigns a provided training $S = \{(xi,yi) \mid i=1, 2,\ldots,n\}$, $xi \in X$, $yi \in Y$, wherein X is sample description while Y is sample representation. $yi \in (0,1)$ in FR using this algorithm represents that 1 denotes a face while 0 denotes a non-face [43].

1.2. Current Study

Together, the studies considered indicate that AdaBoost algorithm is regard as the most efficient [44] and reliable [45,46] for the current development purpose. Consequently, the FR development in this study will employ the AdaBoost technique since, according to the literature review, it was deemed essential for the creation of a solid FR application.

The paper contains customized code in Phyton, using ML with PCA and MySQL with myriad of applications in multiple domains (security, financial, etc.) and illustrates the development steps for a FR module that can be integrated in a wide variety of applications for plenty domains.

This FR system's compactness makes it extremely simple to build and modify. It takes two steps to add a new individual to the database, and the program recognizes it instantly. Furthermore, in contrast with previous studies that simply give theoretical explications of their approach, the authors made the program available for anybody to use, develop, and further investigate this issue.

2. MATERIALS AND METHODS

There is a growing body of literature that recognizes the importance of FR algorithms for the development of a trustworthy face detection application in a myriad of domains. Thus, the authors contribute to the literature in the domain, by building a FR module to fulfil the gap identified in the literature review, namely the financial domain lacks such developments.

The proposed system consists in a live detection of a person, matching the face with the entries in a database. In addition to the code customization that was developed in Phyton, this practical study brings some contributions to the literature in the domain as it implements a skin tone identification feature for the advanced database search optimizations. Moreover, the development cand be used as an input module for any (sector) application, not just financial, that requires user authentication based on face image recognition.

In the current and following Section 3 (Results) will be illustrated the development phases for the proposed FR module. The dataset used was Our Database of Faces [3] and was obtained freely from AT&T Laboratories Cambridge [35].

The architecture of the proposed FR system developed in this paper is illustrated in Figure 4. Firstly, the sign-up in the application is working similar to any modern mobile banking app, where the user adds an existing photo of himself or even take one, instantly. Most applications ask the user to set an account and a picture is loaded in a special database for faces. Later, the information provided by the client such as first name, last name, address, job, and birthplace are loaded in the MySQL Workbench database which keeps all the user's information, together.

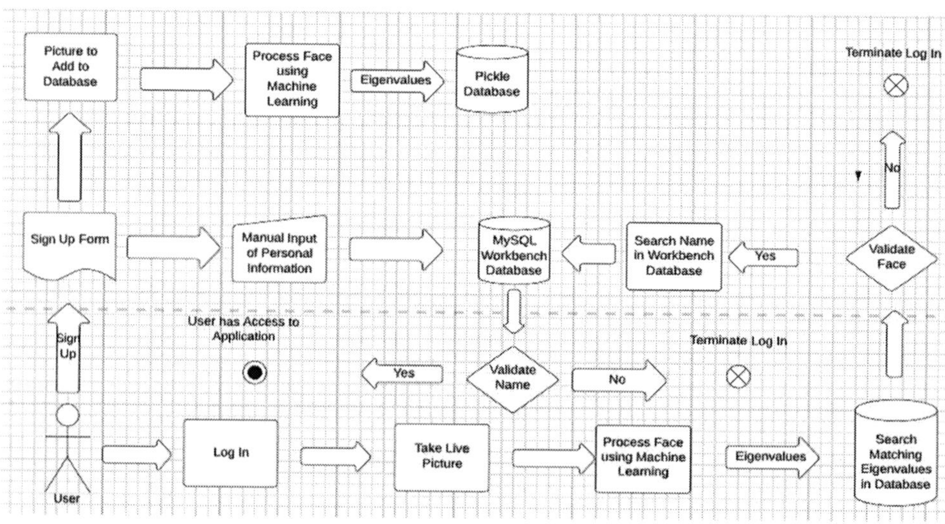

Figure 4.: *Architecture of the developed FR Software.*

After the face is loaded into the Pickle Database, it is analyzed using FR technology and algorithms from Python packages. Furthermore, an ONNX file loads an improved ML and DL model for analyzing the face as explained in the literature review section. Once the face is analyzed, the points of the face that have an outmost importance, usually the ones that do not change, are transformed into eigenvalues, and stored in an array. At this point, everything is set for the user and every time the login function is used, the software will take a live picture of the person that sits in front of the camera or passes by. After the picture is taken, the system will analyze and interpret the face from the photo by using ML. Furthermore, it will crop the face, eliminating the background and other irrelevant information from the picture. After this step, the application will map the eigenvalues of the user and try to match it with the existing information from the database. If any of the faces in the database match the one that is currently being used, this step is verified. Additionally, the system will check that the name and face match so that it can prevent other database users from accessing this user's content. After this phase confirms, the user has complete access to the program and all necessary application's features.

Face verification or face identification are the two general purposes for which FR systems are developed [47]. Verification, often referred to as 1:1 matching, is used to authenticate a person's true identification. Since the person is typically aware that is being scanned and may position properly to ensure that the camera can clearly see his face, FR algorithms typically have excellent accuracy on verification tasks approaching 99%. The challenge arrives for the identification case. The process of identifying someone is known as 1:N or 1:many matchings, and it involves using software to compare an unknown face to a database of known faces. Only under perfect circumstances, with consistent lighting and location, as well as when the participants' face features are visible and not covered, is the degree of precision achievable. Accuracy rates are often far lower in real-world installations. In this respect, we elaborated a chronological analysis of accuracy, and the results are included in Table 1. The purpose is to place the current development accuracy among the existing research.

Table 1.: *A comparison of algorithms accuracy for FR.*

Researchers	Year	Dataset(s)	AI Technique	Accuracy
Yin et al. [48]	2017	NSL-KDD	Recurrent neural network	83.28% (binary), 81.29% (multiclass)
Jia et al. [49]	2019	KDD Cup 99 and NSL-KDD	Deep Neural Network	98%
Vinayakumar et al. [50]	2019	KDD Cup 99, NSL-KDD, Kyoto, UNSW-NB15, WSN-DS and CICIDS 2017	Deep neural network	Big variations between datasets
Kasongo et al. [51]	2019	NSL-KDD	Deep neural network	86.76% (binary), 86.62% (multiclass)
Kanimozhi et al. [52]	2019	UNSW-NB15	Deep neural network	89%

Researchers	Year	Dataset(s)	AI Technique	Accuracy
Mahalakshmi et al. [53]	2021	UNSW-NB15	Convolutional neural network	93.5%
Fu et al. [54]	2022	NSL-KDD	Deep neural network	90.73%
Mijalkovic J., et al. [55]	2022	NSL-KDD and UNSW-NB15	Deep neural network	97% for UNSW-NB15

In the current research, the authors evaluated the algorithm on a small group of persons. The environment was stable, but the algorithm was also checked when the environment alternates and the person (to be recognized) does not look at the camera or has his face tilted in other direction, simulating an involuntary photo. The algorithm proved to recognize the face even in the case of the involuntary photo, maintaining the accuracy of 96%. There have been made multiple tests for each person and the accuracy remained consistent at 96%.

The authors reveal that during the tests, there were few instances when the program failed to identify the face, although the subject was in a stable setting and was looking directly at the camera. This indicates that it was a software error not an algorithm issue. These are the cases that conducted to lowering the accuracy to 96%.

The CSIS [47] test, which was conducted at an airport's boarding gates, is extremely comparable to the test conducted by the authors of this study since it compares a live snapshot with the photo bank. The best FR algorithm in terms of accuracy, according to CSIS's report, obtained a score of 94.4% and this implementation benefited from a variety of FR algorithms. The present algorithm has a higher accuracy than CSIS's where the technology of airport cameras is significantly more sophisticated than the ones used for this research. Thus, the authors consider that the existing algorithm can operate more efficiently and accurately with more sophisticated hardware based on the aforementioned reference [47].

Since the confidence interval for this study was set at 0.3, which is relatively small, the algorithm has a high security rate, which was further demonstrated by the fact that there were never encountered instances of false negative results. This suggests that the application never recognizes a different individual or grants access to a user who is not authorized.

Regarding the accuracy analysis in Table 1, every research study that was conducted evaluated on datasets that compare stable images rather than live images with images from databases. The current model proposes a real time FR system, and it is not built for photo comparison. The authors believe that the proposed model will be at least as competitive in matter of accuracy with the other algorithms that score higher [49,55] if it will be programmed to analyze datasets.

3. RESULTS

The developed application was written in Python programming language and the code editor chosen is Visual Studio Code. Python is a general-purpose [56], high-level, interpreted programming language. Its design concept prioritizes code readability by employing heavy indentation. Python is garbage-collected and flexibly typed. It covers a wide variety of computing paradigms, including organized (especially procedural), object-oriented, and functional programming. Due to its extensive standard library, it is frequently referred to as a "batteries included" language. Python is routinely ranked among the top programming languages and because of the growing popularity of ML and AI an increased number of authors and software developers name it the programming language of the future.

Visual Studio Code, a.k.a. VS Code, is a source-code editor developed by Microsoft for Windows, Linux, and macOS. It provides support for debugging, syntax highlighting, intelligent code completion, snippets, code refactoring, and integrated Git are among the features.

The Python version used in this manuscript is Python 3.9.7 and the package installer used is Pip 21.2.3. The packages installed through pip in the computer's environment are the following (Figure 5):

```
from xml.dom import NotFoundErr
import cv2
import numpy as np
import k_means as km
import mysql.connector
import pickle
import face_recognition as fr
import onnx
import onnxruntime
from onnx_tf.backend import prepare
```

Figure 5.: *Python libraries used.*

- OpenCV—a programming function library targeted mostly at real-time computer vision, this library uses ML algorithms to search for a face in the given picture;
- NumPy—a Python library that adds support for big, multi-dimensional arrays and matrices, as well as a wide variety of high-level mathematical functions to operate on these arrays;

- MySQL Connector—a Python library that provides interaction between the MySQL Workbench Database and the application;
- Pickle—a library that serializes and deserializes Python object structures. It is used in this material to serialize the array of face coordinates for the database of faces loaded in the application;
- Open Neural Network Exchange (ONNX) library—an open-source AI ecosystem comprising of technology businesses and academic groups that build open standards for describing ML techniques and software tools to foster AI innovation and cooperation.
- ONNX Runtime—a cross-platform network accelerator for DL with a versatile interface for integrating hardware-specific libraries.

The database used for this development is a MySQL Workbench database (Figure 6). MySQL Workbench is a visual database design system that involves SQL programming, administration, database design, construction, and maintenance for the MySQL database system in a single integrated working environment. The database is loaded with 5726 different persons and their information (details are displayed on Figure 6).

```
1 •    SELECT * FROM persons.persons;
```

Result Grid | Filter Rows: | Export: | Wrap Cell Content: | Fetch rows:

firstname	lastname	age	skin_tone	job	birth_place	address
Jason	Petty	49	light	Barristerâ€™s clerk	FeteÈ™ti	1300 Gilmer Ave, Tallassee AL 36078
Teri	Garr	38	light	Amenity horticulturist	Breaza	890 Odum Road, Gardendale AL 35071
Rafael	Vinoly	47	light	Public affairs consultant (research)	Covasna	6140A Univ Drive, Huntsville AL 35806
Jason	Petty	38	light	Museum/gallery exhibition officer	Bragadiru	7855 Moffett Rd, Semmes AL 36575
Teri	Garr	58	light	Personal assistant	Tulcea	2900 S Mem PkwyDrake Ave, Huntsville AL 35801
Rafael	Vinoly	31	light	Homeless support worker	Solca	70 Pleasant Valley Street, Methuen MA 1844
Joey	Mantia	18	light	Illustrator	Ovidiu	350 E Fairmount Ave, Lakewood NY 14750
Laura	Bush	27	light	Secretary	Uricani	450 Highland Ave, Salem MA 1970
Didier	Defago	37	light	Biotechnologist	VaÈ™cÄƒu	780 Lynnway, Lynn MA 1905
Roger	King	45	light	Marketing manager (social media)	Beclean	67 Newton Rd, Danbury CT 6810
Catherine	Woodard	49	light	Clinical biochemist	Reghin	655 Boston Post Rd, Old Saybrook CT 6475
Paul	Wals	27	light	Nanoscientist	Podu Iloaiei	3300 South Oates Street, Dothan AL 36301
Janet	Leigh	41	light	Lecturer (further education)	Huedin	1818 State Route 3, Fulton NY 13069
Vladimir	Putin	46	light	Debt/finance adviser	BoldeÈ™ti...	145 Kelley Blvd, Millbrook AL 36054
Jean	Carnahan	36	light	Human resources officer	Brad	6140A Univ Drive, Huntsville AL 35806

Figure 6.: *MySQL Workbench Database.*

The application consists of six Python files that contain different classes and methods that made the FR possible, an ONNX file which loads the ML algorithms, other files responsible for loading data in the database, and pictures used in the process. An overview of these can be depicted from Figure 7.

Firstly, the ONNX File ultra_light_640.onnx was added into the application for the application to have the trained ML algorithm available. Secondly, the model was loaded by executing the file onnxModelLoader, and the loader can be seen in Figure 8.

When the model is loaded, the database entry ("person") was created in MySQL Workbench and the software was connected to it with the SQL Database loading the database with the 5726 entries/persons (Figure 9).

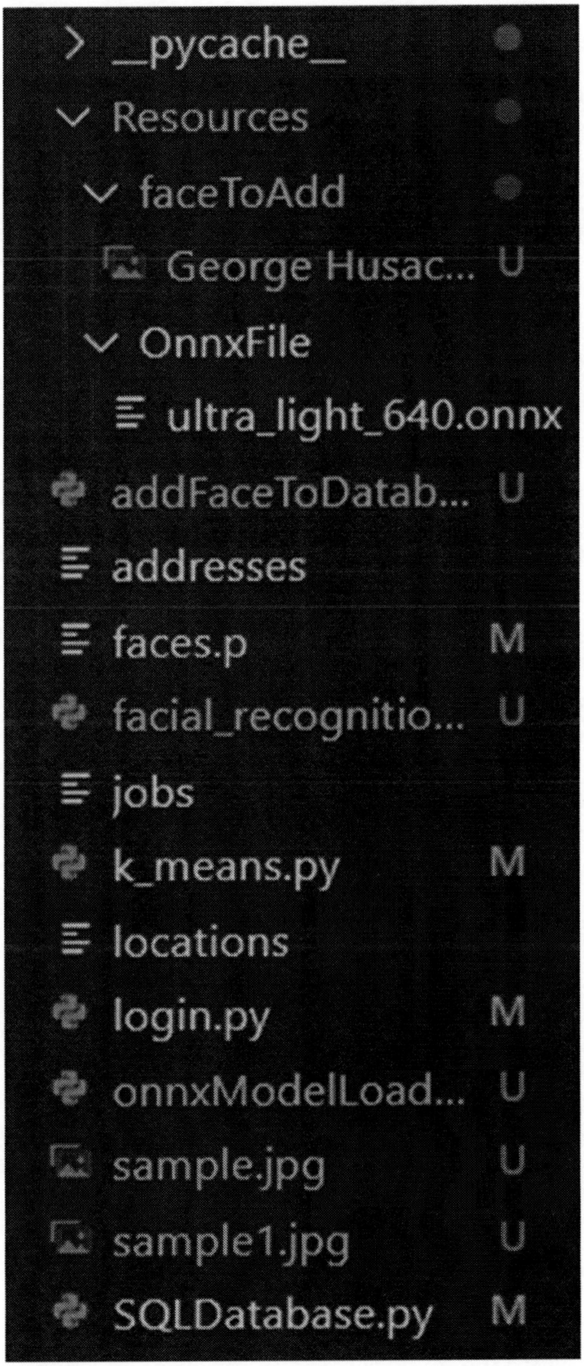

***Figure 7.:** An overview of application files.*

```
import onnx
import onnxoptimizer

onnx_model = onnx.load("Resources/OnnxFile/ultra_light_640.onnx")
passes = ["extract_constant_to_initializer", "eliminate_unused_initializer"]
optimized_model = onnxoptimizer.optimize(onnx_model, passes)

onnx.save(optimized_model, "Resources/OnnxFile/ultra_light_640.onnx")
```

Figure 8.: *Code of the model loader.*

```
try:
    conn = mysql.connector.connect(host = "localhost",
                                   database = "persons",
                                   user = "test",
                                   password = "test")

    if conn.is_connected():
        print("Connected to mysql")

        addresses = open("addresses", "r").read().split("\n")
        locations = open("locations", "r").read().split("\n")
        jobs_file = open("jobs", "r").read().split("\n")
        jobs = list()
        for j in jobs_file:
            jobs.append(j.split(":")[0])

        persons = pickle.load(open("faces.p", "rb"))

        mycursor = conn.cursor()

        for person in list(persons):

            names =person.split(" ")
```

Figure 9.: *Partial Code of loading SQL Database File.*

In the next step, the file addFaceToTheDatabase was created by the person/ user to load his face into the database (1) and for authentication purpose (2). The coordinates of the newly entered face were stored in an array and loaded into the database of faces (Figure 10).

```
import pickle
import os
import face_recognition as fr

RESOURCE_PATH = 'Resources/faceToAdd/'

name = [x[2] for x in os.walk(RESOURCE_PATH)][0][0]

person_image = fr.load_image_file(RESOURCE_PATH + name)
person_encoding = fr.face_encodings(person_image)[0]

print (name)

persons = pickle.load(open("faces.p", "rb"))

persons[name.split('.')[0]] = person_encoding

pickle.dump(persons,open('faces.p','wb'))

print (persons)
```

Figure 10.: *Partial Code of the added face to the database file.*

When all the above prerequisites are set, the developer can commence building the FR file, which is responsible for taking pictures (1), recognizing the face (2) while cropping out the face and removing everything else, analyzing the given face (3), and transforming the face into eigenvalues and coordinates (4). Later, while algorithm has all these actions fulfilled, it queries the database for matching arrays of eigenvalues with a small confidence level of 0.3. While most modern FR systems use a higher confidence level (0.53 for, e.g.,), this proves that the system built by is more precise and has a smaller chance of authorizing the wrong person. After it tries to match the faces, it will send a message to the login file. This file has a class named FR and uses four specialized functions: recognize_feed, hard_nms, approximate and searchInDatabase. Few samples of code can be seen in Figure 11.

Lastly, the message from the FR class is sent to the login class where it will be validated if the face matches a database record (1) and if the name matches the face (2). When both conditions are met, the app will authorize the user and print a welcome message. Else, when the validation process fails the app will unauthorize the user attempt to log in and terminate the process. The login class example can be seen in Figure 12.

```
def recognize_feed(self, video_capture):
    onnx_model = onnx.load(self.MODEL_PATH)
    onnx_rt_session = onnxruntime.InferenceSession(self.MODEL_PATH)
    input_name = onnx_rt_session.get_inputs()[0].name

    ret, frame = video_capture.read()

    cv2.imwrite("sample1.jpg", frame)

    if frame is not None and frame.any():
        height, width, _ = frame.shape

        img = cv2.cvtColor(frame, cv2.COLOR_BGR2RGB)
        img = cv2.resize(img, (640, 480))
        img_mean = np.array([127, 127, 127])
        img = (img - img_mean) / 128
        img = np.transpose(img, [2, 0, 1])
        img = np.expand_dims(img, axis=0)
        img = img.astype(np.float32)

        confidences, boxes = onnx_rt_session.run(None, {input_name: img})
        boxes = self.approximate(width, height, confidences[0], boxes[0], 0.7)

        box = boxes[0]

        x1, y1, x2, y2 = box
        frame[0:(y2 - y1), 0:(x2-x1)] = frame[y1:y2, x1:x2]
        cv2.imwrite("sample.jpg", frame[y1-25:y2+25, x1-25:x2+25])

        match = self.searchInDatabase("./sample.jpg")
```

```
def hard_nms(self, box_probs):
    overlap_thresh = 0.3

    if len(box_probs) == 0:
        return list()

    picked = list()

    x1 = box_probs[:, 0]
    x2 = box_probs[:, 1]
    y1 = box_probs[:, 2]
    y2 = box_probs[:, 3]

    area = (x2 - x1) * (y2 - y1)
    indexes = np.argsort(y2)
    while len(indexes) > 0:
        last_index = indexes[-1]
        picked.append(last_index)
        last_index_index = len(indexes) - 1
        ignore = [last_index_index]

        for pos in range(0, last_index_index):
            current_index = indexes[pos]

            max_x1 = max(x1[last_index], x1[current_index])
            max_y1 = max(y1[last_index], y1[current_index])
            min_x2 = min(x2[last_index], x2[current_index])
            min_y2 = min(y2[last_index], y2[current_index])

            width = max(0, min_x2 - max_x1)
            height = max(0, min_y2 - max_y1)
```

```
def approximate(self, width, height, confidences, boxes, probability_th):
    chosen_boxes_prob = list()

    for index in range(1, confidences.shape[1]):
        probabilities = confidences[:, index]
        mask = probabilities > probability_th
        probabilities = probabilities[mask]

        if probabilities.shape[0] != 0:
            mini_boxes = boxes[mask, :]
            box_prob = np.concatenate([mini_boxes, probabilities.reshape(-1, 1)], axis=1)
            chosen_boxes_prob.append(self.hard_nms(box_prob))

    if chosen_boxes_prob:
        chosen_boxes_prob = np.concatenate(chosen_boxes_prob)
        chosen_boxes_prob[:, 0] *= width
        chosen_boxes_prob[:, 1] *= height
        chosen_boxes_prob[:, 2] *= width
        chosen_boxes_prob[:, 3] *= height
        return chosen_boxes_prob[:, :4].astype(np.int32)

    return np.array([])
```

Figure 11.: *Code Samples of FR class.*

This study provides new insights into FR code, as it uses a k means class (Figure 12) that investigates the facial color of the person to generate the skin color. This information facilitates faster search, thus optimizes the database queries. Future developments of the current application will bring contributions towards age, race, and gender evaluation.

When the application is used for analyzing the skin color, improves the search process within the database. Thus, this function improves the speed of matching the right record because it searches among the entries from the same skin color making the search by 50% faster. This mechanism also increases the security of the application. A code sample of this class can be seen in Figure 13.

```
import cv2
import facial_recognition as fr

recognizer = fr.facial_recognition()

def login():
        resultedName = recognizer.recognize_feed(video_capture= cv2.VideoCapture(0))

        return validate(resultedName)

def validate():
        resultedName = recognizer.recognize_feed(video_capture= cv2.VideoCapture(0))
        print(resultedName)
        if resultedName == "George Husac":
            return (True, resultedName)
        return (False, resultedName)

valid = validate()

if valid[0] == True:
        print('Welcome to the App ' + valid[1] + '!')

else: print("Unauthorized Access")
```

Figure 12.: *Login class.*

4. DISCUSSION

The present research extracts the essential information (technologies, algorithms, programming environments, functions, etc.) from the specialized literature towards the development of a FR application. Consequently, the central thesis of this paper is the development of a customized FR application, with skin color features for increasing the search speed, and its application in various fields including financial sector. Therefore, in the following Section 4.1, Section 4.2, Section 4.3 and Section 4.4 several potential implementations of the developed application will be illustrated and delivered as case studies that can be used in classes in the teaching process of technical disciplines.

4.1. Authorization Access for Employees, in Any Domain

One potential real-world application of this study is the replacement of RFID access cards used in offices around the world to authorize employees access in the office buildings. In this case, the system can be implemented at the entrance doors and the software will be a cost-efficient solution and a safer alternative.

According to a study [57] in the RFID Journal, the market for RFID cards, readers, and software is expected to reach 10.7 billion USD by the end of 2022 and 17.4 billion USD by 2026. These predicaments are announced by similar websites in the RFID industry, stating that this sector is continuously growing. Our implementation can serve companies, hospitals, airports, stores, shopping malls, educational institutions and basically any entity that need to restrict access of people to rooms or buildings.

```
def k_means(img_path):
    k = 1

    img = Image.open(img_path, 'r')

    width, height = img.size
    basewidth = 300

    if width > basewidth:
        wpercent = (basewidth/float(img.size[0]))
        hsize = int((float(img.size[1])*float(wpercent)))
        height = hsize
        width = basewidth
        img = img.resize((basewidth, hsize), Image.ANTIALIAS)

    pixels_value = list(img.getdata())

    miu = k_means_pp(pixels_value, k)
    former_miu = [None] * k
    clusters = list()
    former_clusers = list()
    for i in range(k):
        clusters.append(list())
    J = 0
    previous_J = (None, None, None)

    iter = 0
    shouldContinue = True

    while shouldContinue:
```

Figure 13.: *K Means Class.*

A fast cost calculation shows that the median price as revealed by the RFID Journal [57] of a low-frequency reader type and a circuit board, can cost around 100 USD, while a fully complete standalone reader can cost up to 750 USD. The active tags are 15–25 USD depending on the packaging of the tag and if it is labeled. Taking into consideration that the average-size company has around 5000 employees only the tag cost led to 100.000 USD without adding the cost of the receivers. In addition, the maintenance of the whole RFID system can become expensive, and the companies would need a verified company to do this. In the meantime, a camera to be attached to the door is around 25 USD and this cost is not even necessary for companies as most of them already have implemented some sort of video surveillance.

Surveillance cameras can be used as the technology that captures the image of the person that require institutional access, and the only cost remaining would be that of a PC (laptop, desktop computer) and a database connected to it.

Such a solution can save companies billions of USD and increase security check as the RFID tags have a major flaw, anyone with the tag can enter and the system cannot verify if it is truly the person that is authorized to enter the facility. A conceptual implementation scheme is included in Figure 14.

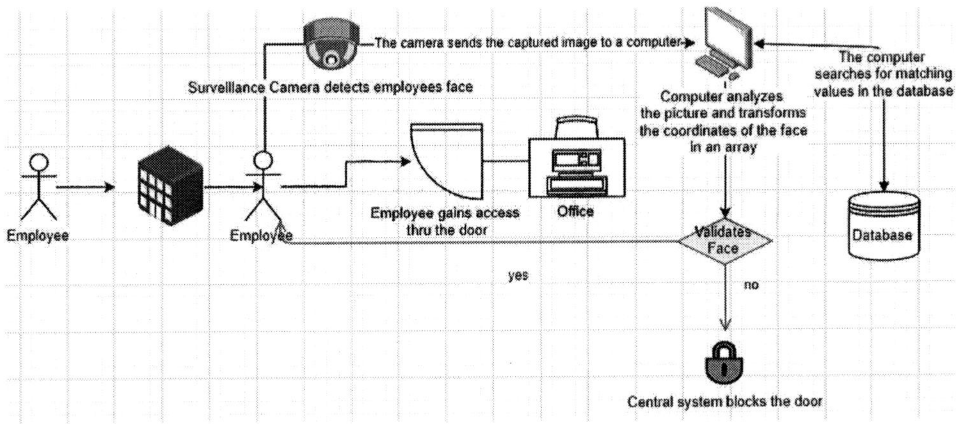

***Figure 14.**: The author's vision on the implementation of an authorization system for employees.*

4.2. Airport Security

Customs and border screening is one of the most unpleasant aspects of any traveler's trip. Passenger embarkation is one of the numerous obstacles to air transportation security checks. Indeed, such a proposal cannot fully replace the need for physical presence of customs agents because the FR software is flawless in 99% of the cases but such implementation will speed up the authentication process. In such an implementation, the customs agents will deal only with the software errors (around 1% of the cases) while the vast majority will pass. The literature states that human error is much higher than software error. Thus, the proposed implementation made possible throughout our application will make airports a lot more efficient in authenticating the passengers. Briefly, a solution based on our app will require the following steps: user scan the passport (1), and then step in front of a camera (2) to pass the photo verification and name match (3). If the last step is successful, the passenger is allowed to pass the security area. Contrary, will returned and be processed by a human customs employee. As a result, the time required by the identification process will be reduced substantially.

4.3. Law Enforcement

FR software can help law enforcement agencies to identify and, later, catch fugitive in a lot of different situations. For example, if the police are seeking for a person with a criminal record, the surveillance cameras installed in almost any city on the planet can identify the person by the FR software built in this study. Moreover, cameras installed at the country borders can prevent a fugitive from exiting a country if they are banned. Another use case for this system related to law enforcement is that it can help track phone thieves. For example, if a user's phone is stolen, the software can be set to take a picture of the one who stole the phone. When the thief tries to use the phone, his photo is uploaded automatically to the phone's cloud. Having the photo of the prospective thief, the phone owner can ask authorities for help and identify the thief.

4.4. Financial Sector

Regarding the financial sector, the users of financial or other types of customer-oriented applications are willingly giving their fingerprints, facial scans, or other biometric information. This proves that in the commercial sector of these technologies the advancement is purely oriented around security and effectiveness. It is visible from the market trend that increased applications are implementing FR software as a security measure. Commercial banks are the most common financial institutions. Banking used to be carried out in huge rooms of buildings, which was a time-consuming chore for both clients and banking staff, but today people choose to use online banking instead of going to the bank, which makes it easier for users to complete transactions. The pandemic context and the growing popularity and demand of online banking and mobile applications forced commercial banks to invest in technology and IT development. Most of these financial institutions developed applications to make financial operations easier and more efficient in matters of time and costs. However, due to a significant increase in fraudulent operations, there has been a perceived lack of security in the network as demand for online banking has grown. According to the numbers published by the FBI and backed by Cybersecurity Ventures and Accenture the losses of victims of internet crime are estimated at 4.2 billion dollars. In addition, The Federal Communications Commission reported that 40% of theft in 2020 in the U.S.A. involved smartphones, this can be reduced by using FR software and can help law enforcement rapidly identify the thieves.

One of the many ways that financial institutions may improve security and accessibility is through FR. Most of them are using, now, this biometric authentication method which proves that the technology is useful and secure. This scientific study proposes to examine the use of FR as a method of authentication across the financial sector of this technology with the focus on tracking unauthorized access in a financial application. The suggested system's major goal is to provide secure banking authentication to end users while also tracking fraudulent login operations. This will be achieved by understanding the software and the literature related to it and creating an application that can easily recognize faces to grant permission in a financial application as well as to keep track of unauthorized access in that application by sending the ungranted permissions with the captured photo to a database that can easily be accessed from another device.

5. CONCLUSIONS

The aim of the present research was to examine the literature review in the FR domain for identifying the main algorithms, programming environments and domains that require human authentication. The results of the literature analysis were fructified in the development of a customized FR solution. Several case studies where such an application can be implemented were presented in Section 4.

This article's primary concepts are simplicity and efficiency in code development, and it applies the principles of clean code presented by Robert C. Martin in [58,59]. The developed application can be used with a device capable of establishing a person's identification and it is designed to overlay extra information about the scanned individual with the user's vision. The software was built in order to achieve FR proved to be efficient, reliable, and useful for future adaptations. The accuracy rate is 96% and is among the best according with the study included in Table 1. Although other studies have found higher accuracy, they lack the real-time photo shoot and authorization that the present study provides.

In this material, the solution was explained, and the positive or negative arguments were illustrated. Furthermore, the fundamental algorithms of this technology were explained and detailed. The proposed system used a Single-Shot Detector model that was utilized to identify the boundary coordinates of the items within the picture for FR. As mentioned in Section 3, the proposed system uses a Visual Studio Code editor, was written in Python programming language with the necessary libraries to fulfill its purpose, used an ONNX trained ML model and a MySQL Workbench Database in order to store the information provided.

Section 4 displays numerous examples of how the proposed method may be applied in the real world while providing substantial financial advantages. The following are only a few of the contributions this paper makes to the field:

- firstly, such a solution proves to be smart, safe, and a very affordable access control tool that can be applied in any business or entity throughout the world;
- secondly, this software can facilitate the embarking process safer, quicker, and more efficient in any airport;
- thirdly, the proposed system can help law enforcement agencies to prevent criminal activities and to catch fugitive persons faster by reducing the costs and the time used by the Law Enforcement Agencies;
- fourthly, this application can prove to be very efficient in the banking system and in smart retail domains, too.

Considering the use cases of this application in the financial sector, the resources that it will save in any of the domains listed, and the fact that it will make any FR operation safer, cheaper, and more effective proves that this software has utility in the real world.

Future development of code will bring additional features, such as age, race, and gender recognition.

Author Contributions

Conceptualization, V.-D.P. and G.H.; methodology, V.-D.P.; software, G.H.; investigation, G.H.; resources, G.H.; writing—original draft, G.H.; writing—review & editing, V.-D.P.; project administration, V.-D.P. All authors have read and agreed to the published version of the manuscript.

REFERENCES

1. Pati, R.; Pujari, A.K.; Gahan, P. Face recognition using particle swarm optimization based block ICA. Multimed. Tools Appl. 2021, 80, 35685–35695.
2. Face Processing: Advanced Modeling and Methods, 1st ed.; Zhao, W.; Chellappa, R. (Eds.) Academic Press: Cambridge, MA, USA, 2011; pp. 15–36.
3. Samaria, F.S.; Harter, A.C. Parameterisation of a stochastic model for human face identification. In Proceedings of the 1994 IEEE Workshop on Applications of Computer Vision, Saratosa, FL, USA, 5–7 December 1994; pp. 138–142.
4. AT&T Laboratories Cambridge. The Database of Faces.
5. Clarivate Web of Science.
6. Monkeylearn. No-Code Text Analytics.
7. Bowyer, K.W.; Chang, K.; Flynn, P. A survey of approaches and challenges in 3D and multi-modal 3D+2D face recognition. Comput. Vis. Image Underst. 2006, 101, 1–15.
8. Bowyer, K.W.; Chang, K.; Flynn, P. A survey of 3D and multi-modal 3D + 2D face recognition. In Proceedings of the International Conference on Pattern Recognition (ICPR) 2004, Cambridge, UK, 26 August 2004.
9. Abate, A.F.; Nappi, M.; Riccio, D.; Sabatino, G. 2D and 3D face recognition: A survey. Pattern Recognit. Lett. 2007, 28, 1885–1906.
10. Cheng, Z.; Zhu, X.; Gong, S. Face re-identification challenge: Are face recognition models good enough? Pattern Recognit. 2020, 107, 107422.
11. Krishna, I.M.V.; Kanth, R.M.; Sowjanya, V. Machine Learning Based Face Recognition System. ECS Trans. 2022, 107, 19979.
12. Lee, G. Fast and more accurate incremental-decremental principal component analysis algorithm for online learning of face recognition. J. Electron. Imaging 2021, 30, 043012.
13. Gang, A.; Bajwa, W.U. A linearly convergent algorithm for distributed principal component analysis. Signal Process. 2022, 193, 108408.
14. Kumar, R.S. Principal Component Analysis: In-Depth Understanding through Image Visualization.
15. Derksen, L.; Xifara, D. Visualising High-Dimensional Datasets Using PCA and t-SNE.
16. Pan, Z.; Healey, G.; Prasad, M.; Tromberg, B. Face recognition in hyperspectral images. IEEE Trans. Pattern Anal. Mach. Intell. 2003, 25, 1552–1560.
17. Medioni, G.; Waupotitsch, R. Face modeling and recognition in 3-D. In Proceedings of the 2003 IEEE International SOI Conference, Nice, France, 17 October 2003.

18. Lu, X.; Jain, A.K.; Colbry, D. Matching 2.5D face scans to 3D models. IEEE Trans. Pattern Anal. Mach. Intell. 2005, 28, 31–43.
19. Chang, K.J.; Bowyer, K.W.; Flynn, P.J. Effects on facial expression in 3D face recognition. In Biometric Technology for Human Identification II, Proceedings of the Defense and Security Conference, Orlando, FL, USA, 28 March–1 April 2005; Jain, A.K., Ratha, N.K., Eds.; Society of Photo-Optical Instrumentation Engineers: Bellingham, WA, USA, 2005; Volume 5779, pp. 132–143.
20. Tsalakanidou, F.; Tzovaras, D.; Strintzis, M.G. Use of depth and color eigenfaces for face recognition. Pattern Recognit. Lett. 2003, 24, 1427–1435.
21. Papatheodorou, T.; Rueckert, D. Evaluation of automatic 4D face recognition using surface and texture registration. In Proceedings of the Sixth IEEE International Conference on Automatic Face and Gesture Recognition, Seoul, Republic of Korea, 19 May 2004; pp. 321–326.
22. Bronstein, A.M.; Bronstein, M.M.; Kimmel, R. Expression-invariant 3D face recognition. In Audio- and Video-Based Biometric Person Authentication; Kittler, J., Nixon, M.S., Eds.; Lecture Notes in Computer Science Volume 2688; Springer: Berlin/Heidelberg, Germany, 2003; pp. 62–70.
23. Beumier, C.; Acheroy, M. Automatic 3D face authentication. Image Vis. Comput. 2000, 18, 315–321.
24. Wang, Y.; Pan, G.; Wu, Z.; Han, S. Sphere-Spin-Image: A Viewpoint-Invariant Surface Representation for 3D Face Recognition. In Computational Science–ICCS 2004, Proceedings of the 4th International Conference on Computational Science (ICCS 2004), Kraków, Poland, 6–9 June 2004; Bubak, M., van Albada, G.D., Sloot, P.M.A., Dongarra, J., Eds.; Springer: Berlin/Heidelberg, Germany, 2004; pp. 427–434.
25. Lu, R.; Zhu, F.; Hao, Y.; Wu, Q. Simple and efficient improvement of spin image for three-dimensional object recognition. Opt. Eng. 2016, 55, 113102.
26. Papoulis, A.; Pillai, S.U. Probability, Random Variables, Stochastic Processes; McGraw Hill: New York, NY, USA, 2002; pp. 120–151.
27. Haykin, S. Neural Networks: A Comprehensive Foundation; Macmillan Publishing: New York, NY, USA, 1999.
28. Bera, S.; Shrivastava, V.K. Analysis of various optimizers on deep convolutional neural network model in the application of hyperspectral remote sensing image classification. Int. J. Remote Sens. 2020, 41, 2664–2683.
29. Eleyan, A.; Demirel, H. PCA and LDA Based Neural Networks for Human Face Recognition. In Face Recognition; Delac, K., Grgic, M., Eds.; IntechOpen: London, UK, 2007; pp. 93–106.
30. Delac, K.; Grgic, M.; Grgic, S. Image compression effects in face recognition systems. In Face Recognition; Delac, K., Grgic, M., Eds.; IntechOpen: London, UK, 2007; pp. 75–92.
31. Sharma, R.; Patterh, M.S. A Systematic Review of PCA and Its Different Form for Face Recognition. Int. J. Sci. Eng. Res. 2014, 5, 1306–1309.

32. Bazama, A.; Mansur, F.; Alsharef, N. Security System by Face Recognition. AlQalam J. Med. Appl. Sci. 2021, 4, 58–67.
33. Patel, V.M.; Chen, Y.-C.; Chellappa, R.; Phillips, P.J. Dictionaries for image and video-based face recognition. J. Opt. Soc. Am. A 2014, 31, 1090–1103.
34. Sirovich, L.; Kirby, M. Low-dimensional procedure for the characterization of human faces. J. Opt. Soc. Am. A 1987, 4, 519–524.
35. ORL: Our Database of Faces by AT&T Laboratories Cambridge.
36. Bing, H.; Xianfeng, H.; Ruizhen, H. Research of Face Detection Based on AdaBoost and ASM. Open Cybern. Syst. J. 2014, 8, 183–190.
37. Gormley, M. Lecture Notes on Introduction to Machine Learning: PCA + AdaBoost. 2018.
38. Mahmood, Z.; Ali, T.; Khattak, S.; Khan, S.U. A comparative study of baseline algorithms of face recognition. In Proceedings of the 2014 12th International Conference on Frontiers of Information Technology, Islamabad, Pakistan, 17–19 December 2014; pp. 263–268.
39. Ehlers, A.; Baumann, F.; Spindler, R.; Glasmacher, B.; Rosenhahn, B. PCA enhanced training data for adaboost. In Computer Analysis of Images and Patterns, Proceedings of the 2011 International Conference on Computer Analysis of Images and Patterns (CAIP 2011), Seville, Spain, 29–31 August 2011; Real, P., Diaz-Pernil, D., Molina-Abril, H., Berciano, A., Kropatsch, W., Eds.; Springer: Berlin/Heidelberg, Germany, 2011; pp. 410–419.
40. Kao, I.-H.; Chan, C.-Y. Comparison of Eye and Face Features on Drowsiness Analysis. Sensors 2022, 22, 6529.
41. Yang, Y. Smart community security monitoring based on artificial intelligence and improved machine learning algorithm. J. Intell. Fuzzy Syst. 2020, 38, 7351–7363.
42. He, D.; He, X.; Yuan, R.; Li, Y.; Shen, C. Lightweight network-based multi-modal feature fusion for face anti-spoofing. Vis. Comput. 2022.
43. Wang, C.; Xu, S.; Yang, J. Adaboost Algorithm in Artificial Intelligence for Optimizing the IRI Prediction Accuracy of Asphalt Concrete Pavement. Sensors 2021, 21, 5682.
44. Natras, R.; Soja, B.; Schmidt, M. Ensemble Machine Learning of Random Forest, AdaBoost and XGBoost for Vertical Total Electron Content Forecasting. Remote Sens. 2022, 14, 3547.
45. Ahmad, I.; Ul Haq, Q.E.; Imran, M.; Alassafi, M.O.; AlGhamdi, R.A. An Efficient Network Intrusion Detection and Classification System. Mathematics 2022, 10, 530.
46. Ding, Y.; Zhu, H.; Chen, R.; Li, R. An Efficient AdaBoost Algorithm with the Multiple Thresholds Classification. Appl. Sci. 2022, 12, 5872.
47. Crumpler, W. How Accurate are Facial Recognition Systems–and Why Does It Matter? Strategic Technologies Blog. 2020.
48. Yin, C.; Zhu, Y.; Fei, J.; He, X. A Deep Learning Approach for Intrusion Detection Using Recurrent Neural Networks. IEEE Access 2017, 5, 21954–21961.

49. Jia, Y.; Wang, M.; Wang, Y. Network intrusion detection algorithm based on deep neural network. IET Inf. Secur. 2019, 13, 48–53.

50. Vinayakumar, R.; Alazab, M.; Soman, K.P.; Poornachandran, P.; Al-Nemrat, A.; Venkatraman, S. Deep Learning Approach for Intelligent Intrusion Detection System. IEEE Access 2019, 7, 41525–41550.

51. Kasongo, S.M.; Sun, Y. A Deep Learning Method With Filter Based Feature Engineering for Wireless Intrusion Detection System. IEEE Access 2019, 7, 38597–38607.

52. Kanimozhi, V.; Jacob, P. UNSW-NB15 dataset feature selection and network intrusion detection using deep learning. Int. J. Recent Technol. Eng. 2019, 7, 443–446.

53. Mahalakshmi, G.; Uma, E.; Aroosiya, M.; Vinitha, M. Intrusion Detection System Using Convolutional Neural Network on UNSW NB15 Dataset. In Advances in Parallel Computing Technologies and Applications; Hemanth, D.J., Elhosney, M., Nguyen, T.N., Lakshmann, S., Eds.; IOS Press: Amsterdam, The Netherlands, 2021; Volume 40, p. 1.

54. Fu, Y.; Du, Y.; Cao, Z.; Li, Q.; Xiang, W. A Deep Learning Model for Network Intrusion Detection with Imbalanced Data. Electronics 2022, 11, 898.

55. Mijalkovic, J.; Spognardi, A. Reducing the False Negative Rate in Deep Learning Based Network Intrusion Detection Systems. Algorithms 2022, 15, 258.

56. Lin, C.-L.; Huang, Y.-H. The Application of Adaptive Tolerance and Serialized Facial Feature Extraction to Automatic Attendance Systems. Electronics 2022, 11, 2278.

57. Gough, S. Current RFID Trends and Challenges You Should Know About, in RFID JOURNAL LIVE! 2021.

58. Martin, R.C. Clean Code: A Handbook of Agile Software Craftsmanship; Pearson Education: London, UK, 2009.

59. Martin, R.C. Clean Code-Refactoring, Patterns, Testen und Techniken für sauberen Code: Deutsche Ausgabe; MITP-Verlags GmbH & Co. KG: Bonn, Germany, 2013. (In German)

10

A Context-Aware Android Malware Detection Approach Using Machine Learning

Mohammed N. AlJarrah [1], **Qussai M. Yaseen** [1,2], **and Ahmad M. Mustafa** [1]

[1]*CIS Department, Jordan University of Science and Technology, Irbid 22110, Jordan*

[2]*Artificial Intelligence Research Center (AIRC), Ajman University, Ajman 346, United Arab Emirates*

ABSTRACT

The Android platform has become the most popular smartphone operating system, which makes it a target for malicious mobile apps. This paper proposes a machine learning-based approach for Android malware detection based on application features. Unlike many prior research that focused exclusively on API Calls and permissions features to improve detection efficiency and accuracy, this paper incorporates applications' contextual features with API Calls and permissions features. Moreover, the proposed approach extracted a new dataset of static API Calls and permission features using a large dataset of malicious and benign Android APK samples. Furthermore, the proposed approach used the Information Gain algorithm to reduce the API and permission feature space from 527 to the most relevant 50 features only. Several combinations of API Calls, permissions, and contextual features were used. These combinations were fed into different machine-learning algorithms to show the significance of using the selected contextual features in detecting Android malware. The experiments show that the proposed model achieved a very high accuracy of about 99.4% when using contextual features in comparison to 97.2% without using contextual features. Moreover, the paper shows that the proposed approach outperformed the state-of-the-art models considered in this work.

Keywords: *Android; API Calls; contextual information; machine learning; malware; permissions*

1. INTRODUCTION

The Internet's expansion and the technical revolution in smartphones have led to a tremendous increase in the number of smartphone users. This encouraged competition among various software industries to serve customers by releasing powerful platforms for their smartphones. Android is the most popular mobile operating system, with millions of users around the world taking advantage of its services. Google created and developed the Android operating system in 2005, and the first Android smartphone was introduced in 2008 [1]. By 2021, there were approximately 2 Billion Android-based devices (smartphones and tablets), indicating that Android applications are rapidly growing and exceeding other mobile operating systems such as IOS, Windows, and others [2]. As the most popular and powerful platform, Android provides a vast number of mobile applications in various categories to be available for all android-based mobile users of various ages worldwide.

Android malware is growing immensely due to the vast growth of Android users, which poses threat to the security and privacy of Android users. Android malware is known for sending fraudulent SMS, misusing users' private information, devouring traffic, downloading malicious applications, remote control, data exploitation, and other dangerous behaviors [3]. According to some statistics [4], the number of Android-based malware cases rises every year. About 3.5 million Android malware samples were observed in the first quarter of 2021, up from 1 million in 2019 and 2020.

Android malware differs in various ways; it acts differently, hacks differently, and performs different damage. Some Android malware infiltrates the device by exploiting the user and then launching an assault via malicious applications, while others replicate and clone themselves in various locations before installing malicious applications in these locations to inflict and spread damage as broadly as possible. Table 1 shows a list of mobile malware types and their behaviors, as well as an example of each one.

Table 1.: *Types of mobile malware.*

Mobile Malware	Behavior	Example
Trojan [5]	Looks to be a harmless application that convinces users to download it and then installs malware on their mobile devices.	Android.Counterlank
Worms [6]	Worms can infect additional devices while they are operating on infected systems, and they can carry a payload that degrades mobile network capacity.	Ikee.B

Mobile Malware	Behavior	Example
Adware [7]	Deceives the user through malicious advertising.	UAPush
Spyware [8]	Collects user's data and behavior, such as email and passwords, and sends it to another location across the network.	Zitmo
Botnet [9]	Comprises many internet-connected cellphones controlled by a malicious user; it gains full access to the device and its contents and sends data to the malicious controller.	Not compatible

The diversity and complexity of Android malware, as well as the employment of various strategies to elude detection, make traditional malware detection techniques ineffective, necessitating the development of more efficient and powerful ways to overcome this constraint [10]. Existing malware detection methods are limited and only reveal malware after it has been infected. Automated detection techniques, such as the use of supervised and unsupervised machine learning algorithms, operate effectively by extracting app features using both static and dynamic analysis to execute an optimal and clear classification of Android apps into two groups: malware or benign [11]. Current detection software is unable to detect zero-day attacks. As a result, most researchers use various machine learning classifiers in the detection of Android-based malware, such as Support Vector Machines (SVM), Naïve Bayes (NB), Random Forest (RF), and Decision Trees (DT) [12]. Machine learning algorithms take advantage of features and characteristics learned from malware and benign samples during training.

Machine learning detection techniques rely on static, dynamic, and hybrid analysis to extract and gather application features that are used to classify and detect malicious behaviors. System API Calls, permissions, privileges used, and contextual information are some of the extracted features that machine learning-based algorithms use [13]. The main machine-learning approaches used to detect Android malware are static and dynamic approaches.

Static analysis involves extracting features from Java bytecode or the AndroidManifest.xml file, which contains contextual information and a collection of features, such as permissions required by the app [14]. The static analysis of Android applications to extract static features is shown in Figure 1.

Dynamic analysis is used to discover harmful behavior in applications while they are running. It collects the system calls that the application makes while it is executing. Furthermore, the dynamic analysis also works well with unidentified application signatures [15]. Figure 2 illustrates the dynamic analysis of Android applications.

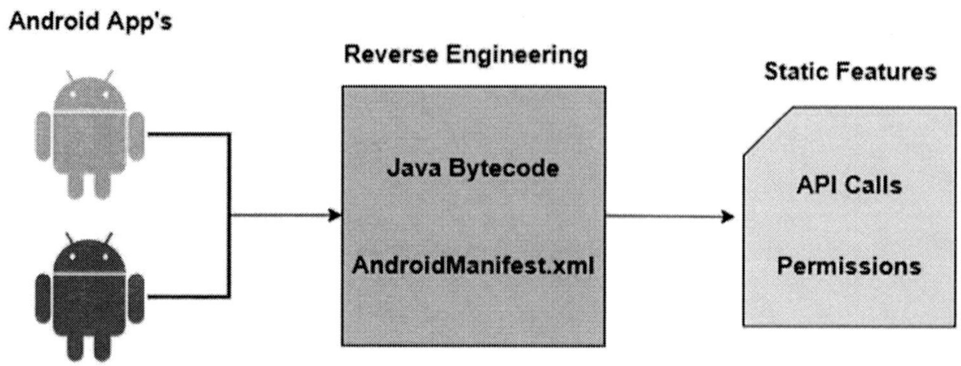

Figure 1.: *Features extraction-based static analysis.*

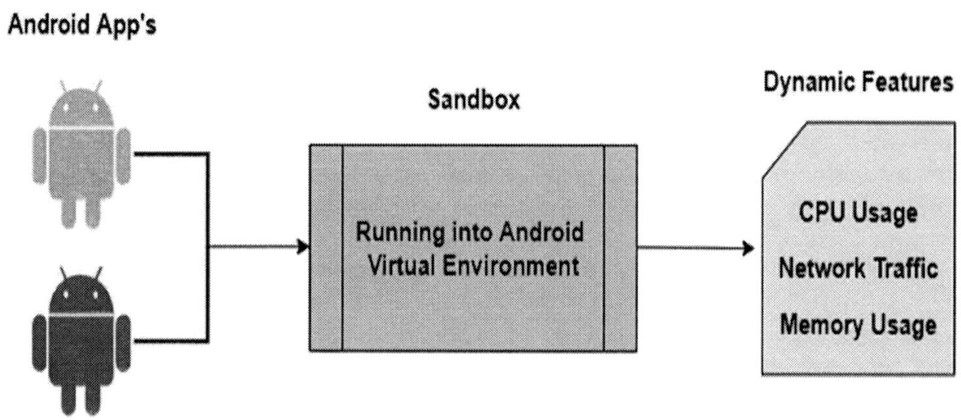

Figure 2.: *Features extraction-based dynamic analysis.*

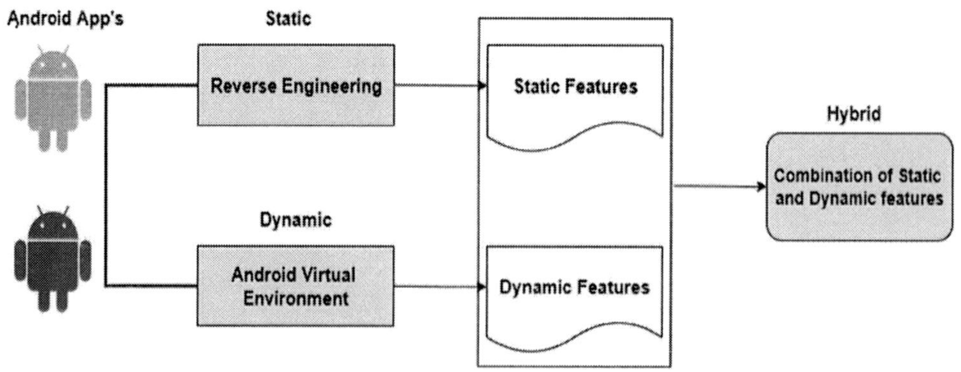

Figure 3.: *Features extraction-bdased hybrid analysis.*

The hybrid technique combines static and dynamic features to improve malware detection results and prevent flaws that can occur when using either a static or dynamic approach alone. The hybrid analysis of Android applications is illustrated in Figure 3.

The benefits of a static analysis include the ability to detect malware before it executes, as well as the ability to detect unknown malware and code vulnerabilities. A dynamic analysis has the advantage of being able to detect undiscovered malware as well as zero-day attacks [16]. However, a dynamic analysis can be time-consuming and resource-intensive usage.

1. The contribution of the paper is summarized as follows:
2. The paper created a new dataset of static API Calls and permissions features from a large number of Android APKs.
3. The paper selected and used the most relevant contextual features along with the API Calls and permissions to test the efficacy of using contextual information in detecting Android malware.
4. The proposed model used the Information Gain algorithm [**17**] to reduce the feature space from 527 API Calls and permissions to 50 features only and achieve a very close accuracy to what was achieved using 527 features.
5. The paper tested several machine learning algorithms, which are Random Forest, Logistic Regression, SVM, K-NN, and Decision Trees using different combinations of API Calls, permissions, and contextual features to evaluate their accuracy in detecting Android malware.
6. The experiments show that using the selected contextual features, the proposed model achieved a high accuracy of about 99.4% in detecting Android malware.
7. The paper considers different state-of-the art models that used contextual features or the same dataset used in this work, and it shows that the proposed models outperformed the state-of-the art models.

The rest of the paper is organized as follows. Section 2 discusses some related work. Section 3 describes the methodology of the proposed approach, discusses the dataset, data pre-processing, features extraction, features selection, and machine learning algorithms. Section 4 shows and discusses the experiments and results. Finally, Section 5 concludes the work.

2. RELATED WORK

Many research approaches have been conducted on detecting Android malware using machine learning. This section discusses some related work in this direction.

Le et al. [18] proposed an approach for Android malware detection that employs different machine learning methods as detectors to identify and detect malicious Android applications. They extracted the features using the static analysis technique by decompiling source files into snail code and using some C++ libraries to read the information from AndroidManifest.xml. In their work, Decision Tree, Naïve Bayes, and an ensemble of Random Forest, Stochastic Gradient Boosting, and AdaBoost were trained based on some application features such as behavior, permission, the size of the application, the class number in the application, and the user interface number of the application. The used dataset contained about 16,589 malicious Android applications collected from different sources, such as Virusshare [19] and Koodous [20], in addition to 12,290 benign Android applications installed from Google Play. The results of their approach showed that the Random Forest classifier achieved the best accuracy at about 98.66%.

Kaushal et al. [21] used permissions from AndroidManifest.xml files as features of Android applications to build an automated Android malware detection system. They trained two machine learning algorithms (Support Vector Machine (SVM) and Naïve Bayes) with a deep learning algorithm (Recurrent Neural Network with LSTM architecture). Then, they used the extracted permissions to perform malware classification into malicious or benign. Their results showed that the Recurrent Neural Network achieved the best results with an accuracy of 95%, outperforming other machine learning classifiers.

Hyoil et al. [22] used Support Vector Machines (SVM) for Android malware detection. They have used a dataset of two samples of Android applications (malicious and benign), where the number of malicious samples is 30,113 applications from the AMD [23] and Drebin [24] dataset, and the benign samples contain 28,489 applications downloaded from Google Play, the Amazon AppStore, and APKPure [25]. Then, they employed a static analysis technique to extract 133,227 API Calls to be used as features for classification. They claimed that the experiments showed that their approach outperformed existing approaches by obtaining an accuracy of 99.97% in detecting malicious Android applications.

Bilal et al. [26] used static and dynamic analysis techniques to propose an approach for Android malware detection using machine learning algorithms based on a hybrid of static, dynamic, and some intrinsic features. They extracted 20 different features from a sample of about 600 Android applications (malicious and benign) that were collected from the Androtracker project [27] and Google Play store [28]. After extracting these features, two machine learning classifiers, which are the K-Nearest Neighbor and Logistic Regression, were created as detection models to perform malware classification. The experiments showed that the proposed approach performs well, and both machine learning classifiers achieved the same accuracy of 97.5% in malware detection on the same training dataset, while the Logistic Regression classifier outperformed other classifiers over the testing dataset.

Fang et al. [29] proposed a method based on the Dalvik Executable file (Dex file) for Android malware family classification. The method extracted the Dex files of 24,553 Android malicious samples from the Android Malware Dataset (AMD) [23] and obtained RGB images and plaintext from the DEX file. Next, it extracted the text features of plaintext, as well as the color and texture features of images. To perform the classification, the study used the feature fusion algorithm based on multi-kernel machine learning. The experiments showed that the proposed method achieved an accuracy of about 96%.

Danish et al. [30] proposed an image-based malware families multiclassification detection method using fine-tuning Convolutional Neural Network (CNN). The method transformed the raw malware binary files into color images to be used as inputs to the CNN for classification. The experiments were performed on two different datasets. The first one is the Malimg malware dataset [31], which consists of 9435 malicious samples, while the other dataset is the IoT-Android mobile dataset, which includes 14,733 malicious samples and 2486 benign samples. The data augmentation technique was adopted by the proposed method during the fine-tuning process. The experiments showed that the proposed method achieved an accuracy of about 98.82% on the Malimg malware dataset, while on the IoT-Android mobile dataset achieved an accuracy of about 97.35%.

Halil et al. [32] proposed an approach for Android malware classification and detection based on a visualization technique and various machine-learning algorithms. They converted some Android application files (Manifest.xml, DEXcode, and Resources (ARSC)) into grayscale images to extract different types of global and local image-based features to be used for training. Before training the algorithms, they normalized the extracted global features in one feature vector and applied the Bag of Visual Words (BOVW) algorithm to build one feature vector from the extracted local features descriptors. To test the model, they performed the experiments on three grayscale image datasets that consisted of 4850 benign samples and 4580 malicious samples for each one. Six machine learning algorithms, Random Forest, K-Nearest Neighbor, Decision Tree, Bagging, AdaBoost, and Gradient Boost, were tested. The experiments showed that the model achieved an accuracy of about 98.75%.

Nuren et al. [33] proposed a machine learning-based approach for Android malware detection. They extracted the application permissions from the AndroidManifest.xml file using static analysis and loaded them in WEKA, where the top 15 permissions were used as malware features. Five machine learning classifiers, Random Forest, J48, Multi-Layer perceptron, Decision Table, and Naïve Bayes, were trained for classification. Using a dataset of 10,000 malicious Android applications and 10,000 benign applications, the Random Forest classifier achieved the best accuracy of about 89.36%.

Talal et al. [34] conducted an empirical study for Android malware detection using various supervised machine-learning algorithms. They employed static analysis to extract some features from the AndroidManifest.xml and Dex files. The extracted features were permissions, intents, and API Calls. Then, they evaluated and compared the performance of six different supervised machine learning classifiers, K-Nearest Neighbour, Support Vector Machine, Decision Tree, Naïve Bayes, Random Forest, and Logistic Regression, on a dataset of 1260 malicious Android applications and 2539 benign Android applications. The results showed that the Random Forest classifier achieved the best accuracy of about 99.21%, while the Naïve Bayes classifier achieved the lowest detection accuracy of about 95.45%.

Other methods in this field were performed by Du et al. [35], Narayanan et al. [36], Mahdavifar et al. [37], and Hadiprakoso et al. [38]. Du et al. [35] proposed a context-based approach that used the semantics and contextual information of the network flow of Android applications. Similarly, Narayanan et al. [36] proposed a contextual-based approach that used a multiple kernel learning method to detect malicious code patterns. Mahdavifar et al. [37] and Hadiprakoso et al. [38] used the same dataset that is used in this work, which is CIC_Maldroid2020 [39]. However, both approaches did not use contextual information. The aforementioned approaches in this paragraph are selected as the state-of-the-art models and are explained in detail in Section 5.

3. METHODOLOGY

This section introduces and discusses the methodology of the proposed approach. Figure 4 shows an illustration of the methodology, and each step is discussed in the following subsections.

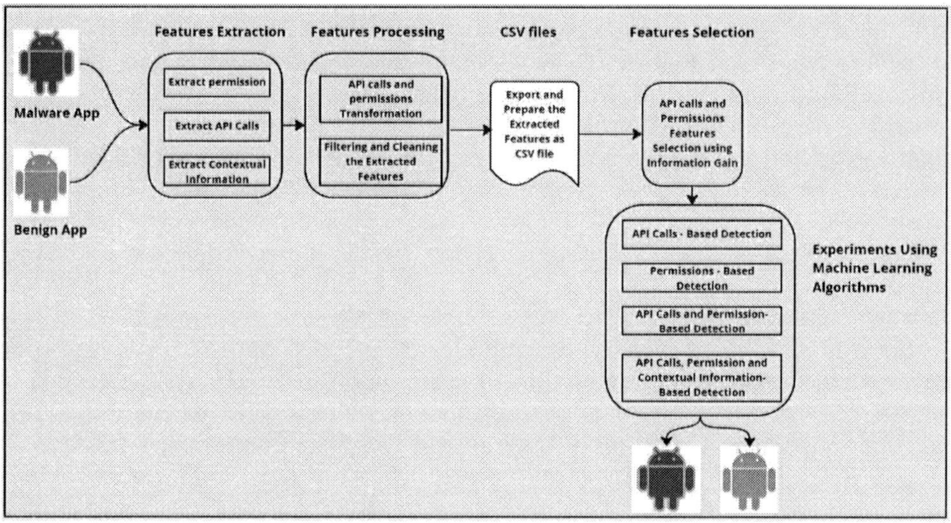

Figure 4.: *A framework for context-aware Android malware detection approach using machine learning techniques.*

3.1. Datasets

Unlike many studies conducted in this field, which used small datasets, this paper used a large dataset of APK samples of malicious and benign Android applications (APKs) called CICMalDroid2020 [39] and extracted a new dataset of API Calls and permissions features. The APKs were collected and published by Mahdavifar et al. [37] and provided by the Canadian Institute for Cybersecurity [40]. It consists of about 16,900 Android samples in different categories; 12,800 samples of the dataset are malware applications, while the rest of the 4100 samples are benign applications. The dataset was collected from 2017 to 2018 from different sources such as MalDozer [41], AMD [23], the VirusTotal service [42], and the Contagio security blog [43]. The collected Android application samples include various application categories, such as advertising, social, educational, etc. The dataset categories samples and their numbers are shown in Figure 5. Table 2 provides a brief explanation of each category of malware inspected in this paper.

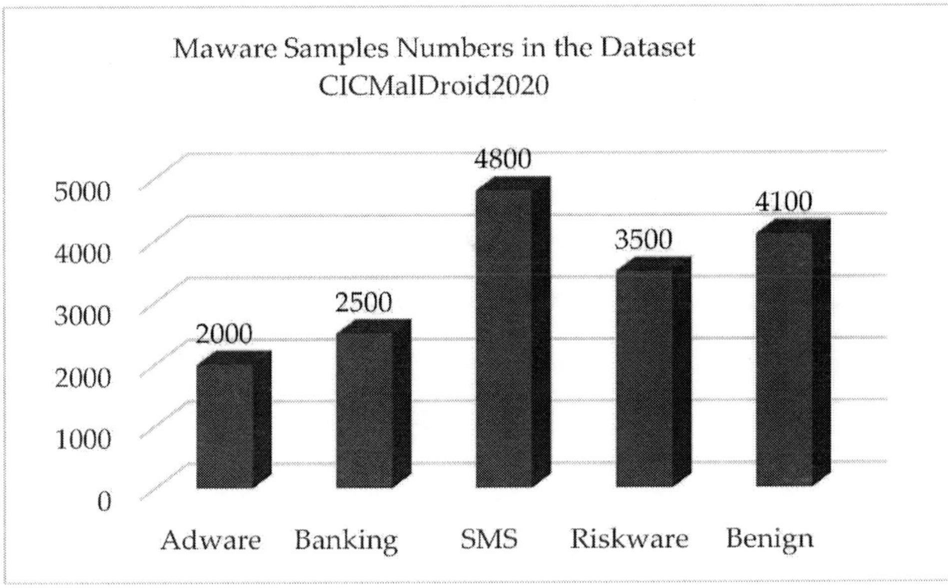

Figure 5.: *Dataset description.*

Table 2.: *Malware categories.*

Android Malware Category	**Concept**
Adware	Malware uses advertising to exploit the user.
Banking	Malware exploits the banking accounts of the user.
SMS	Malware exploits the user by sending a malicious SMS.
Riskware	A program that behaves as good but is malware.

3.2. Features Extraction

The samples of Android applications are in the form of an Android Application Package (APK). An APK is a file that holds all files and components that are responsible for running the application. Figure 6 illustrates the structure of the Android application (APK) [44]. APKs need to be converted and analyzed to get the features that will be used for detection.

Static analysis is a technique to extract static application features from the APK files without running the application. This paper adopts a static analysis approach to extract static features from the applications such as API Calls, permissions, and some contextual information, using Python programming language. The feature extraction process produced a total of 531 distinct features, as shown in Table 3. More information about the extracted features is provided next.

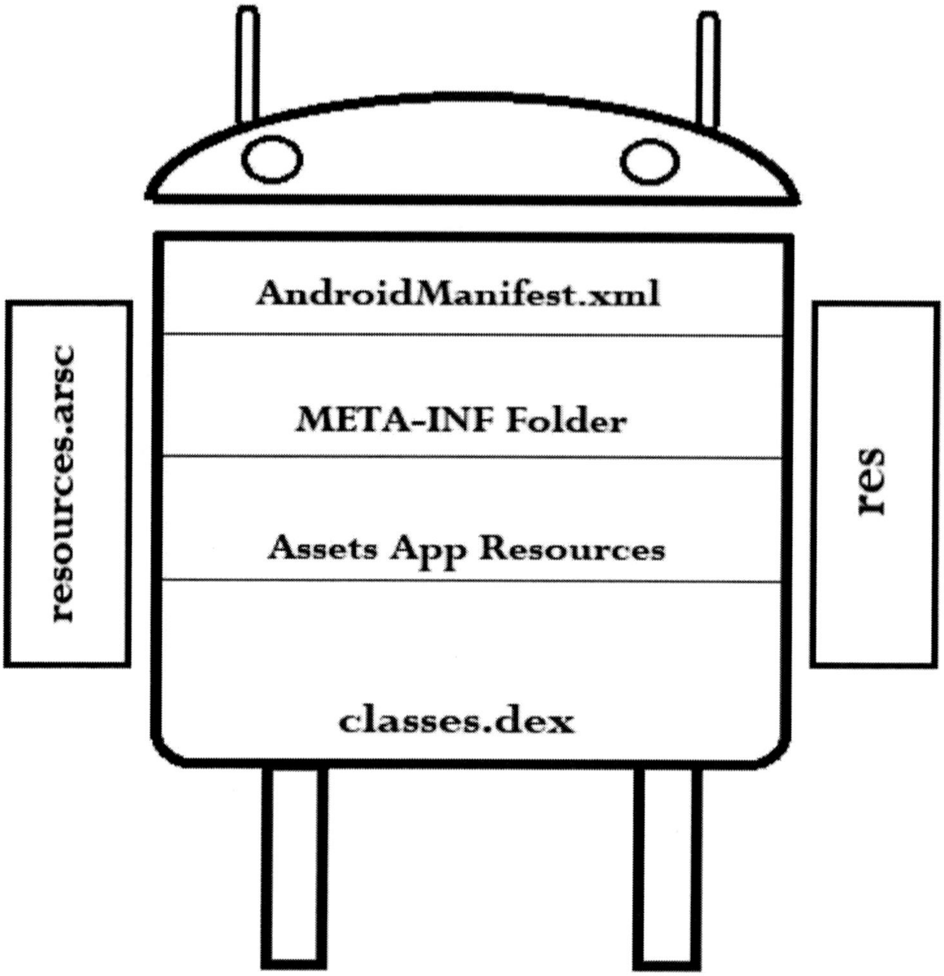

Figure 6.: *Android Application Package (APK) structure.*

Table 3.: *Number of extracted features.*

Application Features Set	Number of Extracted Features
API Calls	15
Permissions	512
Contextual Information	4
Total	531 Features

3.2.1. API Calls Features

The Application Programming Interface (API) is a set of rules that the application uses for communication. API Calls are considered a significant indicator to distinguish between malware and benign applications and to reveal any suspicious behavior [45]. Therefore, we extracted a set of API Calls from Android APK samples to be used for malware detection. Table 4 shows the extracted API Calls. The API Calls for each application were extracted using a script code written in Python using "Androguard", which is a full-featured Python utility for manipulating and handling Android files [46]. It uses reverse engineering by analyzing the DEX file of each APK file [47]. Then, API Calls were converted into binary values (0 or 1) that indicate the presence of API Calls in an APK. A total of 15 API Call features were extracted from 15,836 Android samples, resulting in 11,800 malicious applications and 4036 benign applications. Table 5 displays the number of Android application samples for each category from which API Call features were extracted.

Table 4.: *Extracted API Call categories.*

API Calls	Desc.
startService	Requests the launch of a specific app service.
getDeviceId	Gets the device ID from which an event originated.
createFromPdu	Sending an SMS message using the Protocol Data Unit (PDU), which is a cellular data transmission technology.
getClassLoader	Returns a class loader that can be used to get classes from a package.
getClass	Returns the object's runtime class.
getMethod	Returns a method object that represents the class or interface represented by this class object's public member method.
getDisplayOriginatin-gAddress	Gives the message's originating address, or the email address if it was sent through an email gateway.
getInputStream	Returns a read-only input stream from any of the open connections.
getOutputStream	Returns a write-only output stream to the specified connection.
killProcess	The process with the supplied ID will be terminated.
getLine1Number	For line 1, this function returns the phone number string.
getSimSerialNumber	Gives the SIM serial number.
getSubscriberId	Provides the subscriber's unique ID.
getLastKnownLoca-tion	Returns the data from the last known location retrieved from the supplied source.
isProviderEnabled	Returns if the given provider is enabled or disabled.

***Table 5.:** Number of Android application samples from which API Call features were extracted.*

Android Application Category	Number of Samples from Which API Call Features Were Extracted
Adware	1499
Banking	2277
SMS	4761
Riskware	3263
Benign	4036
Total	**15,836**

3.2.2. Permissions Features

Android application permissions grant apps access to the phone's hardware and data, as well as the ability to control the phone. Permissions can be legitimate or malicious. For example, when an application asks for permission to access sensitive data, such as the phone book or the camera, the application could be suspicious and potentially malicious. Therefore, permissions are powerful indicators for detecting malicious apps and separating them from benign ones. Figure 7 shows examples of some requested permissions by an Android application.

***Figure 7.:** Android application permissions.*

A large set of permissions were extracted from Android application samples for use in malware detection. Table 6 and Table 7 provide a brief description of some normal and dangerous permissions extracted from various Android applications [44]. Each application's used permissions were extracted using a Python script code using "Androguard" and then converted to binary representation "0 or 1". About 700 permissions features were extracted from 16,703 Android samples, including 12,692 malicious apps and 4011 benign apps. The number of Android application samples from which permissions features were extracted is shown in Table 8.

Table 6.: Sample of normal extracted permissions.

Normal Permission	Desc.
'android.permission.INTERNET'	This permission opens network ports for applications.
'android.permission.ACCESS_WIFI_ STATE'	Permits Wi-Fi network information to be accessed by apps.
'android.permission.ACCESS_NET-WORK_STATE'	Allows apps to gain access to network information.
'android.permission.SET_WALLPA-PER'	Allows apps to change the background image.
'android.permission.SET_TIME_ ZONE'	Allows apps to change the time zone of the phone.

Table 7.: Sample of extracted dangerous permissions.

Dangerous Permission	Desc.
'android.permission.READ_CON-TACTS'	Allows apps to access the contact information of the user.
'android.permission.CAMERA'	Allows apps to gain access to the phone camera.
'android.permission.READ_ CALL_LOG'	Allows apps to see the call log of a user.
'android.permission.SEND_SMS'	This permission enables apps to send text messag-es.
'android.permission.READ_ PHONE_STATE'	Gives apps access to the current state of the phone, such as the device's phone number, cellular net-work, and active calls.

Table 8.: Number of Android application samples from which permissions features were extracted.

Android Application Category	Number of Samples from Which Permissions Features Were Extracted
Adware	1499
Banking	2494
SMS	4803
Riskware	3896
Benign	4011
Total	**16,703**

3.2.3. Contextual Features Extraction

Contextual Information refers to information that characterizes the state of an Android application, such as the activities that the app launches, the system services that the app uses, the resources that the app loads, and so on. Because many studies relied solely on API Calls and permissions to distinguish between malware and benign applications, this paper combines application contextual information with API Calls and permissions to enhance the detection performance and detect malicious behavior in Android applications with high accuracy. The authors of the dataset used in this paper employed a dynamic analysis technique to run all Android application samples in a VMI-based dynamic analysis system using CopperDroid, and then recorded the results in JSON format [40]. In this paper, we parsed and analyzed the massive chunk of JSON data for each Android application (APK) using Python scripting codes to extract related contextual information that helps in improving Android malware detection. As indicated in Table 9 below, four categories of application contextual information were selected from various Android application samples. Table 10 shows the number of Android application samples from which contextual information was extracted.

Table 9.: *Extracted contextual features.*

Android Application Contextual Information
num_services
num_receivers
num_activities
num_providers

Table 10.: *Number of APK samples from which the contextual features were extracted.*

Android Application Category	**Number of Samples from Which Contextual Features Were Extracted**
Adware	1243
Banking	1878
SMS	3908
Riskware	2498
Benign	494
Total	**10,021**

3.3. Features Processing

The term "features preprocessing" refers to the act of preparing and transforming features so that they may be trained by machine learning algorithms. Features transformation, or converting features from one format to another, is one of the feature preprocessing mechanisms used in this paper. All extracted API Calls and permissions were converted to binary representation (0 or 1). In other words, if an application calls a specific API (for example, startService), the value will be 1; otherwise, it will be 0. Similarly, if an application uses a specific permission (for example, SEND SMS), the value will be 1; otherwise, it will be 0. An example of the binary representation process of the extracted API Calls and permissions features is shown in Table 11 and Table 12. In this example, as shown in Table 11, the first Android application uses API Call 1 and API Call 2, the second Android application only uses API Call 3, and the third Android application uses all API Calls (1, 2 and 3). According to Table 12, the first Android application only uses permission 3, the second Android application uses all permissions (1, 2 and 3), and no permission have been used by the third Android application.

Table 11.: *Binary representation of the extracted API Calls.*

Android Application (APK)	API Call 1	API Call 2	API Call 3
Application 1	1	0	1
Application 2	0	0	1
Application 3	1	1	1

Table 12.: *Binary representation of the extracted permissions.*

Android Application (APK)	Permission 1	Permission 2	Permission 3
Application 1	1	0	1
Application 2	0	0	1
Application 3	1	1	1

3.4. Feature Extraction and Selection

Many application API Calls and permissions have been extracted. Therefore, this paper uses feature selection on the API Calls with permissions to eliminate duplicate and inconsistent API Calls and permissions features that reduce classification efficiency. To achieve this task, Information Gain (IG) was used. IG is a feature evaluation method that evaluates the quantity of information about the class prediction and the projected reduction in entropy if the only information provided is the presence of a feature and the accompanying class distribution [48]. IG is based on entropy, which is calculated by determining how much of a term may be used for the classification of data [49]. It is a method for selecting the optimal API Calls and permissions features that have been adopted in this paper. The results of using IG in the API Calls and permissions selection, where the top 50 ranked were selected, are shown in Figure 8. Each API Call and permissions feature has an IG value with a high value indicating a significant impact on classification. The proposed method employed mutual information to measure the correlation between variables, where a higher value means higher dependency.

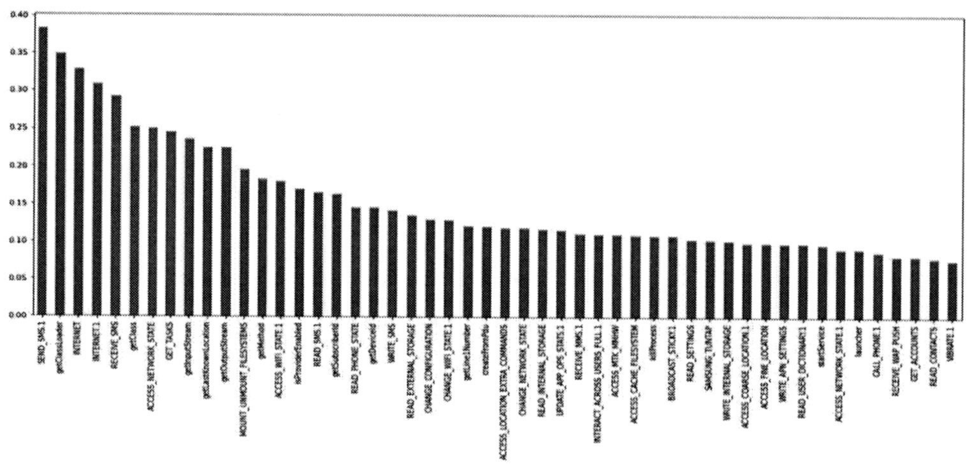

Figure 8.: Top 50 ranked-selected API and permissions based on Information Gain (IG).

3.5. Machine Learning Algorithms

Supervised and unsupervised learning are two types of machine learning algorithms. This paper relies entirely on the supervised technique, which predicts the class of problem-based on related input examples of similar objects. Machine learning classifiers use many features extracted from static analysis to accomplish training for malware classification. This section discusses the various machine learning algorithms used in this paper.

3.5.1. Random Forest RF

RF is one of the most powerful and versatile supervised machine-learning algorithms for classification and regression. Random Forest fits the forest of numerous decision trees, in which the number of trees increases the robustness of the prediction, resulting in improved accuracy and avoiding overfitting [50]. The Random Forest classifier is the best machine learning discriminator between malware and benign applications, according to the results of a literature review performed on Android malware detection, as described by [51,52,53,54]. This paper sets the value of the n_estimators to 100, after testing 10, 50, 100, and 200.

3.5.2. Support Vector Machines SVM

SVM is a supervised learning model used for classification analysis by creating the hyperplane to divide the data into classes [55]. SVM are solid classifiers that give accurate results, but their computations are complex and they work slowly with huge datasets [56]. This paper applied the linear support vector classification SVC, with kernel = "linear"; this has more flexibility in the choice of the loss functions and is better to scale with large numbers of samples.

3.5.3. Logistic Regression LR

LR is a statistical machine learning classification technique used for predicting binary dependent variables. This classifier excels at linear problems, delivering accurate results while consuming minimal computer resources [57].

3.5.4. Naïve Bayesian NB

This is a Bayes Theorem-based probabilistic supervised machine learning algorithm that gives the conditional probability of an event A given event B, and is used for classification tasks [57]. The NB classifier is quick to calculate and can deal with noisy data, but it performs poorly when the data includes many features [56].

3.5.5. K-Nearest Neighbor KNN

The K-Nearest Neighbors (KNN) technique is a simple, easy-to-implement, and commonly used supervised machine learning algorithm that calculates the similarity between training and testing samples to handle classification and regression tasks [58]. This paper set the value of *n_neighbors* to 10.

3.5.6. Decision Trees DT

DT is a supervised machine learning algorithm and a type of tree structure classifier, which is used to accomplish classification and regression tasks. DT splits the data into subsets and presents the results as a tree with two entities: decision nodes for data splitting and leaf nodes for final decisions [59,60].

4. EXPERIMENTS AND RESULTS

This section discusses the experiments conducted to evaluate the model and analyzes the results. The first subsection goes over each experiment that was performed in order to detect malicious Android apps based on their features. The second subsection summarizes all the experiments and determines which one had the highest detection accuracy.

4.1. Results and Analysis

Different metrics were computed to measure and evaluate the performance and effectiveness of each machine learning classifier in order to select the best and most accurate one. The mathematical calculations of the various evaluation metrics are shown in the following equations:

$$\text{Accuracy} = \frac{TP + TN}{TP + TN + FP + FN}$$

$$\text{Recal} = \frac{TP}{TP + FN}$$

$$\text{Precision} = \frac{TP}{TP + FP}$$

$$\text{F1} - \text{Score} = \frac{2 \times \text{Precision} \times \text{Recall}}{\text{Precision} + \text{Recall}}$$

where

- TP (True Positive) is the number of malware detections that are correctly labeled as malware,
- TN (True Negative) is the number at which benign is accurately identified as benign,
- FP (False Positive) is the number of benign that are mistakenly identified as malware, and
- FN (False Negative) is the number at which malware is incorrectly identified as benign.

The most intuitive evaluation metric is accuracy, which reflects the correctly predicted ratio. In some circumstances, accuracy is not always a reliable indicator; instead, alternative metrics should be evaluated, such as Precision, which is the rate of correctly predicted positive outcomes to all positive outcomes. The F1-Score (F-Measure) is the average of Precision and Recall, with Recall referring to the percentage of properly recognized outcomes across all samples [61].

4.1.1. API Calls-Based Android Malware Detection

In this part, Android API Calls features were used to classify the applications. A dataset of 15 features from 15,836 Android application APKs (11,800 malware and 4036 benign) were been used to train various machine learning classifiers. The outcomes of the classification using the Random Forest classifier, along with the confusion matrix, are shown in Figure 9.

The classification report in Figure 9 shows the Random Forest classifier detection performance for each class of Android applications. For example, on adware, the Random Forest obtained 80% Precision, which means it can identify 80% of the adware dataset. Similarly, it shows a 78% Recall, which means it correctly predicts 78% of the adware. Random Forest on adware also earned a 79% F1-Score, which implies it properly predicts 79% of the data.

The number of correct and incorrect predictions for each type of Android application is shown in the confusion matrix in Figure 9. For example, the number of true adware predictions achieved by Random Forest is 477 out of 600, while the number of incorrect predictions is 123. Here are some examples of faulty predictions of adware: seven adware are falsely labeled as banking, fifty-six adware are labeled as benign, fifty-four adware are labeled as riskware, and four adware are labeled as SMS.

	precision	recall	f1-score	support
Adware	0.80	0.78	0.79	600
Banking	0.91	0.84	0.87	911
Benign	0.84	0.91	0.88	1614
Riskware	0.84	0.72	0.78	1305
SMS	0.92	0.98	0.95	1905
accuracy			0.87	6335
macro avg	0.86	0.85	0.85	6335
weighted avg	0.87	0.87	0.87	6335

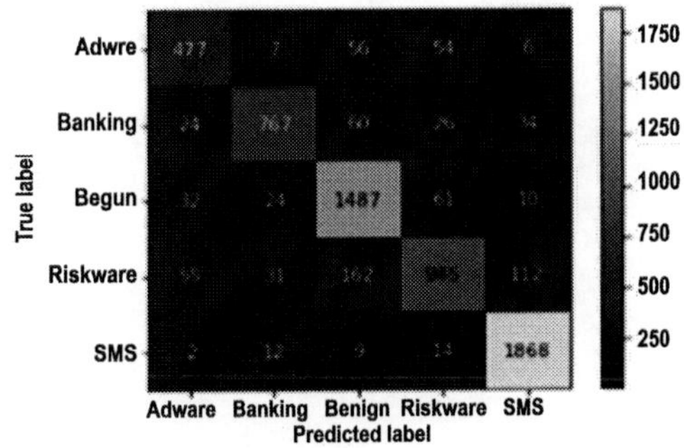

Figure 9.: *Android application permissions classification report and confusion matrix for the Random Forest classifier—API Calls only.*

Table 13 and Figure 10 show how API Calls-based Android malware detection compares to different machine learning classifiers. They show that employing API Calls only to detect malicious applications is insufficient to produce accurate detection results. The Random Forest classifier had the best Accuracy, Precision, Recall, and F1-Score, but overall, this experiment performed poorly over different machine learning algorithms. The results show that the algorithm's detection accuracy is between 75% and 87%, implying that the percentage of inaccurate predictions is about 25%, which is not excellent. Furthermore, the algorithms attained a precision of 75–87%, implying that they were able to identify 75–87% of the data during testing. The different algorithms have achieved a Recall of 75–87%, which implies they properly detect 75–87% of malicious applications.

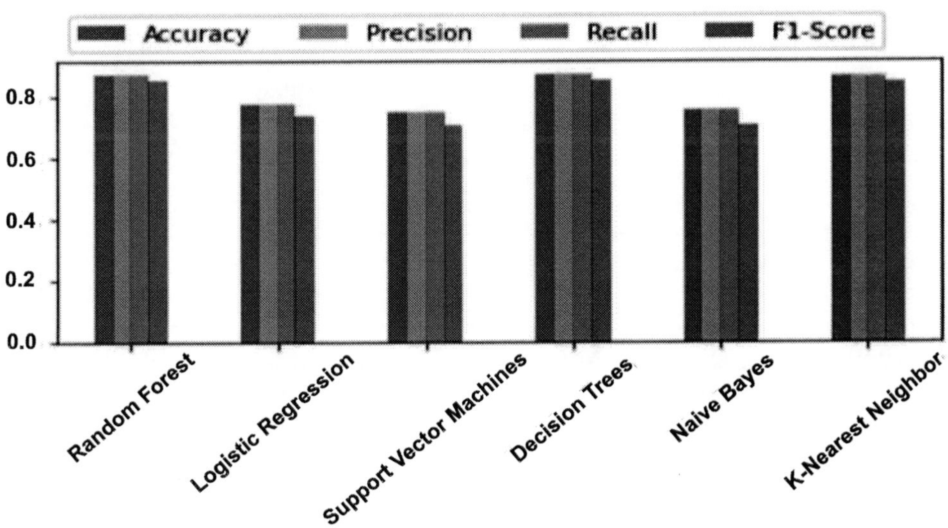

Figure 10.: *Other machine learning classifier results in detecting malicious Android applications—API Calls only.*

***Table 13.**: Machine learning classifiers results—API Calls only.*

	Accuracy	Precision	Recall	F1-Score
RF	0.873244	0.873244	0.873244	0.855546
LR	0.776796	0.776796	0.776796	0.738052
SVM	0.753118	0.753118	0.753118	0.708540
DT	0.871665	0.871665	0.871665	0.853826
NB	0.754854	0.754854	0.754854	0.705594
K-NN	0.865509	0.865509	0.865509	0.846865

4.1.2. Permissions-Based Android Malware Detection

This experiment involves extracting permissions from Android apps to train various machine-learning algorithms to classify whether the app is malicious or benign. For training, a dataset of 512 features from 16,703 Android application APKs (12,692 malicious and 4011 benign) was employed. Figure 11 shows the results of the classification using the Random Forest classifier, as well as the confusion matrix.

```
              precision    recall  f1-score   support

      Adware       0.97      0.98      0.97       600
     Banking       0.96      0.93      0.95       998
      Benign       0.98      0.97      0.98      1605
    Riskware       0.95      0.98      0.97      1558
         SMS       0.99      0.99      0.99      1921

    accuracy                           0.97      6682
   macro avg       0.97      0.97      0.97      6682
weighted avg       0.97      0.97      0.97      6682
```

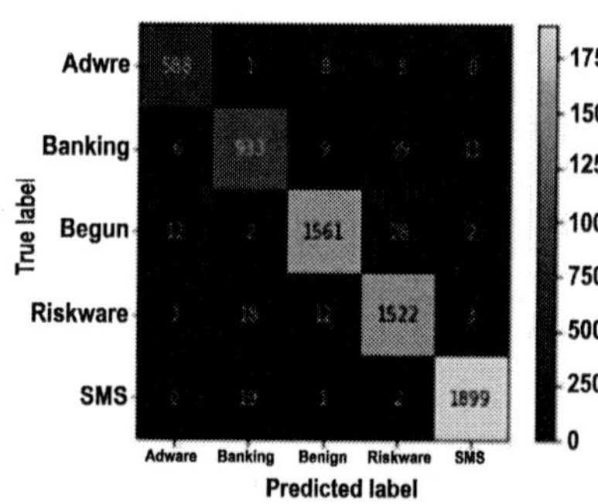

***Figure 11.**: Android application permissions classification report and confusion matrix for Random Forest classifier—permissions only.*

The detection performance of the random forest classifier for each class of Android applications is shown in Figure 11. For riskware, for example, the Random Forest achieved 95% precision, which means it can properly predict 95% of the riskware dataset, and 98% Recall, which means it can identify 98% of the riskware dataset. Random Forest on riskware received an F1-Score of 97%, indicating that it correctly predicts 97% of the data.

The confusion matrix in Figure 11 shows the number of correct and wrong predictions for each type of Android application. The number of genuine riskware predictions made by Random Forest, for example, is 1522 out of 1558, with 36 incorrect predictions. Here are some examples of riskware predictions that were incorrect: three riskware are incorrectly categorized as adware, eighteen riskware are incorrectly labeled as banking, twelve riskware are benign, and three riskware are incorrectly labeled as SMS.

The performance of different machine learning classifiers in detecting Android malware applications is shown in Table 14 and Figure 12. Table 14 and Figure 12 show that using application permissions to discriminate between malicious and benign programs is effective and yields reliable detection results. The Accuracy, Precision, Recall, and F1-Score of the Random Forest classifier were the best. The detection accuracy of the algorithms is between 95% and 97%, meaning a low percentage of incorrect predictions, which is desirable. Furthermore, the algorithms achieved a precision of 95–97% during testing, meaning that they were able to recognize 95–97% of the data. The various methods have a recall of 95–97%, indicating that they correctly detect 95–97% of the malicious programs.

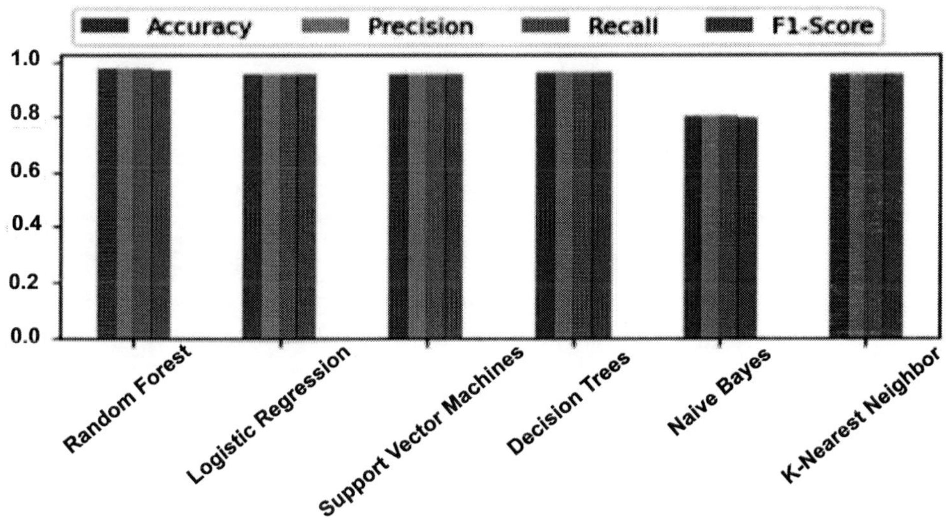

Figure 12.: Other machine learning classifier results in detecting malicious Android applications—permissions only.

Table 14.: Other machine learning classifier results in Android malware detection—permissions only.

	Accuracy	Precision	Recall	F1-Score
RF	0.973810	0.973810	0.973810	0.971126
LR	0.953607	0.953607	0.953607	0.950187
SVM	0.954205	0.954205	0.954205	0.951107
DT	0.961838	0.961838	0.961838	0.955036

	Accuracy	Precision	Recall	F1-Score
NB	0.801556	0.801556	0.801556	0.792031
K-NN	0.955253	0.955253	0.955253	0.949705

4.1.3. API Calls and Permissions-Based Android Malware Detection

In this experiment, we leveraged the existing API Calls and permissions in the apps and combined them so that the machine learning algorithms learn to achieve better efficiency in detecting harmful Android applications. Various machine learning algorithms have been trained with 527 features from 11,781 malware and 4008 benign real-world Android applications. The classification report, as well as the confusion matrix using the Random Forest classifier, is shown in Figure 13.

	precision	recall	f1-score	support
Adware	0.98	0.98	0.98	600
Banking	0.97	0.93	0.95	906
Benign	0.97	1.00	0.98	1603
Riskware	0.96	0.97	0.97	1302
SMS	0.99	0.99	0.99	1905
accuracy			0.98	6316
macro avg	0.98	0.97	0.97	6316
weighted avg	0.98	0.98	0.98	6316

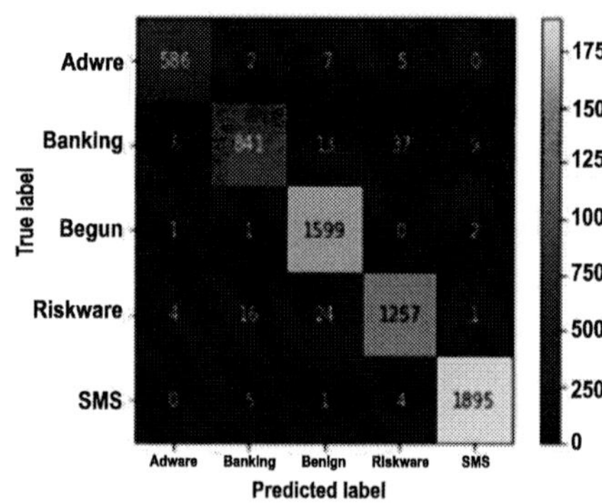

Figure 13.: Android application permissions classification report and confusion matrix for the Random Forest classifier—API Calls with permissions.

Figure 13 displays the random forest classifier detection performance for each class of Android applications. For SMS, for example, the Random Forest obtained 99% precision, meaning it can correctly predict 99% of the dataset and 99% Recall, meaning it can correctly identify 99% of the dataset. The F1-Score for Random Forest on SMS was 99%, showing that it correctly predicts 99% of the data. Moreover, the number of correct and incorrect predictions for each type of Android application is shown in the confusion matrix in Figure 13. Random Forest, for example, produced 1895 genuine SMS predictions out of 1905, with only 10 wrong guesses. Here are a few examples of wrong SMS predictions: four SMSs were wrongly classified as riskware, one SMS was incorrectly classified as benign, five SMSs were classified as banking, and no SMSs were classified as adware.

Table 15 and Figure 14 demonstrate that combining API Calls and permissions improves the detection of Android malicious apps. The Random Forest classifier has the best Accuracy, Precision, Recall, and F1-Score. The algorithm's detection accuracy ranges from 96% to 98%, indicating a high percentage of correct predictions. Furthermore, during testing, the algorithms were able to recognize 96% to 98% of the data with a Precision from 96% to 98%. The various approaches have a Recall from 96% to 98%, meaning that 96% to 98% of harmful applications are correctly detected.

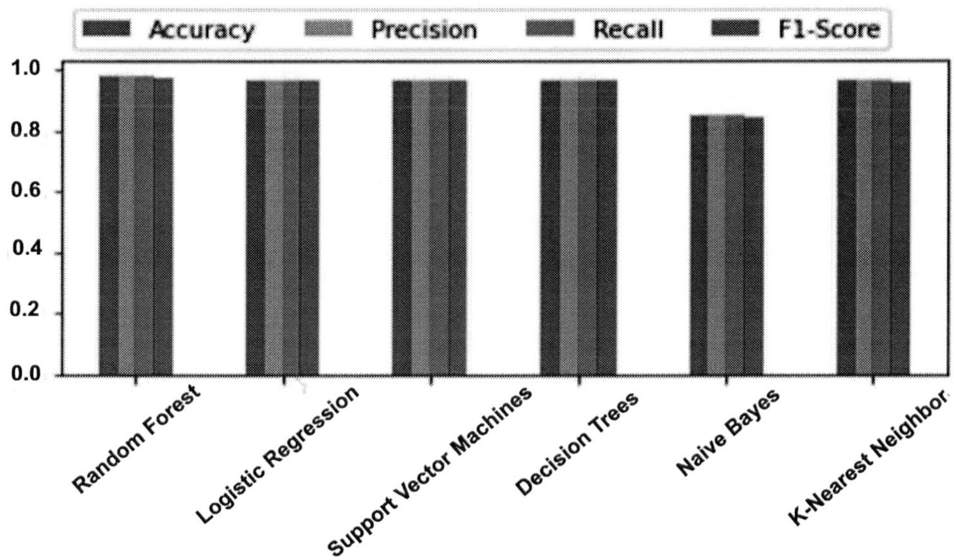

Figure 14.: *Other machine learning classifier performance in Android malware detection—API Calls with permissions.*

Table 15.: *The results of using machine leaning algorithms in detecting Android malware—API Calls with permissions.*

	Accuracy	Precision	Recall	F1-Score
RF	0.980526	0.980526	0.980526	0.977692
LR	0.966276	0.966276	0.966276	0.963571
SVM	0.967226	0.967226	0.967226	0.964235
DT	0.969601	0.969601	0.969601	0.965232
NB	0.852913	0.852913	0.852913	0.841969
K-NN	0.963743	0.963743	0.963743	0.958180

4.1.4. API Calls and Permissions-Based Android Malware Detection with Feature Selection

To reduce the dimension of the feature and improve detection performance, we used the feature selection method (mutual information gain) on the combined API Calls and permissions in this experiment. The top-ranked 50 API Calls and permissions features were picked from 11,781 malware and 4008 benign real-world Android applications; refer to Figure 8 for more information. They were picked after experimenting with different feature dimensions, as shown in Figure 15. This experiment shows an increased efficiency with no discernible effect on classification accuracy.

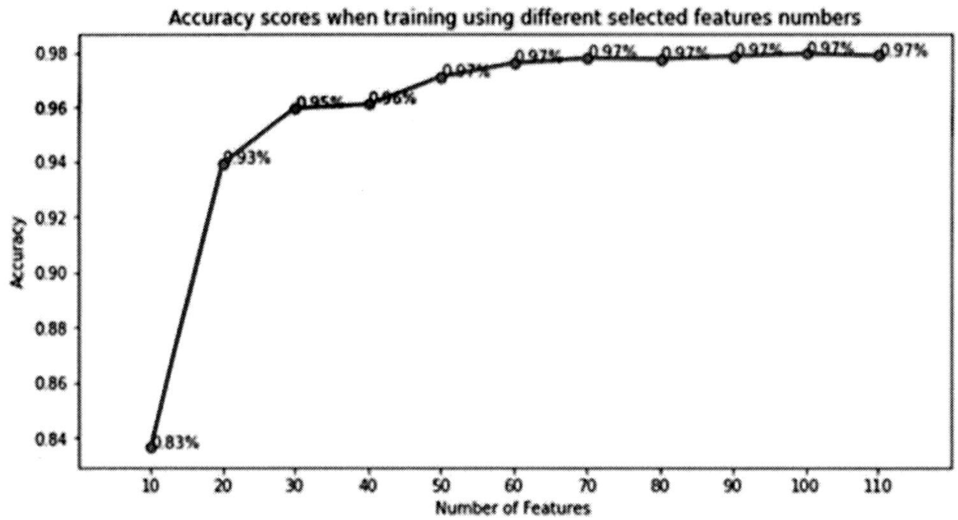

Figure 15.: Accuracy scores when training with different feature dimensions.

	precision	recall	f1-score	support
Adware	0.96	0.96	0.96	600
Banking	0.97	0.91	0.94	906
Benign	0.97	1.00	0.98	1603
Riskware	0.96	0.96	0.96	1302
SMS	0.99	0.99	0.99	1905
accuracy			0.97	6316
macro avg	0.97	0.96	0.97	6316
weighted avg	0.97	0.97	0.97	6316

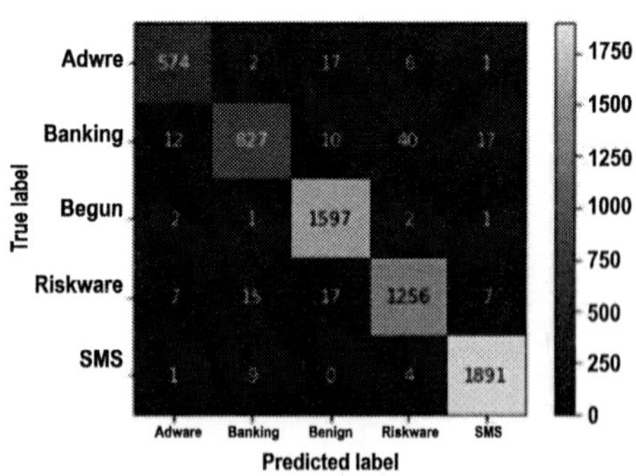

Figure 16.: Classification report and confusion matrix for the Random Forest Classifier—API Calls with permissions (with feature selection).

Figure 16 shows the confusion matrix as well as the classification report using the Random Forest classifier. The results of various machine learning classifiers in detecting fraudulent Android applications are shown in Table 16 and Figure 17.

The adoption of the feature selection technique did not increase detection accuracy, as shown in Table 16 and Figure 17. The findings of this experiment are nearly identical to those of the prior experiment (without feature selection), in which the Random Forest classifier had the best Accuracy, Precision, Recall, and F1-Score. The only advantage we can see in this experiment is that the algorithm's performance, i.e., the time it takes to predict, has improved. That is, while this experiment did not enhance the accuracy results, it improved performance.

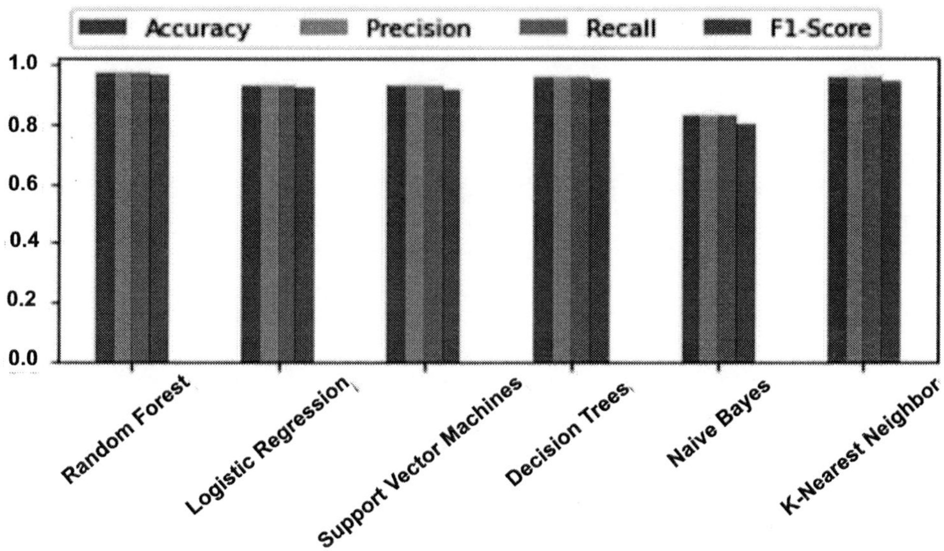

Figure 17.: *Machine learning classifiers results in detecting Android malware—API Calls with permissions (with feature selection).*

Table 16.: *The results of the other machine learning algorithms in Android malware detection—API Calls with permissions (with feature selection).*

	Accuracy	Precision	Recall	F1-Score
RF	0.972451	0.972451	0.972451	0.967090
LR	0.932394	0.932394	0.932394	0.923305
SVM	0.929544	0.929544	0.929544	0.918958
DT	0.960735	0.960735	0.960735	0.955430
NB	0.826314	0.826314	0.826314	0.802296
K-NN	0.955668	0.955668	0.955668	0.946952

4.1.5. API Calls and Permissions with Feature Selection and Contextual Information-Based Android Malware Detection

In this experiment, four contextual information features, num_services, num_receivers, num_activities, and num_providers, were selected and used along with the selected 50 API Calls and permissions features (used in the previous experiment) to show the effectiveness of using contextual information on the detection accuracy. These four features represent the number of times the application performs a certain activity, making them crucial and high-indication features for detecting malicious behavior and distinguishing between malware and benign applications. The number of applications used in this experiment is 842 benign samples and 5866 malware samples.

Table 17 and Figure 18 show that using features along with API Calls and permissions increases detection accuracy and delivers better results. The Random Forest classifier produced the greatest results, with an accuracy of 99.4%. Figure 19 compares the accuracy results of all tested algorithms according to the use of API and permissions features only, without feature selection (527 features), with feature selection (50 features), with feature selection (50 features), and contextual features. The figure shows that using the contextual features with 50 API and permissions features only enhances the accuracy of all algorithms and outperforms the accuracy of the other models (with using feature selection and without using feature selection). In addition, an important finding is obvious in the results, which is the rise of the accuracy of NB when using contextual information. The results show that when we used the contextual features, the accuracy of NB increased sharply from 82.6% to 92.5%, which is an outstanding enhancement.

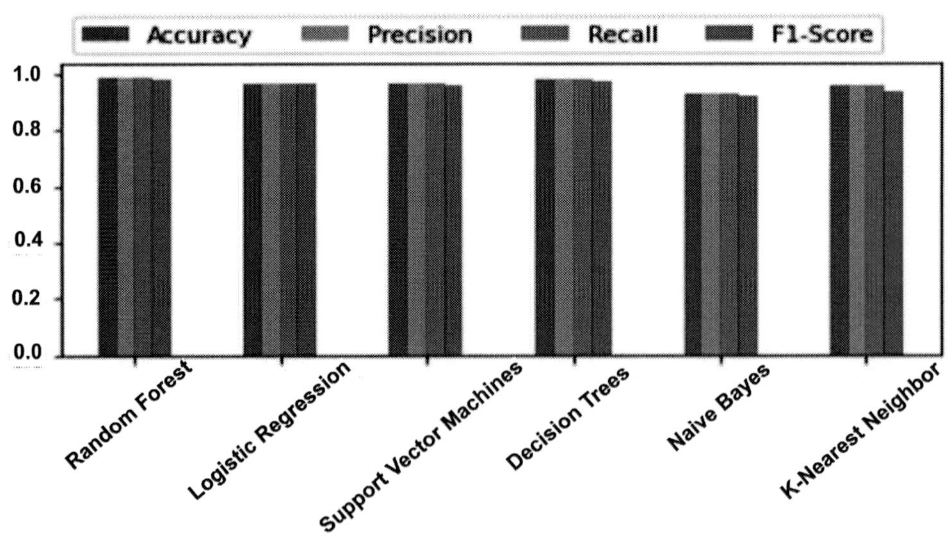

Figure 18.: *Detection of Android malware results with other machine learning algorithms—API Calls, permissions, and contextual information.*

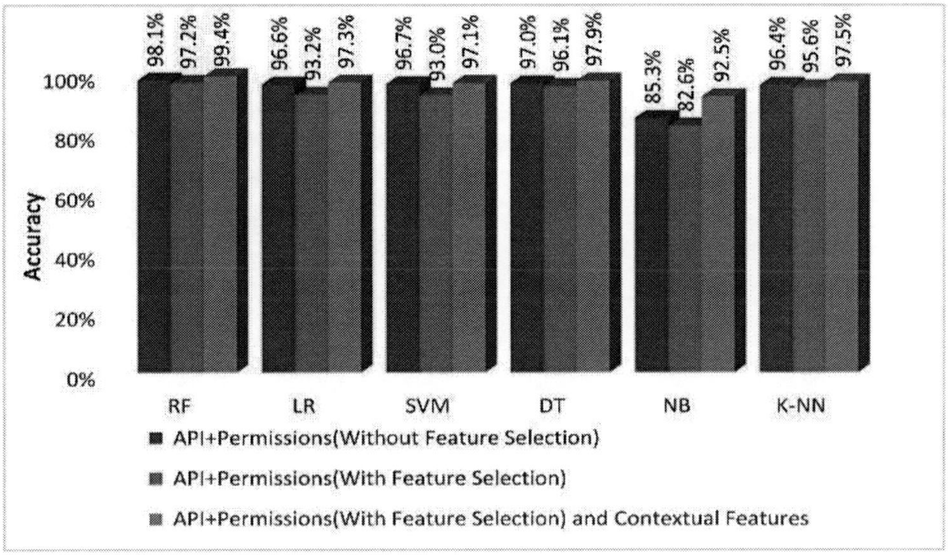

Figure 19.: *Enhancement of the accuracy of the proposed model using contextual features.*

Table 17.: *Android malware detection results with other machine learning algorithms—API Calls, permissions, and contextual information.*

	Accuracy	Precision	Recall	F1-Score
RF	0.994220	0.994220	0.994220	0.991228
LR	0.972598	0.972598	0.972598	0.971393
SVM	0.971247	0.971247	0.971247	0.970111
DT	0.978740	0.978740	0.978740	0.969944
NB	0.925197	0.925197	0.925197	0.914010
K-NN	0.975449	0.975449	0.975449	0.958354

Figure 20 shows the confusion matrix as well as the Random Forest classifier classification results. As shown in the Figure, the detection results for each Android application category are outstanding, with a very small proportion of wrong predictions. The Random Forest algorithm was capable of successfully identifying 99.4% of malicious apps. Moreover, the number of incorrect predictions for all Android malware categories is modest, as illustrated in the confusion matrix in Figure 20. For example, just 6 predictions out of 1331 are incorrect predictions for SMS, and only 8 predictions out of 426 are wrong predictions for adware.

	precision	recall	f1-score	support
Adware	0.98	0.98	0.98	426
Banking	0.98	0.97	0.97	584
Benign	0.98	0.96	0.97	193
SMS	0.99	1.00	0.99	1337
accuracy			0.99	2540
macro avg	0.98	0.98	0.98	2540
weighted avg	0.99	0.99	0.99	2540

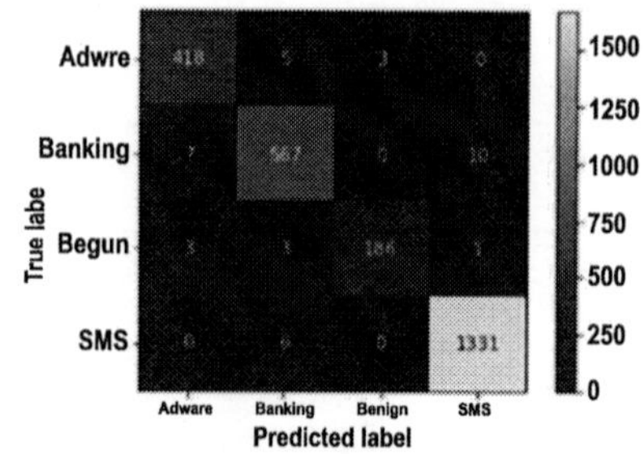

Figure 20.: *The classification results and confusion matrix for the Random Forest Classifier—API Calls, permissions, and contextual features.*

4.2. Results Summary

The results of many experiments conducted in this paper show that using API Calls to identify suspicious applications is insufficient; the results were not accurate enough, and there were numerous incorrect predictions. Meanwhile, the results of detection based on application permissions only were better than those of using API Calls only. However, the results of Android malware detection based on API Calls and permissions together were clearly better, which was higher by 1% and reached around 98% accuracy using the Random Forest algorithm. The features selection approach did not enhance the security. However, it achieved a close accuracy of about 97.2% using 50 features only, instead of 98% using 527 features.

The interesting results were achieved when the contextual features were used along with the selected 50 API Calls and permissions. Using this combination, the highest results reached about 99.4% using the Random Forest algorithm. This proves that using the selected contextual features enhances the classification and detects Android malware with very high accuracy when it is used with API Calls and permissions features. Moreover, using contextual features enhanced Naïve Bayesian accuracy sharply from 82.6% to 92.5%.

4.3. State of Art

The proposed model in this work has achieved very high accuracy, as discussed in the previous section. To show the significance of this work, four stat of art models are considered, which are Du et al. [35], Narayanan et al. [36], Mahdavifar et al. [37], and Hadiprakoso et al. [38].

Du et al. [35] proposed a context-based approach, called FlowCog, that used natural language processing and deep learning methods to analyze the semantics and contextual information of the network flow of Android applications. Their approach used a large dataset of more than 8000 samples collected from different sources, such as the ICC-bench dataset [62], Google Play, and Drebin. The results of their approach showed that their proposed model achieved an accuracy of about 95.4%. Similarly, Narayanan et al. [36] proposed a contextual-based approach, called MKLDroid, which used a multiple kernel learning method that extracted the contextual subgraph features from the applications' dependency graphs to detect malicious code patterns. MKLDroid was applied using two datasets, Drebin and Virusshare. The authors claimed that MKLDroid achieved an accuracy of about 97%.

Mahdavifar et al. [37] and Hadiprakoso et al. [38] used the same dataset used in this work, CIC_Maldroid2020. However, both methods did not use contextual information in their approaches. The authors in [37] proposed a deep neural networks method that used about 470 features, such as system calls, binders, and composite behaviors. Their results showed that their proposed method achieved an accuracy of about 97.84%. Meanwhile, Hadiprakoso et al. [38] proposed a machine-learning model and tested several machine-learning algorithms such as SVM, KNN, RF, and XGBoost. Their model used many static and dynamic features such as API Calls, permissions, and system calls. The authors claimed that their model achieved an accuracy of about 96%.

Table 18 shows a comparison between the accuracy of the proposed model and the state-of-theart models. The table shows that the proposed work outperformed the approaches that used contextual features, which are [35] and [38], which achieved an accuracy of about 95.4% and 97%, respectively. However, these approaches did not use the MalDroid2020 dataset that was used in this work, and they did not use conventional machine learning algorithms. This proves the significance of the machine learning model that has been proposed in this work and the significance of the chosen contextual features in detecting Android malware with very high accuracy. Moreover, the table shows that the proposed work outperformed the approaches that used the same dataset in this work. These approaches used deep learning algorithms and conventional machine learning methods, but they did not use contextual features. This proves the significance of using contextual features in achieving very high accuracy in Android malware detection.

Table 18.: *Comparison with the state-of-the-art methods.*

Work	**Year**	**Dataset**	**Features**	**Number of Features**	**Methods**	**Accuracy**
[35]	2022	Modified ICC-Bench dataset [61] Drebin [24]	Network flow semantics, such as flow contexts and inter-component communication	NA	Natural language processing and deep learning approaches	95.4%
[37]	2020	CICMal-Droid2020 [39]	System calls, binders, and composite behaviors	470	Deep neural networks	97.84%

Work	Year	Dataset	Features	Number of Features	Methods	Accuracy
[38]	2020	Drebin [24] Malgenome [63] CICMAL-DROID2020 [39]	Static (permissions, API Calls, intent, command signatures, and binaries) Dynamic (system calls, binder calls, and composite behaviors)	261	SVM, KNN, MLP, RF DT, and Naïve Bayes XGBOOST	96%
[36]	2018	DREBIN [24] Virusshare [19]	contextual information (contextual subgraph features)	NA	Multiple lernel learning	97%
The proposed work	2022	CICMal-Droid2020 [39]	API Calls, permissions, and contextual features	54	Random Forest	99.4%

5. CONCLUSIONS

The accuracy of Android malware detection methods using machine learning depends on the features used. API Calls and permissions are two of the most important features that are used in Android malware detection. However, most machine learning methods use these features without considering the context. This paper has shed light on the importance of using contextual features with API Calls and permissions on the detection accuracy of machine learning models. The paper has proposed a machine learning model based on the use of four important contextual features and fifty API Calls and permission features, which were extracted from a large dataset of 12,800 malicious and 4100 benign Android apps. To test the model, the paper has used several machine learning algorithms, Random Forest, SVM, Linear Regression, Naïve Bayesian, K-NN, and Decision Tree. The results have shown that when using the proposed model with API Calls and permissions only, the best results achieved were 98.1% using the Random Forest algorithm. Moreover, the results have shown that after applying the Information Gain selection algorithm to select the best relevant features, only 50 features out of 527 can be used to achieve a close accuracy of about 97.2%. Furthermore, the results have shown that using contextual features along with the 50 API Calls and permissions achieved a very high accuracy of about 99.4% when using the Random Forest algorithm. In addition, the results have shown that the most affected algorithm by using contextual features was the Naïve Bayesian algorithm, where its accuracy raised sharply from 82.6% to 92.5%, which is an interesting change for the Naïve Bayesian. Moreover, this paper considered four important methods as state-of-theart models. The comparison has shown that the proposed model outperformed the state-of-the-art models.

Author Contributions

All authors provided equal contributions. All authors have read and agreed to the published version of the manuscript.

REFERENCES

1. Singh, R. An Overview of Android Operating System and Its Security Features. J. Eng. Res. Appl. 2014, 4, 519–521.
2. Mobile Security Review 2021—AV-Comparatives.
3. Singh, P.; Tiwari, P.; Singh, S. Analysis of Malicious Behavior of Android Apps. Procedia Comput. Sci. 2016, 79, 215–220.
4. 2021 Mobile Malware Evolution: Fewer Attacks, Escalating Dangers.
5. Sk, H.K. A Literature Review on Android Mobile Malware Detection using Machine Learning Techniques. In Proceedings of the 6th International Conference on Computing Methodologies and Communication (ICCMC), Erode, India, 29–31 March 2022; pp. 986–991.
6. Salah, Y.; Hamed, I.; Nabil, S.; Abdulkader, A.; Mostafa, M. Mobile Malware Detection: A Survey. Int. J. Comput. Sci. Inf. Secur. 2019, 17, 56–65.
7. Moses, A.; Morris, S. Analysis of Mobile Malware: A Systematic Review of Evolution and Infection Strategies. J. Inf. Secur. Cybercrimes Res. 2021, 4, 103–131.
8. Kambar, M.E.; Esmaeilzadeh, A.; Kim, Y.; Taghva, K. A Survey on Mobile Malware Detection Methods using Machine Learning. In Proceedings of the IEEE 12th Annual Computing and Communication Workshop and Conference (CCWC), Las Vegas, NV, USA, 26–29 January 2022; pp. 0215–0221.
9. Yerima, S.Y.; Alzaylaee, M.K. Mobile Botnet Detection: A Deep Learning Approach Using Convolutional Neural Networks. arXiv 2020, arXiv:2007.00263.
10. Alzaylaee, M.K.; Yerima, S.Y.; Sezer, S. Dynalog: An automated dynamic analysis framework for characterizing android applications. In Proceedings of the International Conference On Cyber Security and Protection of Digital Services (Cyber Security), London, UK, 13–14 June 2016; pp. 1–8.
11. Kosmidis, K.; Kalloniatis, C. Machine learning and images for malware detection and classification. ACM International Conference Proceeding Series. In Proceedings of the 21st Pan-Hellenic Conference on Informatics, Larissa, Greece, 28–30 September 2017.
12. Chumachenko, K. Machine Learning Methods for Malware Detection and Classification. Bachelor's Thesis, South-Eastern Finland University of Applied Sciences, Kouvola, Finland, 2017.
13. Narayanan, A.; Chandramohan, M.; Chen, L.; Liu, Y. Context-Aware, Adaptive, and Scalable Android Malware Detection Through Online Learning. IEEE Trans. Emerg. Top. Comput. Intell. 2017, 1, 157–175.

14. Kapratwar, A.; Di Troia, F.; Stamp, M. Static and dynamic analysis of android malware. In Proceedings of the 3rd International Conference on Information Systems Security and Privacy, Porto, Portugal, 19–21 February 2017.
15. Bhatia, T.; Kaushal, R. Malware detection in android based on dynamic analysis. In Proceedings of the 2017 International Conference on Cyber Security and Protection of Digital Services (Cyber Security), London, UK, 19–20 June 2017.
16. Amamra, A.; Talhi, C.; Robert, J.M. Smartphone malware detection: From a survey towards taxonomy. In Proceedings of the 2012 7th International Conference on Malicious and Unwanted Software, Fajardo, PR, USA, 16–18 October 2012.
17. Larose Daniel, T. Discovering Knowledge in Data: An Introduction to Data Mining; Wiley: Hoboken, NJ, USA, 2014; pp. 174–179. ISBN 9780470908747.
18. Le, N.C.; Nguyen, T.M.; Truong, T.; Nguyen, N.D.; Ngo, T. A Machine Learning Approach for Real Time Android Malware Detection. In Proceedings of the 2020 RIVF International Conference on Computing and Communication Technologies (RIVF), Ho Chi Minh City, Vietnam, 14–15 October 2020.
19. Virusshare. Available online: https://virusshare.com/ (accessed on 30 August 2022).
20. Koodous: Collective Intelligence against Android Malware. Available online: https://koodous.com/ (accessed on 30 August 2022).
21. Kavediya, V.; Sadashiv, M.; Mhaskar Kulkarni, K.; Prabhu, S.; Balbudhe, K. Android Malware Detection using Machine learning technique. Int. J. Res. Anal. Rev. 2020, 7, 777–780.
22. Han, H.; Lim, S.; Suh, K.; Park, S.; Cho, S.J.; Park, M. Enhanced android malware detection: An SVM-based machine learning approach. In Proceedings of the 2020 IEEE International Conference on Big Data and Smart Computing (BigComp), Busan, Korea, 19–22 February 2020.
23. Li, Y.; Jang, J.; Hu, X.; Ou, X. Android Malware Clustering through Malicious Payload Mining. In International Symposium on Research in Attacks, Intrusions, and Defenses; Springer: Cham, Switzerland, 2017.
24. Arp, D.; Spreitzenbarth, M.; Hübner, M.; Gascon, H.; Rieck, K. DREBIN: Effective and Explainable Detection of Android Malware in Your Pocket. In Proceedings of the Symposium on Network and Distributed System Security (NDSS), San Diego, CA, USA, 23–26 February 2014.
25. APKPure. Available online: https://m.apkpure.com/ (accessed on 30 August 2022).
26. Mantoo, B.A.; Khurana, S.S. Static, Dynamic and Intrinsic Features Based Android Malware Detection Using Machine Learning. Lect. Notes Electr. Eng. 2020, 597, 31–45.
27. Kang, H.J.; Jang, J.W.; Mohaisen, A.; Kim, H.K. AndroTracker: Creator Information based Android Malware Classification System. In Proceedings of the 15th International Workshop in Information Security Applications, Jeju Island, Korea, 25–27 August 2014.
28. Google Paly Store. Available online: https://play.google.com/store/apps (accessed on 30 August 2022).
29. Fang, Y.; Gao, Y.; Jing, F.; Zhang, L. Android Malware Familial Classification Based on DEX File Section Features. IEEE Access 2020, 8, 10614–10627.

30. Vasan, D.; Alazab, M.; Wassan, S.; Naeem, H.; Safaei, B.; Zheng, Q. IMCFN: Image-based malware classification using fine-tuned convolutional neural network architecture. Comput. Netw. 2020, 171, 107–138.
31. Nataraj, L.; Karthikeyan, S.; Jacob, G.; Manjunath, B. Malware images: Visualization and automatic classification. In Proceedings of the 8th International Symposium on Visualization for Cyber Security, Pittsburgh, PA, USA, 20 July 2011.
32. Ünver, H.M.; Bakour, K. Android malware detection based on image-based features and machine learning techniques. SN Appl. Sci. 2020, 2, pp. 1–15.
33. Nasri, N.; Razak, M.A. Android Malware Detection System using Machine Learning. Int. J. Adv. Trends Comput. Sci. Eng. 2020, 9, 327–333.
34. Ali, W.; Abdulghafor, R.; Abdullah, T. Empirical Study on Intelligent Android Malware Detection based on Supervised Machine Learning. Int. J. Adv. Comput. Sci. Appl. 2020, 11, 215–224.
35. Du, X.; Pan, X.; Cao, Y.; He, B.; Fang, G.; Chen, Y.; Xu, D. FlowCog: Context-aware Semantic Extraction and Analysis of Information Flow Leaks in Android Apps. In IEEE Transactions on Mobile Computing; IEEE: Piscataway, NJ, USA, 2022.
36. Narayanan, A.; Chandramohan, M.; Chen, L.; Liu, Y. A multi-view context-aware approach to Android malware detection and malicious code localization. Empir. Softw. Engg. 2018, 23, 3.
37. Mahdavifar, S.; Kadir, A.; Fatemi, R.; Alhadidi, D.; Ghorbani, A. Dynamic Android Malware Category Classification using Semi-Supervised Deep Learning. In Proceedings of the IEEE International Conference on Dependable, Autonomic and Secure Computing, International Conference on Pervasive Intelligence and Computing, International Conference on Cloud and Big Data Computing, International Conference on Cyber Science and Technology Congress (DASC/PiCom/CBDCom/CyberSciTech), Calgary, AB, Canada, 17–22 August 2020.
38. Hadiprakoso, R.B.; Kabetta, H.; Buana, I. Hybrid-Based Malware Analysis for Effective and Efficiency Android Malware Detection. In Proceedings of the 2nd International Conference on Informatics, Multimedia, Cyber, and Information System, ICIMCIS 2020, Jakarta, Indonesia, 19–20 November 2020.
39. Mahdavifar, A.; Abdul Kadir, R.; Fatemi, D.; Alhadidi, A. Ghorbani, Dynamic Android Malware Category Classification using Semi-Supervised Deep Learning. In Proceedings of the 18th IEEE International Conference on Dependable, Autonomic, and Secure Computing (DASC), Calgary, AB, Canada, 17–24 August 2020.
40. MalDroid 2020, Canadian Institute for Cybersecurity. Available online: https://www.unb.ca/cic/datasets/maldroid-2020.html (accessed on 9 September 2022).
41. Karbab, E.; Debbabi, M.; Derhab, A.; Mouheb, D. MalDozer: Automatic framework for android malware detection using deep learning. Digit. Investig. 2018, 24, S48–S59.
42. VirusTotal. Available online: https://www.virustotal.com/ (accessed on 30 August 2022).
43. Parkour, M. Contagio Mini-Dump. Available online: http://contagiominidump.blogspot.it/ (accessed on 30 August 2022)

44. Saint Yen, Y.; Sun, H.M. An Android mutation malware detection based on deep learning using visualization of importance from codes. Microelectron. Reliab. 2019, 93, 109–114.

45. Thomas, T.; Vijayaraghavan, A.P.; Emmanuel, S. Machine Learning Approaches in Cyber Security Analytics; Springer: Singapore, 2019; pp. 1–209.

46. Welcome to Androguard's Documentation! Androguard 3.4.0 Documentation. Available online: https://androguard.readthedocs.io/en/latest/ (accessed on 9 September 2022).

47. GitHub-Androguard/Androguard: Reverse Engineering, Malware and Goodware Analysis of Android Applications... and More.

48. Sharma, A.; Dash, S.K. Mining API Calls and Permissions for Android Malware Detection. Lect. Notes Comput. Sci. 2014, 8813, 191–205.

49. Lei, S. A feature selection method based on information gain and genetic algorithm. In Proceedings of the 2012 International Conference on Computer Science and Electronics Engineering, Hangzhou, China, 23–25 March 2012.

50. Ho, T.K. Random decision forests. In Proceedings of the 3rd International Conference on Document Analysis and Recognition, Montreal, QC, Canada, 14–16 August 1995.

51. Pandey, S.; Lal, R. Opcode-Based Android Malware Detection Using Machine Learning Techniques. J. Innov. Eng. Techn. 2021, 5, 56–61.

52. Mohamad Arif, J.; Razak, M.F.; Awang, S.; Tuan Mat, S.R.; Ismail, N.S.N.; Firdaus, A. A static analysis approach for Android permission-based malware detection systems. PLoS ONE 2021, 16, e0257968.

53. Singh, D.; Karpa, S.; Chawla, I. Emerging Trends in Computational Intelligence to Solve Real-World Problems' Android Malware Detection Using Machine Learning. In International Conference on Innovative Computing and Communications; Springer: Singapore, 2022.

54. Muzaffar, A.; Ragab Hassen, H.; Lones, M.A.; Zantout, H. Android Malware Detection Using API Calls: A Comparison of Feature Selection and Machine Learning Models. Lect. Notes Networks Syst. 2022, 378, 3–12.

55. Cortes, C.; Vapnik, V.; Saitta, L. Support-vector networks. Mach. Learn. 1995, 20, 273–297.

56. Dutt, S.; Chandramouli, S.; Kumar Das, A. Machine Learning, 1st ed.; Pearson Education: Bengaluru, India, 2018.

57. Agrawal, P.; Trivedi, B. Machine Learning Classifiers for Android Malware Detection. Adv. Intell. Syst. Comput. 2021, 1174, 311–322.

58. Abu Alfeilat, H.A.; Hassanat, A.B.; Lasassmeh, O.; Tarawneh, A.S.; Alhasanat, M.B.; Eyal Salman, H.S.; Prasath, V.S. Effects of Distance Measure Choice on K-Nearest Neighbor Classifier Performance: A Review. J. Big Data 2019, 7, 221–248.

59. Zulkifli, A.; Hamid, I.R.A.; Shah, W.M.; Abdullah, Z. Android Malware Detection Based on Network Traffic Using Decision Tree Algorithm. Adv. Intell. Syst. Comput. 2018, 700, 485–494.

60. Kouliaridis, V.; Kambourakis, G. A Comprehensive Survey on Machine Learning Techniques for Android Malware Detection. Information 2021, 12, 185.
61. Powers, D. Evaluation: From Precision, Recall and F-Factor to ROC, Informedness, Markedness & Correlation. Mach. Learn. Technol. 2008, 2, 37–63.
62. Icc-Bench. Available online: https://github.com/fgwei/ICC-Bench (accessed on 15 September 2022)
63. Malgenome Project. Available online: http://www.Malgenomeproject.org (accessed on 15 September 2022).

Index